EDEXCEL

Ext

Serie
Willi
Stev
Jim Newall, Ray Oliver, Damian Riddle,
Ed Walsh, Gemma Young

ResultsPlus **authors:**

Mark Grinsell
Sue Jenkin
Ian Roberts
Julia Salter
David Swann

Contents

Progress questions can be used to check understanding as you work through the course.

Skills spotlight boxes build How Science Works skills. They match the HSW skill listed in the Learning Outcomes box.

Learning outcomes are taken straight from the specification to make it clear what you need to know for the exam.

P3.1 Radiation in medicine

How is radiation used in medicine?

The 'Interstellar Light Collector' in Arizona, USA, uses mirrors to gather moonlight into one spot. People who are hoping to be cured of various conditions from cancer to eczema stand in that spot to absorb the light. One user said: 'As I was standing there, I could feel myself becoming happier'. There is no scientific proof that it works.

A The 'Interstellar Light Collector'

Visible light is an example of **radiation** – energy carried by waves or particles from a source. Light and other types of radiation are used to identify and treat medical problems.

Radiation for diagnosis

In order to reach a **diagnosis**, doctors may use radiation to produce images that show features inside the body. Some methods are shown in Figure B.

1 Which of the techniques in Figure B seems to be the odd one out? Explain your answer.

Radiation detected	How it forms an image	Where it is used
Visible light	Light reflects off features to form an image	**Endoscopes**
X-rays	X-rays are absorbed by some materials inside the body but not others. A negative image is produced	X-ray photography and **CAT scanners**
Gamma rays	The movement of substances producing gamma rays is detected and the positions shown on a screen	PET scanners
Ultrasound	High-frequency sound waves reflect off features inside the body to form an image	Ultrasound scanners

B Some types of radiation used in medical diagnosis.

Skills spotlight

New technology has benefits as well as risks. Suggest a benefit and a risk of using ionising radiation to create images of the inside of the body.

C A CAT scan in progress

2 Which diagnosis or treatment techniques involve hazardous (ionising) radiation?

Radiation for medical treatments

Some types of radiation are **ionising** – they create reactive ions in the body, which can cause damage. Gamma rays and X-rays are ionising and can be used to damage and destroy cancer cells.

Various types of **non-ionising radiation** (ultrasound) are also used in treatments used in eye surgery to correct vision de absorption of ultrasound is used to tre tissues.

The **intensity** of the radiation decrease from the source. Different cancer tumo with different intensities of gamma rad doctors place the source at different d the tumour. Intensity is also affected b the radiation is travelling through. The medium, the weaker the radiation gets

Intensity is the power of the incomin radiation) divided by the area over w

$$Intensity = \frac{power\ of\ incident\ radiation}{area}$$

$$I = \frac{P}{A}$$

Power is measured in watts (W) and the standard unit of area is metres squared (m²), so intensity will be in watts per square metre (W/m²).

H 5 Calculate the intensity of a 100 W of 5 cm².

H 6 Calculate the intensity of a laser (1 mW) on a board if the dot is a squa

H 7 If the intensity of a torch's beam power output of the bulb?

8 Compare the techniques of using u broken bone in the body.

Learning Outcomes

1.1 Demonstrate an understanding of the including: a CAT scans b ultrasounds

1.2 Use the word 'radiation' to describe ar

1.3 Demonstrate an understanding that th nature of the medium through which it

H 1.4 Use the equation: intensity = $\frac{pow}{}$

HSW 12 Describe the benefits, drawbacks and

180

>>>>>>>>>>>>>>

Higher-tier only questions and outcomes are clearly identified with a small **H** icon.

These pages give you an investigation task, allowing you to complete a specification practical. These tasks can be used as practice Controlled Assessments.

The specification practical is listed in the Learning outcomes box.

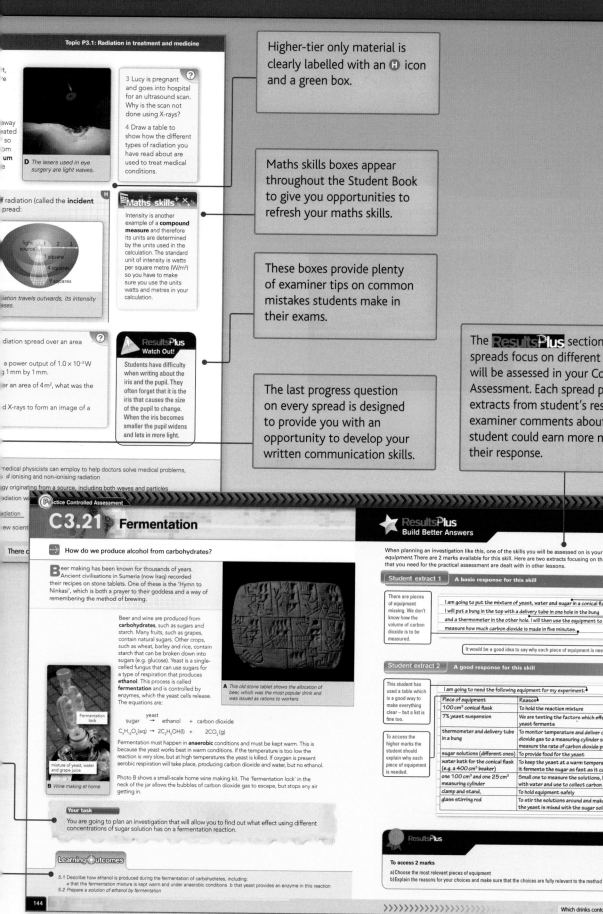

Higher-tier only material is clearly labelled with an **H** icon and a green box.

Maths skills boxes appear throughout the Student Book to give you opportunities to refresh your maths skills.

These boxes provide plenty of examiner tips on common mistakes students make in their exams.

The **ResultsPlus** sections of these spreads focus on different skills that will be assessed in your Controlled Assessment. Each spread provides extracts from student's responses and examiner comments about how the student could earn more marks in their response.

The last progress question on every spread is designed to provide you with an opportunity to develop your written communication skills.

D The lasers used in eye surgery are light waves.

3 Lucy is pregnant and goes into hospital for an ultrasound scan. Why is the scan not done using X-rays?

4 Draw a table to show how the different types of radiation you have read about are used to treat medical conditions.

Maths skills

Intensity is another example of a **compound measure** and therefore its units are determined by the units used in the calculation. The standard unit of intensity is watts per square metre (W/m²) so you have to make sure you use the units watts and metres in your calculation.

ResultsPlus
Watch Out!

Students have difficulty when writing about the iris and the pupil. They often forget that it is the iris that causes the size of the pupil to change. When the iris becomes smaller the pupil widens and lets in more light.

Practice Controlled Assessment

C3.21 Fermentation

How do we produce alcohol from carbohydrates?

Beer making has been known for thousands of years. Ancient civilisations in Sumeria (now Iraq) recorded their recipes on stone tablets. One of these is the 'Hymn to Ninkasi', which is both a prayer to their goddess and a way of remembering the method of brewing.

Beer and wine are produced from **carbohydrates**, such as sugars and starch. Many fruits, such as grapes, contain natural sugars. Other crops, such as wheat, barley and rice, contain starch that can be broken down into sugars (e.g. glucose). Yeast is a single-celled fungus that can use sugars for a type of respiration that produces **ethanol**. This process is called **fermentation** and is controlled by enzymes, which the yeast cells release. The equations are:

$$\text{sugar} \xrightarrow{\text{yeast}} \text{ethanol} + \text{carbon dioxide}$$
$$C_6H_{12}O_6(aq) \rightarrow 2C_2H_5OH(l) + 2CO_2(g)$$

Fermentation must happen in **anaerobic** conditions and must be kept warm. This is because the yeast works best in warm conditions. If the temperature is too low the reaction is very slow, but at high temperatures the yeast is killed. If oxygen is present aerobic respiration will take place, producing carbon dioxide and water, but no ethanol.

Photo B shows a small-scale home wine making kit. The 'fermentation lock' in the neck of the jar allows the bubbles of carbon dioxide gas to escape, but stops any air getting in.

A This old stone tablet shows the allocation of beer, which was the most popular drink and was issued as rations to workers.

Fermentation lock

mixture of yeast, water and grape juice

B Wine making at home

Your task

You are going to plan an investigation that will allow you to find out what effect using different concentrations of sugar solution has on a fermentation reaction.

Learning Outcomes

5.1 Describe how ethanol is produced during the fermentation of carbohydrates, including:
a that the fermentation mixture is kept warm and under anaerobic conditions b that yeast provides an enzyme in this reaction
5.2 Prepare a solution of ethanol by fermentation

ResultsPlus
Build Better Answers

When planning an investigation like this, one of the skills you will be assessed on is your ability to *choose equipment*. There are 2 marks available for this skill. Here are two extracts focusing on that skill. Other skills that you need for the practical assessment are dealt with in other lessons.

Student extract 1 A basic response for this skill

There are pieces of equipment missing. We don't know how the volume of carbon dioxide is to be measured.

I am going to put the mixture of yeast, water and sugar in a conical flask. I will put a bung in the top with a delivery tube in one hole in the bung and a thermometer in the other hole. I will then use the equipment to measure how much carbon dioxide is made in five minutes.

The student has not given the concentrations of the solutions.

It would be a good idea to say why each piece of equipment is needed.

Student extract 2 A good response for this skill

This student has used a table which is a good way to make everything clear – but a list is fine too.

To access the higher marks the student should explain why each piece of equipment is needed.

I am going to need the following equipment for my experiment:

Piece of equipment	Reason
100 cm³ conical flask	To hold the reaction mixture
7% yeast suspension	We are testing the factors which effect how quickly yeast ferments
thermometer and delivery tube in a bung	To monitor temperature and deliver carbon dioxide gas to a measuring cylinder so that we can measure the rate of carbon dioxide production.
sugar solutions (different ones)	To provide food for the yeast
water bath for the conical flask (e.g. a 400 cm³ beaker)	To keep the yeast at a warm temperature so that it ferments the sugar as fast as it can
one 100 cm³ and one 25 cm³ measuring cylinder	Small one to measure the solutions, large one to fill with water and use to collect carbon dioxide gas
clamp and stand,	To hold equipment safely
glass stirring rod	To stir the solutions and make sure that the yeast is mixed with the sugar solution.

ResultsPlus

To access 2 marks

a) Choose the most relevant pieces of equipment
b) Explain the reasons for your choices and make sure that the choices are fully relevant to the method

Which drinks contain the most alcohol?

There is a practice exam paper for both the Foundation and Higher tiers in each unit.

All exam practice questions are written by examiners.

Each exam section has some extended writing questions where you can practise answering this type of question. The extended writing questions are worth 6 marks and are always the last part of a question.

The question parts are colour coded to indicate what grades they can access:
- Orange means you can access grades G-D (Foundation tier) or D-B (Higher tier)
- Light green means you can access grades E-C or B-A*
- Dark green covers the whole grade range, G-C or D-A*.

The Build Better Answers pages present an extended writing question along with three different student answers to the question – a level 1, a level 2 and a level 3 answer.

ResultsPlus Exam Practice

Foundation tier

These questions are indicative of the type of questions used in the exam. Refer to page 6 for information on the grades.

Animal behaviour

1. As soon as a new brood of ducklings is born they follow their mother around. Ducklings will do this with the first animal they see after breaking out of their egg.

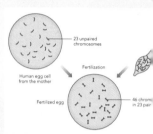

(a) (i) This type of behaviour is known as
   A habituation
   B imprinting
   C classical conditioning
   D operant conditioning
   (1)

   (ii) Describe the benefits to the ducklings of this type of behaviour.
   (2)

(b) (i) Explain why parenting is likely to be a successful evolutionary strategy.
   (2)

   (ii) Use one of the words from the box to complete the sentence on animal behaviour.

   | innate | habituated | imprinted | conditioned |

   The ability to suckle milk from the moment a mammal is born is known as _____ behaviour.
   (1)

(c) The police train animals including dogs and horses to seek out drugs or control riots. Describe the training methods used by the police to make sure the animals carry out the required behaviour.
   (6)

82

Fertilisation

2. The diagram shows the sperm and egg cell (ovum) and the sperm and ovu

- 23 unpaired chromosomes
- Human egg cell from the mother
- Fertilization
- Fertilized egg
- 46 chromo in 23 pair

(a) (i) Sperm cells determine gender. Sperm cells contain

   A Y chromosomes only for gender
   B X chromosomes only for gender
   C both X and Y chromosomes in each sperm cell
   D either X or Y chromosomes in each sperm cell

   (ii) Complete the Punnett square to show how the gender of a child i from the parent

   (iii) What is the p

(b) Describe how the

(c) Many couples are Suggest one ethi of fertility treat

(d) Explain how horm

ResultsPlus Build Better Answers

Here are three student answers to the comments around and after them.

Question   **Tempera**

Joshim investigates how changing with some gas in a syringe and seal how this affects the volume of the g

| Temperature (°C) | |
| Volume (cm³) | |

Suggest how Joshim should proces he could improve the experiment to

Student answer 1   Extract t

Be clear about which axis you are referring to. Extending these results back to absolute zero involves drawing a line through one axis to meet the temperature axis.

Joshim should rep graph on the right temperature of ab line back to the ax temperature. If he He could check the must be correct.

Examiner summary
This answer describes s clear. Unless you are luc not be good; if you all do

Student answer 2   Extract t

You suggest making extra readings, but you don't mention why. This is a good way to spot any anomalies in the readings.

The results of an e took 7 but he need it back until it meet absolute zero whe draw a very straigh would also help. At get less than this.

You should also expla

250

6

Exam practice spreads provide a large bank of the new question types you will encounter in your exams.

The Be the Examiner spread offers a variety of past exam questions along with examiner comments, advice on how to improve an answer and common mistakes that students have made in the past.

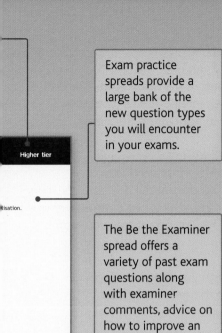

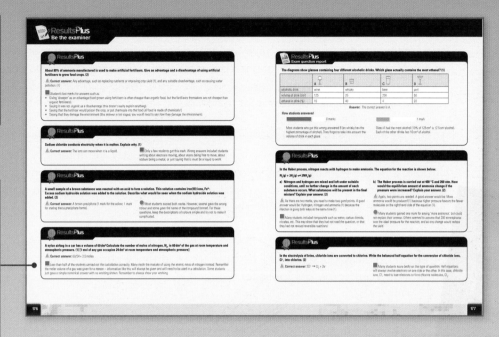

There are examiner comments around and under each student response, making it clear how to progress through the mark scheme to improve your marks.

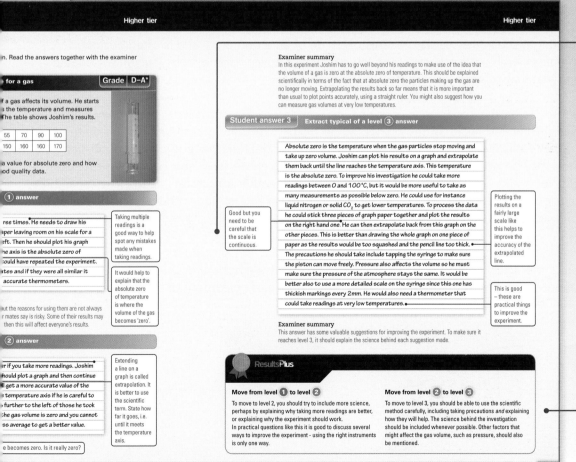

n. Read the answers together with the examiner

for a gas — Grade D–A*

f a gas affects its volume. He starts s the temperature and measures The table shows Joshim's results.

55	70	90	100
150	160	160	170

a value for absolute zero and how od quality data.

① answer

ree times. He needs to draw his aper leaving room on his scale for a eft. Then he should plot his graph ne axis is the absolute zero of could have repeated the experiment. ates and if they were all similar it accurate thermometers.

Taking multiple readings is a good way to help spot any mistakes made when taking readings.

It would help to explain that the absolute zero of temperature is where the volume of the gas becomes 'zero'.

ut the reasons for using them are not always r mates say is risky. Some of their results may then this will affect everyone's results.

② answer

r if you take more readings. Joshim should plot a graph and then continue ll get a more accurate value of the e temperature axis if he is careful to further to the left of those he took he gas volume is zero and you cannot ss average to get a better value.

Extending a line on a graph is called extrapolation. It is better to use the scientific term. State how far it goes, i.e. until it meets the temperature axis.

e becomes zero. Is it really zero?

Examiner summary

In this experiment Joshim has to go well beyond his readings to make use of the idea that the volume of a gas is zero at the absolute zero of temperature. This should be explained scientifically in terms of the fact that at absolute zero the particles making up the gas are no longer moving. Extrapolating the results back so far means that it is more important than usual to plot points accurately, using a straight ruler. You might also suggest how you can measure gas volumes at very low temperatures.

Student answer 3 — Extract typical of a level ③ answer

Absolute zero is the temperature when the gas particles stop moving and take up zero volume. Joshim can plot his results on a graph and extrapolate them back until the line reaches the temperature axis. This temperature is the absolute zero. To improve his investigation he could take more readings between 0 and 100 °C, but it would be more useful to take as many measurements as possible below zero. He could use for instance liquid nitrogen or solid CO_2 to get lower temperatures. To process the data he could stick three pieces of graph paper together and plot the results on the right hand one. He can then extrapolate back from this graph on the other pieces. This is better than drawing the whole graph on one piece of paper as the results would be too squashed and the pencil line too thick. The precautions he should take include tapping the syringe to make sure the piston can move freely. Pressure also affects the volume so he must make sure the pressure of the atmosphere stays the same. It would be better also to use a more detailed scale on the syringe since this one has thickish markings every 2mm. He would also need a thermometer that could take readings at very low temperatures.

Good but you need to be careful that the scale is continuous.

Plotting the results on a fairly large scale like this helps to improve the accuracy of the extrapolated line.

This is good – these are practical things to improve the experiment.

Examiner summary

This answer has some valuable suggestions for improving the experiment. To make sure it reaches level 3, it should explain the science behind each suggestion made.

ResultsPlus

Move from level ① to level ②

To move to level 2, you should try to include more science, perhaps by explaining why taking more readings are better, or explaining why the experiment should work.
In practical questions like this it is good to discuss several ways to improve the experiment - using the right instruments is only one way.

Move from level ② to level ③

To move to level 3, you should be able to use the scientific method carefully, including taking precautions and explaining how they will help. The science behind the investigation should be included whenever possible. Other factors that might affect the gas volume, such as pressure, should also be mentioned.

There is also examiner advice on the things you can improve in your answer to help you move up a level in your response.

Why study science?

If you asked your science teacher why it's important to study and understand science, they may say, 'Everything around you is science.' You might expect a scientist to say that, but there's truth in it.

Just think of what your daily life would be like without advances in science. Even over the last 100 years, the achievements of science have benefited the human race in so many areas: in transport (cars, planes), in medicine (anaesthetics, organ transplants, cures for many diseases, drugs), in electronics (computers, mobile phones), in materials (fabrics such as Gore-Tex ® and Kevlar ®) and in agriculture (fertilisers, pesticides, genetic modification) to name but a few.

However, sceptics will say these advances have come at a price. Alfred Nobel, whose will funds the Nobel Prizes, invented dynamite for the mining industry, yet it rapidly became part of the armaments industry. And a hundred years ago, no one had heard of global warming or the ethical arguments over gene therapy. But in order to understand whether these sceptics are right, it's important that you learn some of the science behind these issues.

So why study science? Firstly, there is the excitement of discovery. Although you may not discover anything new yourself, you'll be able to experience some of the 'buzz' of the great scientists by working out some key ideas for yourself.

Science also gives you the chance to do some practical work: to get your hands dirty with experiments. You can investigate living organisms, create chemical reactions that give off energy or make colour changes, or build a physical model of a phenomenon.

However, learning about science in the new millennium is about more than that – and this is where we return to our sceptics. You need to be able to make informed decisions about how science benefits your life and what to do in situations where science has posed as many questions as it has answered. Much of what you might see in the media presents one side of an argument – and is often designed as a piece of journalism, high on shock value and low on facts! Knowing some facts yourself will enable you to look critically at how science is presented in the media.

It's also important to realise the importance of science to your future. Scientists work in so many fields to try and improve the life and health of the planet. Some will be in research, perhaps working on the cure for cancer or HIV / AIDS, or helping make the chips to power the next generation computer-game technology. Others may be working in industries trying to develop new energy sources or new fabrics and materials. But you'll also find science specialists working as weather forecasters, television researchers, lawyers, medical specialists, teachers, writers, architects, journalists and in many other areas. Increasingly, employers look for applicants with a science background because they know they will have logical, enquiring minds.

Finally, there's one other excellent reason to study science: it's fun! We hope that this book will help you throughout GCSE Science to see the interest, relevance and enjoyment of the subject.

Good luck!

Damian Riddle
Edexcel Science Team

The units

At this stage, as you've worked towards your separate science GCSEs, you'll have taken Unit 1 and Unit 2 in each of Biology, Chemistry and Physics. To finish the separate sciences off, you'll now be working on the Unit 3 content for each science. You'll also complete a unit of practical and investigative work (although you may have done this when you did Unit 2).

As you can probably tell from your studies so far, each of the periods of study of Unit 3 will lead to a written examination in one of the sciences: one each in Biology (B3), Chemistry (C3) and Physics (P3). Again, these examination papers will contain the same types of question that you've already seen in your Unit 1 (Science) and Unit 2 (Additional Science) exams. The fourth unit is a piece of coursework, the Controlled Assessment. It is possible for you to take the Controlled Assessment task from either Unit 2 or Unit 3, so you may have already done this section. If you haven't, then it's very similar to the one you may have done at GCSE Science. Simply, you'll have to develop an idea or hypothesis to test, collect some data, process it and draw conclusions.

Whether you're doing all three sciences as separate GCSEs, or if you're doing just one or two of them; these courses are meant to help you deepen your knowledge and understanding of the whole subjects that you have been studying.

To remind you, here's the diagram to show you how the GCSEs available in the science subjects all fit together.

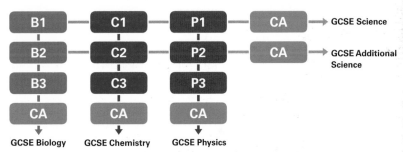

You're probably used to the fact that each of the Units is broken down into smaller topics. Let's start, therefore, by looking at the smaller topics that make up the Units you'll study as you complete the GCSEs in Biology, Chemistry and Physics.

Unit B3

This unit is called 'Using Biology' and it covers some applications of biology in the food industry, as well as looking at how the human body controls different mechanisms using hormones. It also covers how some diseases are inherited and how the body responds to infection. Lastly, there is a section on animal behaviour and conditioning.

Topic 1 asks you to:
• study the structure and function of the kidney, including the role of ADH
• investigate the roles of hormones in the menstrual cycle
• consider the inheritance of some genetic conditions
• learn about the body's response to infection and to immunisation.

In Topic 2, you will:
• study different aspects of animal behaviour such as courtship and conditioning to responses
• look at the ways in which animals communicate
• consider evidence for human evolution.

In Topic 3, you will:
• explore the role of enzymes in aspects of manufacturing items such as cheese, sweets and washing powder
• consider how DNA is manipulated in GM organisms.

Unit C3

In this unit – 'Chemistry in action' - you will see some applications of the chemistry that you studied in C1 and C2. This unit gives plenty of chance to use practical techniques that you have learned at an earlier stage. The unit is broken up into five small topics. These topics cover the following areas:

• further tests for metal cations, especially within the water industry
• hard and soft water and how to calculate concentrations of solutions in water
• electrolysis of salts – both molten and in aqueous solution – and electroplating
• how conditions are chosen for the Haber process
• further organic reactions, especially of alcohols, organic acids and oils.

Unit P3

The idea here, as with Chemistry, is to introduce you to applications of physics linked to what you have already learned in P1 and P2. The unit title 'Applications of Physics' makes this clear. Most of the applications are within the field of medical physics. There are five topics to be covered:

• using lenses to correct vision; and other optical systems using reflection
• the production, use and potential damage from X-rays; and measuring an ECG
• nuclear decay processes and how the nucleus is made up of quarks; and how radiation is used in certain treatments, as the benefits outweigh the risks
• the physics of particle accelerators in terms of circular motion, momentum and conservation of energy in collisions
• applying the ideal gas laws to situations such as bottled gases.

In the next few pages, we'll take an in-depth look at the exams you'll take in GCSE Science.

This will help you get familiar with what the papers look like and will also give you some information on the sorts of questions that you'll be asked, plus the way in which the examiners use key words to test your knowledge and understanding.

Assessment Objectives

Many students think that examiners have the job of trying to catch them out or that examiners set out to write exam papers which are too hard. Nothing could be further from the truth! Examiners try hard to write questions that allow you to show everything you have learned during your GCSE course. However, they also have to make sure that any exam paper is fair for you, past students and future students. The papers need to be the same difficulty and test the same skills.

To help with this, all papers are targeted to test specific skills called Assessment Objectives. They sound a bit complicated, but here's what they mean:

Assessment Objective	The jargon	What it means
AO1	Recall, select and communicate your knowledge and understanding of science.	Essentially, AO1 questions will ask you to write down facts that you have learned.
AO2	Apply skills, knowledge and understanding of science in practical and other contexts.	AO2 questions may ask you to apply what you've learned to new situations, or to practical contexts – it's about showing skills you've learned, rather than repeating facts.
AO3	Analyse and evaluate evidence, make reasoned judgements and draw conclusions based on evidence.	AO3 questions will be about how well you can use data, say what graphs show, or think about arguments with two sides, such as ethical issues.

Your exam papers will be written so that the balance of these AOs is roughly 45% AO1, 35% AO2 and 20% AO3. The Controlled Assessment task will be about 50% AO2 and 50% AO3.

Types of question

Your exam paper will always consist of six questions. The questions will examine different areas of the course which you have studied. Each question will start with some straight-forward question parts, which will slightly increase in difficulty until the end of the question. The six questions themselves will also be 'ramped' slightly in difficulty: this means that Question 6 will be a little more challenging than Question 1. However, each question will start with a question part that puts you at ease and settles you into the question as a whole.

The first two questions will be worth around 8 marks, the next pair around 10 marks and the final pair around 12 marks. Each question could contain the following types of question:

- **Multiple choice**. These ask a question and usually provide four possible answers: A, B, C and D. Some multiple choice questions may ask you to choose words from a box to complete a sentence or to draw lines between statements.

- **Open response**. Like multiple choice, these will usually be worth 1 mark, but you will need to write down your own answer, rather than choose from a selection of answers provided.

- **Short answers**. These questions, worth 2 or 3 marks, will ask you to write slightly longer answers (perhaps three or four lines). Occasionally, at Higher tier, some questions – most likely those involving calculations – may be worth 4 marks.

Two questions in the paper, usually questions 5 and 6, will also have a piece of extended writing.

- **Extended writing**. These questions are worth 6 marks. They will require you to write at greater depth and the questions will be slightly more open to give you the chance to express yourself. In these questions, you will also be assessed on the quality of your written communication.

There is more detail on each type of question, and how to answer them, on pages 14 and 15.

The language of the exams

An exam paper contains precise words. It's important that you understand exactly what the words are asking you to do so that you can answer the question quickly and accurately.

The words are called 'command words' and it's useful for you to know what they mean. Some are simple words designed to allow you to give simple answers, whereas others are more complex terminology, asking you to write at greater length and give more detail.

Let's have a look at the command words you might encounter on a GCSE Science paper. These are in order of complexity below, i.e. they get more difficult.

Give, Name, State	These questions are asking for short answers – often only a few words – but with precise use of scientific terminology.
Complete, Select, Choose	In these questions you are usually asked to fill the gaps in sentences, using words that are given to you.
Draw, Plot	These questions will ask you to put data onto a graph, or draw a diagram. Make sure that your work is accurate and that you use labels, if appropriate.
Calculate, Work out	In GCSE Science, you'll need to use your mathematical skills in solving equations and performing simple calculations. This type of question will test you on these skills.
Describe, Use the graph	In these questions, try to use scientific terminology concisely and accurately. You may be asked to describe a particular process – in which case, remember to think about putting your answers in a logical sequence. Alternatively, you may be asked to describe the trend in a graph – here you will get more marks for using data that you have read from the graph.
Suggest	These questions are often asking you to apply what you have learnt to a new situation, or to put together different facts you have learnt in order to answer the question.
Explain	These questions will be worth 2 or 3 marks. You need to give reasons for your answer and not to simply repeat information given in the question. Imagine that any question that starts 'Explain...' is really asking you 'Why...?' – that should help you understand the depth needed in your answer.
Evaluate, Discuss, Compare	These command words will often be found in the 6-mark extended writing questions. Look carefully at exactly what the question is asking you to do. In many cases, it will be asking you to look at 'pros' and 'cons' surrounding a particular argument, or to give a balanced answer, looking at different aspects of a topic. 'Compare' questions will ask you to look at areas of similarity and difference between two ideas, or two sets of data.

Knowing what to expect: the front page

We know it can feel a bit scary sitting in the exam room with your GCSE paper in front of you, waiting to start. If you know what the paper looks like beforehand and what some of the text on it means, hopefully it won't seem so daunting.

Usually, the centre number will be written clearly somewhere in the exam room. It's a 5-digit number, and it will also appear on the statement of entry that your teacher or form tutor may have given you. If you're not sure, just ask one of the invigilators.

All GCSE Science papers last one hour and contain 6 questions.

All GCSE Science papers are marked out of 60. The mark for each question part is immediately after that part and the total for the whole question is at the end of the question. Questions marked with an asterisk indicate that the examiners will look at how well you express yourself and use technical vocabulary in your answer.

There's also a section here giving you advice how to answer questions.

This is a 4-digit number, unique to you in your school or college. It's important to copy this down correctly because the exam board will use this number to give you your marks.

GCSE Science papers come in two tiers: Foundation (which allows you to score grades G – C) and Higher (which allows you to score grades D – A*). Check you've got the correct tier of paper. Your teacher should have talked to you about the tier you're sitting.

The paper asks you to use a black ink pen or biro. Your exam paper is scanned and marked by a marker on a computer screen and black ink means the marker can read your answers more clearly. It's also important to answer in the spaces provided. Don't feel you always have to fill the entire answer space though!

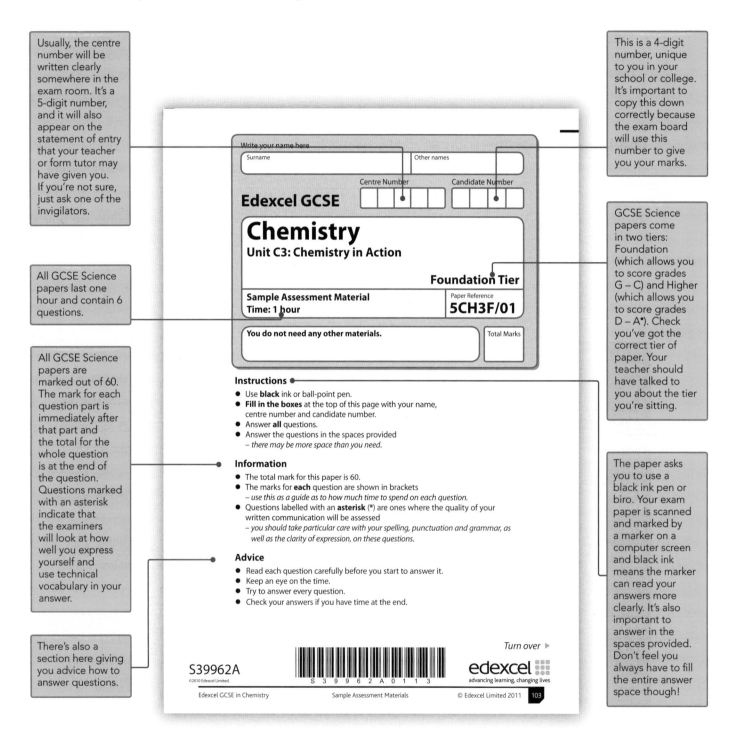

Write your name here

Surname

Other names

Centre Number

Candidate Number

Edexcel GCSE

Chemistry
Unit C3: Chemistry in Action

Foundation Tier

Sample Assessment Material
Time: 1 hour

Paper Reference
5CH3F/01

You do not need any other materials.

Total Marks

Instructions

- Use **black** ink or ball-point pen.
- **Fill in the boxes** at the top of this page with your name, centre number and candidate number.
- Answer **all** questions.
- Answer the questions in the spaces provided
  – there may be more space than you need.

Information

- The total mark for this paper is 60.
- The marks for **each** question are shown in brackets
  – use this as a guide as to how much time to spend on each question.
- Questions labelled with an **asterisk** (*) are ones where the quality of your written communication will be assessed
  – you should take particular care with your spelling, punctuation and grammar, as well as the clarity of expression, on these questions.

Advice

- Read each question carefully before you start to answer it.
- Keep an eye on the time.
- Try to answer every question.
- Check your answers if you have time at the end.

Turn over ▶

S39962A
©2010 Edexcel Limited.

edexcel
advancing learning, changing lives

Edexcel GCSE in Chemistry   Sample Assessment Materials   © Edexcel Limited 2011   103

Knowing what to expect: a sample question

This is called the stem of the question. It lets you know what topic the question is on. In some cases, the stem gives some important information to set the scene for the question.

Examiners use bold text to highlight something they want you to notice. In many cases, it will be a word which you will be asked to define or it will tell you the number of answers you are expected to give.

Each question will contain what examiners call a stimulus. Most often, this will be a photograph or a diagram that should help set the context for the question. In some cases, the stimulus might be some data from an experiment or a short piece of text.

The number of marks for the question part is given on the right-hand side of the exam paper, just under the question part. It's always a good idea to look at how many marks the question part is worth. This will give you some idea of how much you are expected to write, what sort of depth the examiners are looking for and the length of time you should spend on the question part.

Here's an example of one of the command words that we looked at on page 11. It tells you what to do in your answer.

Multiple choice questions are laid out differently – we'll look at these in more detail on the next page.

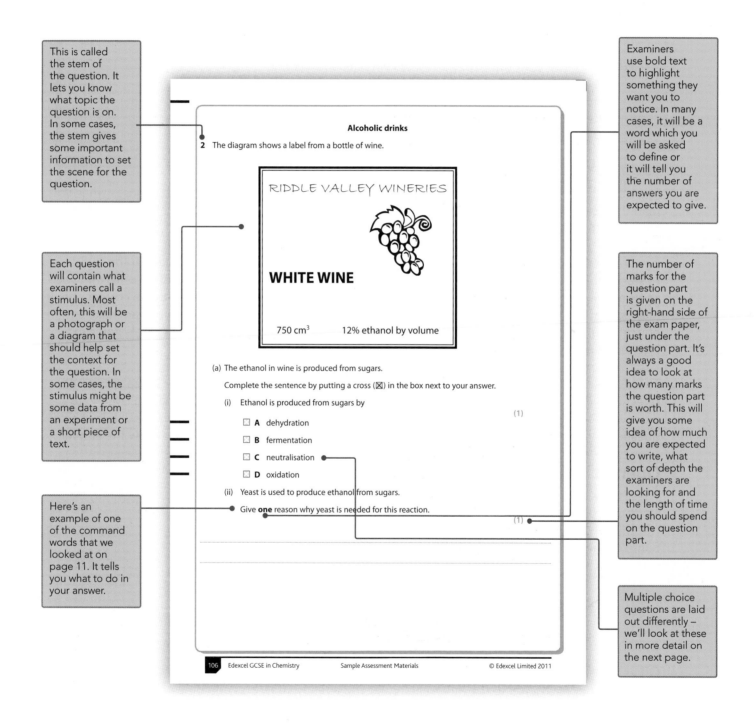

Alcoholic drinks

2 The diagram shows a label from a bottle of wine.

RIDDLE VALLEY WINERIES

WHITE WINE

750 cm³   12% ethanol by volume

(a) The ethanol in wine is produced from sugars.

Complete the sentence by putting a cross (☒) in the box next to your answer.

(i) Ethanol is produced from sugars by

(1)

☐ **A** dehydration

☐ **B** fermentation

☐ **C** neutralisation

☐ **D** oxidation

(ii) Yeast is used to produce ethanol from sugars.

Give **one** reason why yeast is needed for this reaction.

(1)

....

....

On pages 10 and 11, we looked at the types of questions that would come up in your GCSE Science exams. Let's look at each one in a bit more detail, so you understand how to score as many marks as you can.

Multiple choice questions

The most common type of multiple choice question will present you with four alternative answers, one of which is correct. For example:

> Which of these is an addictive substance contained in tobacco?
>   A a cannabinoid
>   B carbon monoxide
>   C nicotine
>   D tar

The best way to answer multiple choice questions is to cover up the four possible responses when you read the question. Think of your answer and then look at the four possible answers: hopefully yours will be among them!

If your answer isn't there – or if you couldn't come up with an answer when you looked at the question to start with – then you have to start looking at the answers one by one and eliminating ones that you know are wrong. Hopefully, you'll be able to eliminate three answers and be left with the correct one. It may be that you're only able to eliminate one or two wrong answers – but at least you can make a more educated guess. The key thing with a multiple choice question is this: don't leave it blank. You can't lose marks if you get it wrong and you may actually guess right!

There are similar questions where you're given the answers as part of the question. These might be selecting words from a box to complete sentences, or drawing lines to join words in one column to those in another. The same principle applies to these types as to the standard 'ABCD' multiple choice questions – look at the question before looking at the answers to see if you already know the answer.

Open response and short-answer questions

These questions might be 1 mark questions, often asking you to recall information. Or they may be worth 2 or 3 marks, if you're being asked for two reasons, or two factors.

Some examples of 1 mark questions might include:

> a Give one form of naturally-occurring calcium carbonate.
> b Which waves in the electromagnetic spectrum have the longest wavelength?

Other types of 1 mark questions might ask you to label or complete diagrams. Some may be of the **Suggest** type, asking you to use information that you already know and combine it with information in the question to come up with an answer.

Remember that these questions are only worth 1 mark – so don't spend too much time going into a great amount of detail. Keep your answer clear and concise. You don't have to answer in full sentences, so you can save time here.

Longer-answer questions

Each question on the paper will have some questions worth 2 or 3 marks. Generally, there will be more of these longer-answer questions towards the end of the exam paper. These types of question will include the following:

Writing or completing equations. Make sure with these that you're clear whether the answer needs a word equation or a chemical equation. Don't forget to look for clues in the question – you'll often find that the words or formulae you need are in the question.

Drawing graphs. Different questions will ask you to do different things with a graph. Read the question carefully to check if you're meant to label axes or draw your own axes. Be careful when you plot the points – there are marks for the accuracy of your plotting. Finally, check to see if you're required to draw a line of best fit – and remember, lines of best fit don't have to be straight lines, they can be curves!

Performing calculations. Two key tips for calculations. Firstly, always show your working. If you make a slip with your calculator (and end up with the wrong final answer), you can often get marks for your working if the examiner can see that you just made a small slip. Secondly, check to see if you need to give units in your answer.

Describe or **Explain** questions. For example, a question like:

> Describe the path taken by a nerve impulse from the receptors to the effectors.

These questions are designed to be a bit more difficult than some of the other types we've seen. However, there's no reason why you shouldn't score well on them. It's always best to spend a few moments planning your answer before starting to write. Make sure you understand exactly what you're being asked to do – you want to keep your answer relevant. Do think about the number of marks that the question is worth: if it's a 3 mark question, then you need to make three different points.

Extended writing questions

There is one final type of question that you'll face in your examination paper – the extended writing question. That may sound a bit daunting, but these questions aren't designed to be really difficult or to set traps for you. Instead, they give you more time and space to show the knowledge and skills you have picked up during your GCSE course. These questions will be written to test you on a variety of different skills.

The other important thing to realise about these questions is that they're not just aimed at A* students. The questions are designed to be open enough to allow all students to be able to write something.

On the next two pages we'll look at the sort of topics that might form the basis of an extended writing question.

Practical-based questions

Much of the time you spend in science lessons, you're doing practical work. Some extended writing questions will therefore ask you about the practical work that you've done. The questions may ask you about how you would set up an investigation or about how a particular practical investigation gives us information about scientific theories.

Opinion-based questions

Many people think that science is all about hard facts and certainties but many areas of science still lead to uncertainty. In some cases, this is because scientists genuinely don't know all the answers or because data that they collect can be interpreted in different ways. In other cases, the discoveries that scientists have made have led to moral or ethical dilemmas.

Opinion-based questions will therefore ask you to use what you have learnt to back up your own opinion or to show that you understand two sides of a particular argument.

Knowledge-based questions

There will be some parts of your GCSE Science course where you will learn quite a lot of detail. Sometimes, 1 or 2 mark questions on these topics mean you can only write about some of the things you know about the topic, rather than all of it. Equally, there are times when the examiners want to ask a general question to allow you to show a variety of things you know or to bring in knowledge across the whole subject.

Hence, some extended writing questions will ask you for more factual responses. This might seem a bit daunting, but the questions may sometimes be phrased in such a way as to allow a variety of answers. There will often be some prompt questions to help you get started.

How they're marked

The extended writing questions are always worth 6 marks. So if you've read the advice given for other questions types, you're probably thinking about the amount that you may have to write, and you're thinking that you have to make sure you make 6 credit-worthy points.

Well, you're half right – the whole point about these questions being called 'extended writing' is that there is the opportunity for you to write at greater length. Note that in many questions, you'll be able to provide diagrams or tables as part of your answer, so don't think it's all about writing essays! But you don't have to think about making six points each time. These questions will be marked with two ideas in mind – one is known as 'levels' and the other as 'QWC'.

Let's look at **levels** first. The mark scheme for each question contains a long list of possible points – the key thing to remember is that you're not expected to write all of these! The examiners will see lots of examples of answers, and they'll use this experience to place your answer in one of three levels: very good (Level 3), good (Level 2) and less good (Level 1). Their judgement will be based on factors such as the number of points you've made, the balance in any argument you've made or how well you've appreciated your practical work. Each level corresponds to 2 marks. Level 1 is 1–2 marks, Level 2 is 3–4 marks, and Level 3 is 5–6 marks. So once your answer is placed in one of the levels, how is the final mark decided?

The other deciding factor is **QWC**. This stands for Quality of Written Communication. What the examiners will look for is your ability to use proper scientific words correctly and use proper spelling, punctuation and grammar, your ability to put your answer in a logical order and how well you express yourself.

How to answer

Let's have a look at a possible question:

> Discuss the advantages and disadvantages of using biofuels instead of petrol for cars.

The question relates directly to a particular part of the specification – the statement about biofuels being renewable but taking up land that could be used for growing crops. However, your answer wouldn't have to involve that. You could, for example, talk about what factors make a good fuel and use this to compare biofuel and petrol; or you could write about the amount of carbon dioxide given off by each fuel and hence talk about the greenhouse effect. Or if you'd learned a lot about the effects of acid rain, you could even write about sulfur impurities in petrol causing this, whereas biofuels (which don't contain sulfur) don't give the same problems.

The key, therefore, is to treat each question as a way for you to display some of the knowledge you've learned, rather than just a black-and-white question with one set answer.

In terms of your exam technique, the most important things to do are: a) think about all the different areas of what you've learned that you can use in your answer, and b) to spend some time planning your answer. The two extended questions are worth a total of 12 marks between them – a fifth of the marks on the paper – so you should spend a reasonable amount of time on them, probably about 6–8 minutes on each. And remember that this is one area where you need to be careful with the logical presentation of your answer. Finally, read the question again before answering – did you notice that it asked for advantages and disadvantages? Remember, therefore, to think about both pros and cons in your answer.

Let's look at a possible answer to this question:

> Biofuel is a renewable fuel. It is often made from fermenting the sugar in sugar beet to produce ethanol. Petrol, however, is not renewable – it is a fossil fuel and, at the rate humans are using it, it will soon be used up. Petrol, however, does give more energy out when it burns than biofuels do. So, although biofuels may be an answer to the problems of energy needs, we'll need to burn a lot of them to get our energy. That means that a lot of land needs to be used to grow the sugar crop – and that means less land for growing food for people or livestock. Many people see biofuels as being "green". It is certainly true that, unlike petrol, they don't contain sulfur impurities, so there is no sulfur dioxide produced when they burn, so no acid rain. Biofuels do, of course, produce carbon dioxide when they're burnt, just like petrol, and this is a powerful greenhouse gas. But, some of the effect of this may be offset as, to grow the next crop of sugar beet, carbon dioxide will be taken in by the plants photosynthesising.

Here is how an examiner responded to this student answer:

This answer looks at some pros and cons about using petrol. Importantly, it also looks at some negatives of using biofuels – such as land use – as well as seeing the positives. This means it should be a top-level response. The presentation of the answer is good, with accurate spelling and grammar, and the answer is logically structured. It should achieve a mark in the top level.

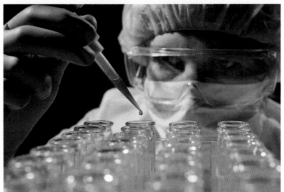

There is an aspect of your course where we try to assess you on your ability to handle practical work and use the results of experiments. This section is known as Controlled Assessment.

If you've got older brothers and sisters or friends in years above you at school, it's quite likely that they'll have told you horror stories about coursework and how much time it took up when they were studying for their GCSEs.

Well, Controlled Assessment is, essentially, a form of coursework, but one which is very different from the coursework used in the past. Hopefully, you'll see that many of the differences are positive ones.

The major differences are:

- In Controlled Assessment, the task is set by the exam board and changes every year. This means that it is the same task for all students, which is much fairer.

- In Controlled Assessment, parts of the work have to be completed in class time and you won't be able to take work home. This means that it is easier to guarantee that it is your own work and means that students who have family members who are good scientists aren't able to get their family to help with their work.

- Controlled Assessment takes up less time – especially because you do not have to do write-ups for several homeworks.

How important is Controlled Assessment?

Controlled Assessment is worth 25% of your GCSE – in other words, it has the same proportion of marks as a written exam.

How many Controlled Assessment tasks do you need to do?

You have to submit one Controlled Assessment mark for GCSE Science and another one if you go on to GCSE Additional Science. This can come from any of the three sciences: Biology or Chemistry or Physics. It is possible that your teachers may complete more than one Controlled Assessment task with you – if this is the case, you submit your best mark. In some cases, you may be able to combine marks for different Controlled Assessments in order to get a higher mark. Your teacher will be able to give you some advice on this.

If you are taking Biology, Chemistry and Physics as separate GCSEs, then you will need one Controlled Assessment for each science.

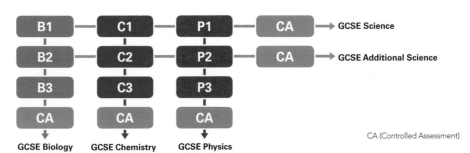

CA (Controlled Assessment)

What sort of practicals will the exam board choose?

The specification for GCSE Science includes a series of suggested practicals. The Controlled Assessment could be set on one of these pieces of practical work, or it may be set on a related experiment. This is another example of us trying to ensure that the Controlled Assessment is as fair as possible. Having asked you to study some pieces of practical work in your course, it seems fair that one of these pieces of work – or something closely related to those pieces of work – will be used as the Controlled Assessment, as all candidates will have the same previous experience of the practical being used.

How will you prepare?

Preparation for the Controlled Assessment is obviously going to be very important. Hopefully, your teacher will give you lots of opportunities to practise the skills you need in order to do well in this section of the course. That's another reason why we've included the suggested practicals in each unit – so that you can use these experiments to help you get better at planning experiments, collecting data and making conclusions based on the data.

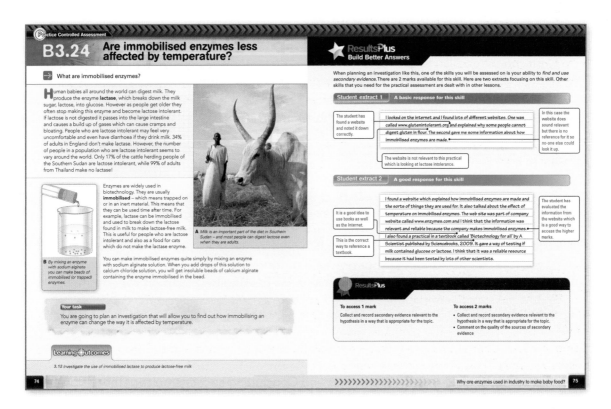

If you've had a flick through this textbook before reading this section, then you'll notice that each of the suggested practicals has a double–page spread in the book and that each of these concentrates on a different area of practical skills. You may do some of these suggested practicals as 'practice' Controlled Assessments to help you prepare for your real Controlled Assessment. Obviously in your real Controlled Assessment you will have a different investigation. Separate science candidates are likely to practice by taking a Science or Additional Science task earlier in the course.

What do you have to do in a Controlled Assessment?

As far as possible, the idea of the Controlled Assessment task is to try and assess how well you have picked up key practical skills during your science course. This means that we have split up each Controlled Assessment into three distinct sections: Part A (planning), Part B (observing) and Part C (concluding).

Planning. In the planning section, you will be asked to develop a prediction (or, as scientists often call it, a hypothesis) to test. You'll also be given some information about the sort of experiment you should be doing to test your prediction. Remember, the Controlled Assessment will often be based on one of the suggested practicals that are in the specification – so you should have a good idea of what the experiment that you're trying to plan is like!

Observing. In this section, you will carry out your plan and collect some data. You'll also research some secondary evidence. Your teacher may give you a pre-prepared plan to follow, rather than using your own. Don't worry if you think your practical skills are a bit basic, or if you know that you work very slowly and carefully when you do a practical. No–one is going to be standing over you to watch exactly what you're doing! We can assess how well you do an experiment by looking at the data that you get.

Concluding. Here, there are some key skills we're looking for: how well you present your data and draw relevant graphs; how you process information in order to make a conclusion; and, finally, whether you think the evidence that you have gathered during your practical supports the prediction or hypothesis you were aiming to test. Your conclusions will need to be based on your data and the secondary evidence that you collected.

It should be pretty clear that the Observing and Concluding sections go together – you can't analyse data if you've not collected any! But the Planning section is separate, so you may end up doing a Planning task based on one practical and the Observing and Concluding tasks on a different practical.

When will you do a Controlled Assessment?

That's up to your teacher – he or she will give you some notice that you'll be taking one of these tasks, so you'll have time to prepare. Doing well in a Controlled Assessment relies on you having picked up a certain number of skills in planning and analysing – so you'll probably be at least a term or so into your GCSE course before you do your first piece of work.

How will the real Controlled Assessment work?

It's possible that you'll do a practice before you do the real thing – or that you may do more than one real piece (because your teacher only has to submit your best mark – so if you do more than one, your best mark counts).

As you know, the Controlled Assessment is split into three parts and it's possible that you'll do the different parts at different times. Indeed, it's possible that you'll do the first part (the planning section) from a different Controlled Assessment task than the other two parts.

Why are practicals important?

One of the key things that marks science out as different to other school subjects is that it is practical.

It's important to realise that scientists do practical work not as a way to liven things up, but because science cannot progress without scientists making observations, collecting data and then using that information to back up (or disprove) a theory or hypothesis.

The philosopher Democrates is credited as first coming up with the idea that all substances are made of small particles called atoms, and that atoms cannot be broken up (in Greek, *atomos* means *indivisible*). Although modern atomic theory bases itself on this two-and-a-half-thousand-year-old idea, modern scientists have shown – practically – that this is not quite true. Indeed, harnessing the energy released by splitting the atom was one of the defining moments of the 20th century and, although humans haven't always used this technology for good, this is a source of energy on which we can rely as fossil fuels begin to be used up.

Throughout history, important discoveries in science have been linked to practical work and observations. By doing practical work and collecting data, scientists are able to put forward theories to explain the data produced. Sometimes, of course, the theory comes first; but the practical work is always there to help give evidence to show the theory is correct.

To think of examples from each science, Harvey could never have proposed the theory of blood circulation in humans without having performed experiments and dissections; Humfrey Davy would never have discovered and isolated so many chemical elements without using electricity to break up substances by electrolysis; and where would Newton's theory of gravity have been without the simple – if unplanned – experiment of dropping an apple on his head?

When designing this GCSE course, one aim has been to encourage your teachers to give you better access to practical work than has often been the case in the past. We think that practical work is very important for your enjoyment of science and, because it's also a great way to learn, we've tried to design our GCSE courses to put practical work back into them.

Part A – Planning

Your teacher will issue you with a student brief. This student brief will give you a bit of background, particularly telling you something about the experiment. It might be that the experiment you're doing is similar to one you've already encountered in your course. You should have some clues, therefore, about the sort of prediction or hypothesis that would be testable.

The planning task is under limited control – this means that you can discuss ideas with people in the class and do some other work as preparation. It's possible that you'll spend some time in class with your teacher discussing ideas which may be important to help you plan. Otherwise, you may be asked to do some research for homework to help you prepare for the planning section. You may be given some prompt questions – some questions for you to think about as you do your preparation.

Some key things for you to consider will be:

- **The apparatus you need to do the experiment**. Think about what you are trying to measure and which apparatus will do this best – and be prepared to justify your choice of equipment. Remember that it's often better to provide a labelled diagram of apparatus rather than a list!

- **How many readings to take**. Here, you want to consider the range of readings that you wish to take as well as whether you want to repeat any readings. Again, be prepared to justify the decisions you come to.

- **How to control factors in the experiment**. As well as thinking about how you're going to change the factor you're investigating, you also need to think about how you're going to make sure that other factors stay the same – in other words, how you make sure that the experiment is a fair test.

- **Any relevant safety factors**. Try to make sure that these are relevant to the experiment you're actually doing and not just general things like "tie your hair back".

- **The scientific theory** which can be used to justify your prediction.

The writing-up of your plan should take place in lesson time – depending on the length of your science lessons, you may be given more than one lesson, but the work will be collected in from you at the end of each lesson.

There are slightly different ways in which the planning exercise will be given to you. You'll already have had the briefing document and your teacher may feel, especially if you've been given some prompt questions, that you've got enough information to write your plan. Some teachers may issue you with the prompt questions again, in written form, just to remind you. Alternatively, you may be given something that looks a bit more like a question paper, with the prompt questions laid out one by one, with blank space left for you to answer each one. Whichever form you get, remember the key questions above and try to write a logical, concise plan that covers all of those points.

Hopefully, you'll get a chance to carry out your plan, so make sure that it's clear to follow and has all the necessary detail.

What makes a good plan?

Let's say that the hypothesis you're planning to test is:

> "The greater the mass of fuel burnt, the greater the rise of temperature in some water heated by the burning fuel."

The following is one possible plan to test the hypothesis. It is not a bad plan, but can you see where it can be improved?

> "I'm going to measure the rise in temperature when I burn 3 different fuels. I will put the burning fuel underneath a beaker of water and use the burning fuel to heat the water. I'll use a thermometer to measure the temperature of the water before the experiment and again once I have burnt the fuel. I'll measure out $100cm^3$ of water each time using the scale on the side of the beaker. I'll use a balance to measure the mass of the fuel burnt. The water being heated in the experiment might get quite hot, so I will have to take care when I handle the beaker containing hot water."

The list of apparatus is not very clear – what is being used to hold the fuel, for example? Also, no justification is given about the apparatus named – especially with regard to how well they make the measurements you need. So, is a beaker really a good piece of apparatus for measuring volume – rather than a measuring cylinder? And how accurate are the thermometer and the weighing balance?

Some factors are controlled – the volume of water is mentioned – but others are not mentioned e.g. using the same beaker each time. If someone else was doing this experiment, they'd need to know when to stop the experiment – this could be when a set mass of fuel has been burned or when there is a set temperature rise in the water. This is an important variable.

There's also no indication of some practical details to improve how well the experiment works e.g. stirring the water as it is heated, or stopping the fuel from evaporating.

It's clear how many fuels are being used – three – but is this a wide enough range of fuels to provide evidence for the hypothesis? There's also no mention of doing the experiment more than once in order to check that the results are correct and can be averaged.

Finally, there is a good, relevant safety feature mentioned; although other risks – especially of the burning fuel – have not been mentioned.

Remember that a good plan also depends on having a good hypothesis!

Part B – Observations

In most cases, your Part B task will follow the Planning task, and you will perform the experiment that you have just planned. However, your teacher may give you a new plan to carry out at this point if you have problems with the plan you wrote.

In some cases you may just complete the planning task because your teacher may choose to take the Planning task from one area of the course e.g. from Biology; and your Observations task from another e.g. Chemistry.

Remember, though, that the Part C (Conclusions) task will be based on the Observations task – so it is important that you collect a good set of data.

In many ways, the Observations task is the most straightforward – you will be following your plan or worksheet for the practical work you have to carry out. There are some things for you to consider when you carry out the practical and collect data or observations.

How many readings will you take for each experimental trial you do?

- If you're taking more than one reading, how are you going to check to see that your results each time are concordant? (Concordant is the scientific way of saying that the results agree with each other).

- You may also need to decide on a range of readings to take. For instance, if the plan tells you to set up a circuit and to vary the voltage in the circuit and measure the current, then you may have to decide on a range of voltages to use e.g. 2V, 4V, 6V, 8V, 10V and 12V.

How are you going to record your observations?

- Think here of whether you need any units in the data you are recording, and how many significant figures or decimal places you need to record.

The Observations task is also under limited control. This means that you may work in a group to collect data; and also discuss the range and number of readings you will take within the group. If you are working in a group, it's important that you take turns to do the stages in the experiment – don't rely on one person to do all the practical work and one person to do all the recording!

The final part of the Observations task will be for you to collect secondary evidence. Secondary evidence is often results from a similar experiment or an experiment testing a similar hypothesis. You'll be given some guidance on where to look for your secondary evidence.

Once you have collected data and observations, your teacher will probably ask you to hand these in. This is because you will need this information in the next part of the Controlled Assessment task and so it's very important that it is not lost, or taken home and accidentally left there!

Part C – Conclusions

In order to do the Conclusions task of the Controlled Assessment, you'll have to have completed the Observations task. Don't worry if you've been away when the Observations task was done – your teacher should be able to provide you with some results taken by other students in your class.

This part of the task is under high control. This means that you will be expected to work entirely by yourself. So if you were working in a group in the Observations task, make sure that the data you collected is written in a form that you can understand. It's a good idea to make sure that, if you worked in a group of two for Observations, that you make two copies of the data you collected.

Just as in the Planning task in Part A, there will be a series of prompt questions to help you with this part of the Controlled Assessment. Again, there will be different formats in which these questions may be given to you – if you are in doubt, ask your teacher.

Don't forget the secondary evidence you researched in Part B. You'll need to use this information, along with the data you have collected in Part B, in order to complete Part C.

The key areas for you to concentrate on as you look at the data or observations you have collected are:

- **How you are going to process and present your results**. Most of the time, you'll want to put your results into a table, so think about column headings and units as you draw your table. With many experiments, you'll have data that you can plot to make a graph – but is it best to have a bar chart or a line graph?

- **How well the data you have collected supports the prediction or hypothesis**. You need to be able to use your knowledge of some scientific principles in order to justify the conclusion you make here.

- **An evaluation of the experiment that you did**. Here, you need to think about two things: how the set-up of the experiment worked well and allowed you to collect data of a high quality; and secondly, if there were some areas where the set-up was not helpful. Try to think about how easy the experiment was to do, but also think about how well the equipment you used worked and how good the results you collected were. When you come to think about things which were not good about the experiment, come up with some suggestions about things that you might like to change in order to make it easier to collect results and to make the results more accurate. Lastly, consider what effects any weaknesses in the experiment had on the data you collected and, therefore, how confident you are that your conclusion is correct.

- Don't forget to use the **secondary data** together with your own data when making your final conclusion. And don't forget to use your scientific knowledge to explain why you have come to this conclusion.

Of the three parts of the Controlled Assessment, Part C is probably the most challenging – mostly because you're doing it by yourself. Remember that you can practise the skills needed to succeed in this part of the Controlled Assessment – use your textbook wisely, as it will have lots of advice on tackling the different aspects of the practical work.

And don't forget that you can have more than one go at any part of the Controlled Assessment – it's your best mark for each part of the task that counts!

Biology 3
Using biology

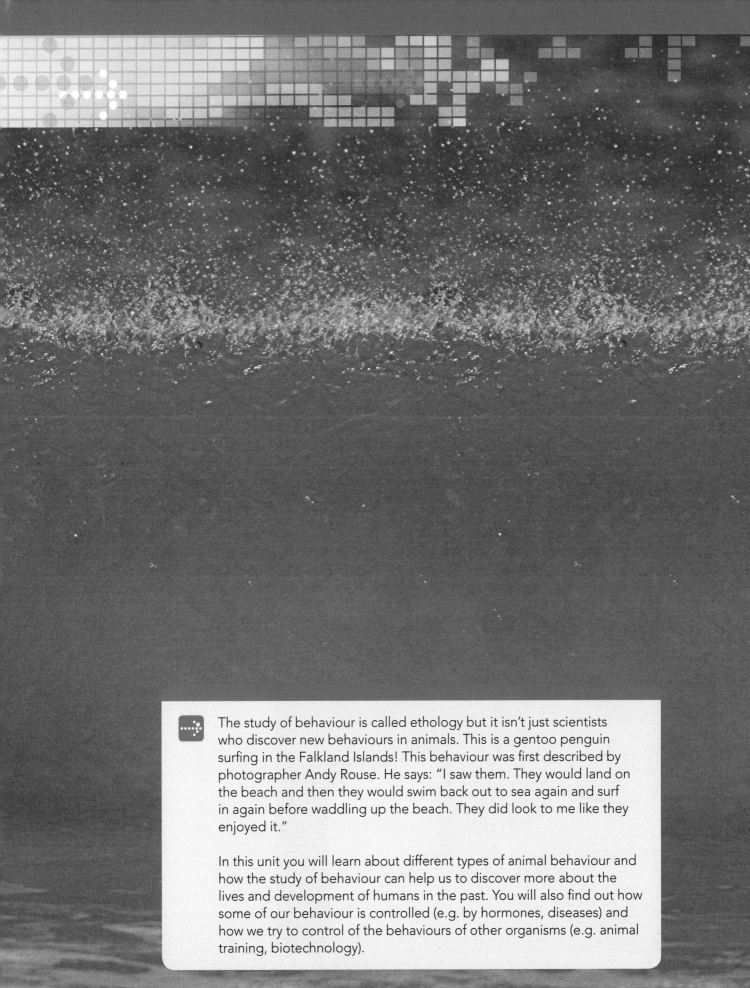

The study of behaviour is called ethology but it isn't just scientists who discover new behaviours in animals. This is a gentoo penguin surfing in the Falkland Islands! This behaviour was first described by photographer Andy Rouse. He says: "I saw them. They would land on the beach and then they would swim back out to sea again and surf in again before waddling up the beach. They did look to me like they enjoyed it."

In this unit you will learn about different types of animal behaviour and how the study of behaviour can help us to discover more about the lives and development of humans in the past. You will also find out how some of our behaviour is controlled (e.g. by hormones, diseases) and how we try to control of the behaviours of other organisms (e.g. animal training, biotechnology).

B3.1 Rhythms

What are circadian rhythms?

This is a palolo worm – a delicacy in the South Pacific. It's only available on one night a year, when the wriggling worms fill the sea as they release egg cells and sperm cells. The islanders scoop the worms up and swallow them raw, or keep them until morning and roast them.

A *A palolo worm*

Biological rhythms

The palolo worms' activity happens only once a year. However, many biological rhythms happen over one day and these are known as **circadian rhythms**.

The human brain contains a timing mechanism called a **biological clock**, which regulates many things that happen in our bodies over a 24-hour period. This includes the release of **hormones**. Hormones are 'chemical messengers' that are made in the body. They are carried in the blood and affect different parts of the body.

For example, at night, usually around 10 pm, we secrete increased quantities of a hormone called melatonin. Melatonin makes us feel sleepy. Levels of melatonin drop in the morning, so we wake up. That's why most people feel sleepy at night and more alert during the daytime.

> **?**
> **1** What is a circadian rhythm?
>
> **2** Give two examples of circadian rhythms in humans.

B *Some people use light therapy and/or melatonin capsules to try to get over jet lag.*

Although our biological clock has its own built-in rhythm, it needs regular exposure to day and night to keep it in sync with a 24-hour cycle. If we travel east or west round the globe, then the day–night cycle comes earlier or later than the one the body is using. This can make a person feel less alert and less able to think clearly. This is called jet lag.

Plants have circadian rhythms too. Flowers often open during the daytime and close at night. This makes sure they are ready for insects to visit them for pollination during the daytime, and the pollen is protected from wind, cold and damp at night. The flowers only produce nectar during the daytime, when insects are likely to visit the flowers.

Photoperiodism

As well as their circadian rhythms, many plants have yearly rhythms. They use change in day length to help them grow or flower at the right time. Responses to changing day length are called **photoperiodism**.

Many species of plants die in the tough conditions of winter, but their seeds survive. In spring, as the days get longer, the seeds sense this and **germinate**.

Some plant species may grow all through the winter, but respond to the lengthening days by growing faster. In the autumn, as days get shorter, other plant species stop growing and get ready to survive the hard times ahead.

In many plant species, flowering is also controlled by the length of dark or light during a 24-hour period.

C *Daisy flowers open during the day and close at night.*

Plant	Flowers when ...
Iris	there are more than 12 hours of light in a day
Poinsettia	there are more than 14 hours of dark in a day
Spinach	there are more than 14 hours of light in a day

D *The number of hours of light needed for some plants to flower.*

Skills spotlight

How could you find out if a plant that produces flowers in spring is responding to changes in day length, or to some other factor that is changing at this time of year?

3 What is photoperiodism?

4 Why is it useful for seeds not to germinate until days are getting longer?

5 Which of the plants shown in Table D flowers in the spring? Explain your answer.

6 Footballers give their peak performances in the afternoon. Match results show that a football team travelling from the west coast of the USA to play a night game against an east coast team at home has a big advantage. Use your knowledge of circadian rhythms to suggest why.

ResultsPlus
Watch Out!

Some students make the mistake of saying that all biological rhythms are called 'circadian rhythms'. However, circadian rhythms are 24-hour cycles.

Learning Outcomes

1.31 Explain the importance of photoperiodicity in plants, including
  a plant germination *b* growth *c* reproduction

1.32 Demonstrate an understanding of circadian rhythms in living organisms

HSW 5 Plan to test a scientific idea, answer a scientific question, or solve a scientific problem

>>>>>>>>>>>>>>>>>>>>>>> If you are unable to move, how can you defend yourself against attack?

B3.2 Plant defences

Why are some plants poisonous?

Many people grow lupins in their gardens for their flowers, but in some countries the seeds are eaten as a snack. However, the seeds contain poisonous chemicals so they have to be elaborately cooked to make them safe. The poison affects the nervous system, causing blurred vision and nervousness.

A *The young leaves and seeds of lupins are poisonous.*

1 Why do plants produce poisonous chemicals?

2 Give one example of a plant that produces poisonous chemicals in its leaves.

Young lupin leaves produce poisonous chemicals called alkaloids. The production of these chemicals follows a circadian rhythm – production starts in the early morning and stops at night.

The chemicals make the leaves poisonous to insect **pests** or larger herbivores that might want to eat them. Even though the plant may have to use a lot of energy and materials to make the chemicals, it is worth it.

stoma (breathing pore) in potato leaf

these swellings of the potato blight pathogen contain spores that will burst out and spread to other plants

B *Parts of the potato blight pathogen grow out through the stomata of a potato leaf to shed spores.*

Many plants also use chemicals to defend themselves against **pathogens** – organisms that cause disease. For example, potato plants are often attacked by a fungus-like organism called potato blight that destroys their leaves, killing the plant. A few varieties of potatoes respond to attack from potato blight by producing chemicals that kill it. Scientists are attempting to produce high-yielding varieties of potatoes that readily produce these chemicals and so are resistant to potato blight.

3 What is meant by the terms 'pathogen' and 'pest'?

4 Scientists are trying to develop more resistant crops. Which of the crops in Figure C would benefit most from such developments?

People depend on plants for much of their food. If pathogens destroy or damage a crop then our food supply is at risk. For example, the famine caused by potato blight in Ireland in 1845 and 1846 is estimated to have killed over 1 million people.

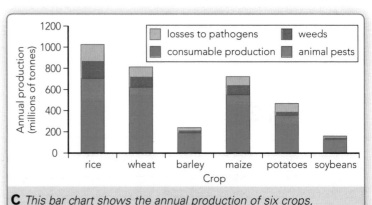

C *This bar chart shows the annual production of six crops, and the quantities lost to pathogens each year.*
Source: Agency BATS, www.bats.ch<http://www.bats.ch>

Making use of plant poisons

Although some chemicals in plants are poisonous to people, in small amounts they may have useful effects. For example, digoxin is a chemical found in foxgloves. At high doses it can kill because it affects how the heart beats. However, at lower doses it was found to improve the heartbeat. So now it is commonly used to treat heart disorders.

We use many different plant poisons as medicinal drugs. For example:
• quinine, produced by cinchona trees, has been used to treat the disease malaria
• aspirin, produced by willow trees, has been used to treat **symptoms** of disease, such as pain and fever.

New possibilities are being researched all the time. For example, potato plants produce poisonous alkaloids in their leaves or in tubers that have been exposed to light. In one incident in 1978, 78 English schoolchildren became ill after eating school lunch containing potatoes that had been left in the light and had gone green. However, research suggests that these alkaloids could be developed as valuable treatments for cancer.

Louis Pasteur

As well as treating diseases, we also try to prevent them. Louis Pasteur (1822 – 1895) showed that microorganisms were responsible for some diseases and for foods going off. He proposed the idea of keeping microorganisms away from people and foods in order to stop some diseases and to preserve foods. Today, we refer to the methods used to keep things free from living microorganisms as **aseptic techniques**. This includes the process of **pasteurisation**, in which foods (such as milk) are heated briefly before being stored in order to kill bacteria in them.

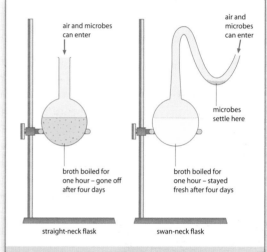

D *The beaver stores chemicals from willow bark in glands for scent-marking its territory. Until aspirin was developed, people ate these glands to reduce pain and fever.*

E *Pasteur carried out an experiment like this in 1864. He concluded that neither the air nor the food itself caused a food to go off.*

---

5 Explain why some poisonous chemicals in plants can be useful for treating human diseases.

6 Explain how Pasteur drew his conclusion from the experiment shown in Figure E.

7 a What are aseptic techniques?
b Suggest two aseptic techniques used in a kitchen.

8 Explain why it is worthwhile for many plants to use up energy in producing poisonous compounds in their leaves. You should refer to two specific examples in your answer.

Skills spotlight

Many native people rely on plants to treat all their symptoms and diseases. Imagine you go on an expedition. How would you find out which wild plants to take back and research for new treatments?

Learning Outcomes

1.27 Demonstrate an understanding of Louis Pasteur's contribution to the development of aseptic techniques

1.29 Demonstrate an understanding that plants defend themselves against attack from pests and pathogens by producing chemicals, some of which can be used to treat human diseases, disorders or relieve symptoms

1.30 Demonstrate an understanding of the impact that attack by pathogens on plants has on human food supply

HSW *1* Explain how scientific data is collected and analysed

B3.3 What affects the rate that microorganisms grow?

 What conditions affect how quickly microorganisms grow in milk?

Microorganisms such as bacteria, can cause diseases in living organisms. It is the bacteria in milk which make it go off so it is important to keep the numbers as low as possible to keep the milk fresh. The milking equipment is sterilised, the cow's udders are washed before milking and the milk is cooled rapidly to slow the growth of the bacteria. Most milk is then pasteurised.

A *In some dairies milking robots milk the cows automatically whenever they come into the parlour.*

If bacteria have everything they need (such as food, oxygen and warmth) they can grow very quickly. When a bacterial cell is large enough, it reproduces by dividing in two. If all the bacterial cells in a culture keep dividing in two, the number of cells increases exponentially. We say the population shows **exponential growth**. In the right conditions some kinds of bacteria can divide every 20 minutes. If milk with high levels of bacteria is drunk it could cause infections of the gut, such as food poisoning, or other illnesses.

One way of measuring how many bacteria there are in a sample is to use resazurin dye. This shows how quickly the oxygen is used up. The more bacteria there are, the more quickly the oxygen levels fall. Resazurin is blue when there is plenty of oxygen. It turns pink and eventually colourless when oxygen levels fall.

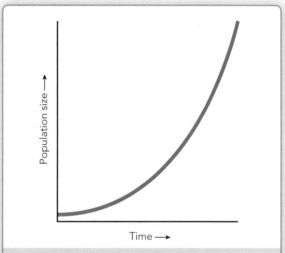

B *In the right conditions one bacterium can form a colony of millions in a few days.*

Your task

You are going to plan an investigation that will allow you to find out about one condition which affects the growth of microorganisms. To do this you will use **resazurin dye** to show up how quickly the bacteria are growing.

Learning Outcomes

1.26 Describe how the exponential growth of a population of bacteria can lead to rapid development of an infection

1.28 *Investigate the conditions affecting growth of micro-organisms (using resazurin dye)*

ResultsPlus
Build Better Answers

When planning an investigation like this, one of the skills you will be assessed on is your ability to *form a hypothesis*. There are 4 marks available for this skill. Here are two extracts taken from two students' controlled assessments.

Student extract 1 — A basic response for this skill

The student has formed a clear hypothesis.

> I think that the way that milk is stored will affect how quickly microorganisms grow in it and how quickly it will go bad. I think this because I know that if I leave milk out of the fridge it goes bad.

The student has then explained why they think their hypothesis is true.

To access the higher marks for this section the student should use some scientific knowledge to explain the hypothesis.

Student extract 2 — A good response for this skill

The student has given a clear and detailed hypothesis.

> I think that if I leave milk samples in warm conditions (i.e. room temperature) then microorganisms are more likely grow quickly. The growth of the microorganisms will eventually turn the milk sour. I think that this will happen because there are a small number of microorganisms in the milk already. I also know that cooling food down slows down the growth of microorganisms because growth rates are changed by temperature. Warm temperatures increase the growth rates.

The student has also used their scientific knowledge to explain the hypothesis.

 ResultsPlus

To access 2 marks

- Provide a hypothesis that is appropriate for most of the task
- Partially justify the hypothesis

To access 4 marks

- Provide a hypothesis that is appropriate for the full scope of the task, based on relevant scientific ideas
- Justify the hypothesis fully using relevant scientific ideas

B3.4 Vaccines

What are vaccines and how do they work?

This is Rahina Banu, from Bangladesh. The photo was taken in 1975, when she was 2 years old and suffering from the deadly disease smallpox. She was one of the very last people in the world ever to get this disease, which was completely eradicated by 1979 as a result of world-wide vaccination.

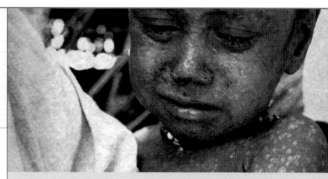

A *Rahina was lucky and survived her smallpox infection.*

> **1** Why was Jenner investigating smallpox?
>
> **2** What observation led Jenner to think that giving someone cowpox might prevent them from getting smallpox?

Smallpox was a common and very serious disease in the 1700s, and even if it did not kill a person it often left them severely disfigured.

Edward Jenner (1749–1823) noticed that milkmaids didn't seem to get smallpox. He thought that perhaps getting cowpox (a mild disease that people caught from cows) might stop you getting smallpox.

In 1796, Jenner took pus from a cowpox blister and rubbed it into the skin of an 8-year-old boy called James Phipps. James got a mild fever but that was all. Some time later, Jenner did the same with pus from a smallpox blister. James did not get smallpox. The cowpox **vaccine** had made him immune to smallpox.

> **3** Explain the difference between an antigen and an antibody.
>
> **4** Explain how vaccination makes you immune to a disease.

Smallpox is caused by a virus. All viruses and cells have chemicals on their outer surfaces, called **antigens**. Our bodies recognise 'foreign' antigens and so destroy foreign viruses and cells, often by using **antibodies** that stick to the pathogen antigens.

A vaccine contains harmless versions of a pathogen, or parts of it. White blood cells, called **lymphocytes**, respond to the vaccine. Some of these become **memory lymphocytes**. The way the body responds to **infection** is called the **immune response**. Making someone immune to a disease is called **immunisation**.

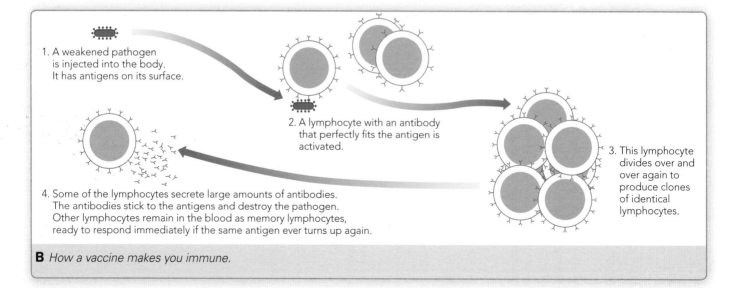

1. A weakened pathogen is injected into the body. It has antigens on its surface.

2. A lymphocyte with an antibody that perfectly fits the antigen is activated.

3. This lymphocyte divides over and over again to produce clones of identical lymphocytes.

4. Some of the lymphocytes secrete large amounts of antibodies. The antibodies stick to the antigens and destroy the pathogen. Other lymphocytes remain in the blood as memory lymphocytes, ready to respond immediately if the same antigen ever turns up again.

B *How a vaccine makes you immune.*

Are vaccines safe?

All young children in the UK are offered immunisation against dangerous childhood diseases, such as measles and whooping cough. Before immunisation was introduced many children died or were harmed by these diseases. For example, about 1 in every 2000 children infected with measles suffered permanent brain damage or died.

Today, very few children are affected by these diseases. However, some react to the vaccines. About 20% of children may get a mild fever or rash from the measles vaccine, and about 1 in a million has a dangerous reaction. Because people have forgotten what the diseases are like, they are more concerned about the risks of immunisation. Media scares about the risks of immunisation can persuade parents to not have their children immunised.

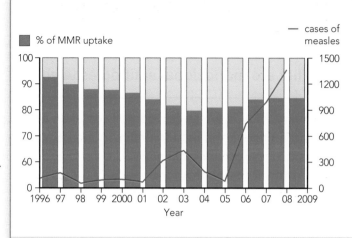

C *This graph shows changes in the proportion of children immunised with MMR vaccine (that protects against measles, mumps and rubella) and the number of cases of measles.*

Risks of immunisation

- It's quite common for a person to get swelling or redness around the site of the vaccination.
- Some children may get a mild form of the disease they are being vaccinated against.
- Very, very rarely a child suffers an allergic reaction – as some people do to bee stings.

Advantages of immunisation

- A child can become immune to a disease without having to suffer from it.
- The chances of any long-lasting harm are much, much less than if a person actually has a disease such as measles, mumps, rubella or diphtheria.
- If enough children are vaccinated against a disease, then it becomes so rare that even unvaccinated individuals are unlikely to get it.

Skills spotlight

In 1998, Andrew Wakefield, a doctor, published an article in which he suggested that the MMR vaccine might cause children to develop autism. Others on his team thought his data didn't show a genuine link between autism and the MMR vaccine and that he had jumped to this conclusion without good evidence. Explain why Wakefield was later condemned for acting 'dishonestly and irresponsibly'.

5 What do vaccines contain?

6 Use Figure C to suggest and explain why the media scare about the MMR vaccine affected vaccination and the number cases of measles.

7 Doctors need to persuade parents to have their children vaccinated. Design a poster to encourage immunisation, explaining how the process works.

Learning Outcomes

1.20 Describe Edward Jenner's contribution to the development of vaccines

1.21 Explain the process of immunisation, including:
  a harmless pathogen or antigenic material introduced
  b the antigens trigger an immune response which causes the production of antibodies
  c the antigens also trigger production of memory lymphocytes

1.22 Demonstrate an understanding of the advantages and risks associated with immunisation

HSW 14 Describe how scientists share data and discuss new ideas, and how over time this process helps to reduce uncertainties and revise scientific theories

What are monoclonal antibodies used for?

In February 2004, a white powder fell out of an envelope that had arrived in the Senate Office in the USA. Tests with biosensors, using monoclonal antibodies, showed that it was ricin, a powerful poison from the seeds of the castor oil plant.

A *US Marines searched the Senate Office for any other suspicious envelopes.*

> **1 a** Use Figure B to *describe* how the production of antibodies differs between the first and second infections.
> **b** Now *explain* these differences.

The entry of a pathogen into the body is known as infection. The first time a pathogen infects a person, only one or two lymphocytes recognise the antigens on it. It takes a while for them to multiply and secrete enough antibodies to destroy the pathogens. This is the **primary response**.

B *Primary and secondary responses to infection.*

After an infection or immunisation, memory lymphocytes remain in the blood, sometimes for the rest of a person's life. They can immediately make the right antibodies if the same pathogen re-enters the body. This is the **secondary response**. It's more than likely that the lymphocytes will be able to produce enough antibodies to destroy the pathogens before they have a chance to increase in numbers enough to make the person ill.

Monoclonal antibodies

Since antibodies are very specific, scientists can use them to identify particular substances. To do this, scientists need large quantities of identical antibodies. These are called **monoclonal antibodies**.

A lymphocyte can divide over and over again to make identical copies (**clones**) of itself. However, once it has started to make antibodies it becomes a **B lymphocyte**, and can't divide anymore.

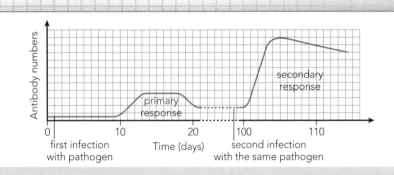

stage 1

A particular antigen (for example, HGH) is injected into a mouse. The mouse produces lymphocytes that make antibodies against HGH.

antigen injected into mouse

myeloma (cancer) cells growing in culture medium

stage 2

B lymphocyte from mouse

cancer cell

stage 3

The hybridoma cell can both divide and make antibodies against HGH. These are monoclonal antibodies.

fusion

hybridoma cell

C *How monoclonal antibodies are made.*

To get round this problem in the laboratory, a B lymphocyte is fused with a cancer cell that can divide hundreds of times. The resulting cell is called a **hybridoma**.

Using monoclonal antibodies

Pregnancy testing kits use monoclonal antibodies to detect a hormone called HGH, found in the urine of pregnant women. A dipstick is dipped into some urine and, if there is any HGH in it, it binds to the monoclonal antibodies on the stick and causes a colour change.

Monoclonal antibodies can be made slightly radioactive. Some monoclonal antibodies bind to substances found in the membranes of platelets or cancer cells. (Platelets are fragments of cells that help to form blood clots – in the wrong places, such as the brain or heart, these can kill.) The antibodies are injected into the patient's body, where they stick to the platelets or cancer cells. Radiologists can then detect where the antibodies are (which then tells them where any blood clots or cancer cells are) so they can be treated.

Many people with cancer are given drugs (chemotherapy) or ionising radiation (**radiotherapy**) to kill cancer cells. With both of those types of treatment, it's difficult to make sure that only the cancerous cells are targeted.

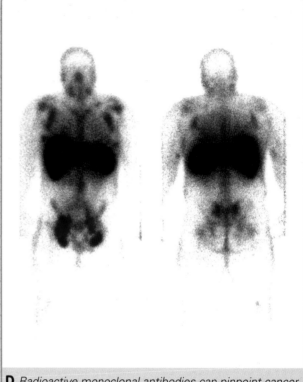

D *Radioactive monoclonal antibodies can pinpoint cancer cells. The red and black areas show where there are cancer cells.*

However, drugs can be attached to monoclonal antibodies, to deliver the drug only to the cells that need to be destroyed. This means that less of the drug is needed, as none of it is wasted in parts of the body that are healthy. There is also much less risk of harming healthy cells.

2 What are monoclonal antibodies?

3 Why are hybridoma cells needed to produce monoclonal antibodies?

4 Explain how monoclonal antibodies are used to diagnose and treat cancer.

Skills spotlight

New scientific techniques are developed to be beneficial. Explain the advantages of using monoclonal antibodies for treating cancer, rather than using standard drugs or ionising radiation.

H *1.23* Describe the role of memory lymphocytes in secondary responses to antigen; interpret data showing variation in blood antibody levels in response to first and subsequent infections

H *1.24* Describe the production of monoclonal antibodies, including:
   a use of B lymphocytes which produce desired antibodies but do not divide
   b production of hybridoma cells
   c hybridoma cells produce antibodies and they divide

H *1.25* Demonstrate an understanding of the use of monoclonal antibodies, including:
   a in pregnancy testing
   b use in diagnosis including locating the position of blood clots and cancer cells and in treatment of diseases including cancer
   c the advantages of using monoclonal antibodies to target specific cells compared to drug and radiotherapy treatments

HSW 12 Describe the benefits of using new scientific and technological developments

What happens if your kidneys stop working?

In the 1980s, an ancient human skeleton was dug up in South Africa. This skeleton had two lumps of a calcium-rich substance where its kidneys would have been. They were probably kidney stones, big enough to kill.

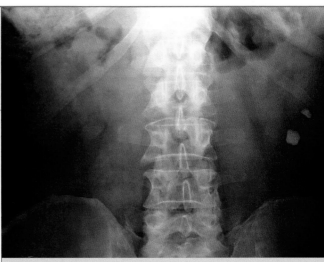

A The red blobs on this X-ray are kidney stones. They can be very painful and can stop the kidneys from working properly.

> **?**
>
> 1 Where is urea made, and what is it made from?
>
> 2 Which organs remove urea from the body?
>
> 3 Explain the difference between urea and urine.

Getting rid of waste

The chemical reactions happening inside the body (**metabolic reactions**) produce waste products. For example, respiring cells produce carbon dioxide and liver cells produce **urea** from excess amino acids. Both of these waste products are put into the blood. Carbon dioxide is removed in the lungs and the kidneys filter out the urea.

Blood is brought to the kidneys in the **renal arteries**. Urea and other substances are filtered out of the blood and form **urine**. The cleaned blood flows out of the kidneys in the **renal veins** and the urine is excreted.

Treating kidney failure

Sometimes (e.g. due to an infection) both of a person's kidneys stop working properly. The person's life will be in danger, because poisonous urea starts to build up in the blood. If the kidneys cannot be repaired the best treatment is a **kidney transplant**.

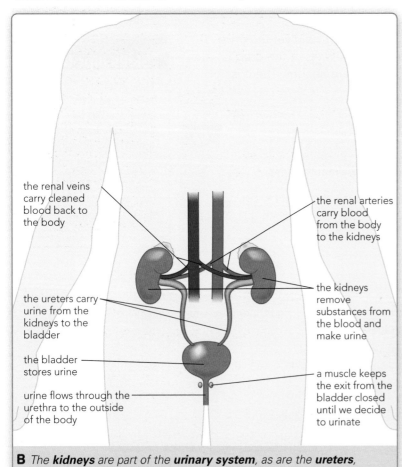

the renal veins carry cleaned blood back to the body

the renal arteries carry blood from the body to the kidneys

the ureters carry urine from the kidneys to the bladder

the kidneys remove substances from the blood and make urine

the bladder stores urine

a muscle keeps the exit from the bladder closed until we decide to urinate

urine flows through the urethra to the outside of the body

B The **kidneys** are part of the **urinary system**, as are the **ureters**, **bladder** and **urethra**.

C The man on the right is about to donate one of his kidneys to his 13-year-old brother. The man on the left is one of the doctors who will perform the operation.

You can't put just any kidney into a person's body. Kidney cells, like all cells, have antigens on them, and the cells in the immune system quickly recognise any strange antigens. They attack the foreign cells and kill them – we say the organ has been **rejected**.

The antigens on the donated organ must therefore be very similar to those on the patient's cells. This means it can take a long time to find a suitable kidney for a patient. Sometimes a family member may be able to donate a kidney (you can manage perfectly well with just one kidney). Close relatives are more likely to have similar antigens than strangers.

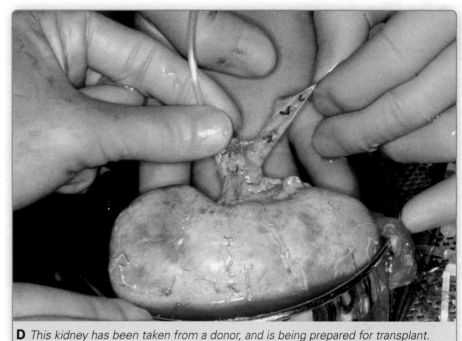

D *This kidney has been taken from a donor, and is being prepared for transplant.*

Even with a good match, the patient will need life-long medication to prevent the kidney being rejected. This medication affects the body's response to infection, so the patient may catch diseases like colds more easily.

While a person is waiting for a kidney transplant, they will be treated with a kidney **dialysis** machine that removes waste products from their blood. Dialysis machines are expensive, and the patient will have to be connected to one for several hours, several times a week.

4 Explain why a recipient's body sometimes attacks and destroys a transplanted kidney.

5 Most people with kidney failure would prefer a kidney transplant to dialysis. Discuss the reasons for this, and explain why many people are unable to have a kidney transplant.

Skills spotlight

Developments in science and technology often make us face difficult ethical issues. People in some parts of the world may be tempted to sell a kidney for use by someone who needs a transplant. Buying organs for transplant in the UK is illegal at the moment. Do you think this practice should be legalised? Construct an argument 'for' or 'against' legalisation.

Learning Outcomes

1.1 Demonstrate an understanding that cell metabolism leads to the build-up of waste products in the blood, including carbon dioxide and urea

1.2 Recall that urea is produced from the breakdown of excess amino acids in the liver and is removed by the kidneys

1.3 Describe the structure of the urinary system, including:
 a renal artery and vein
 b kidneys
 c ureters
 d bladder
 e urethra

1.4 Describe possible treatments for kidney failure, including kidney dialysis and organ donation

HSW **13** Explain how scientific evidence is used to guide decisions about the use and application of science and technology, for example whether kidneys for transplant could be bought

Inside the kidneys

How do kidneys clean the blood?

If someone was ill in the Middle Ages, the first thing a doctor might do when he examined them was to taste their urine. He'd look at it as well – the colour and taste would give clues about what was wrong with them.

A *A 15th-century urine colour chart. Doctors still use urine in diagnosis today – but they don't usually taste it!*

> **1** What is a nephron, and where are they found? ?

How kidneys work

Each kidney contains thousands of tiny, microscopic tubes called **nephrons**.

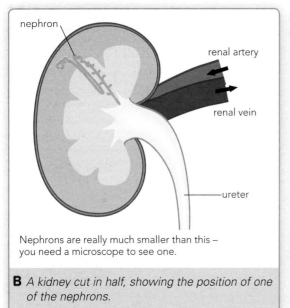

Nephrons are really much smaller than this – you need a microscope to see one.

B *A kidney cut in half, showing the position of one of the nephrons.*

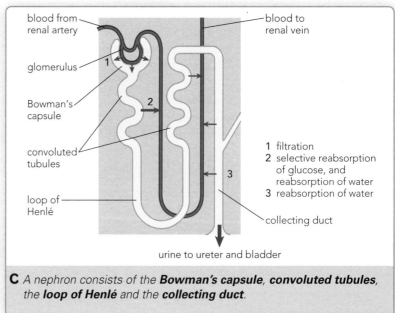

1 filtration
2 selective reabsorption of glucose, and reabsorption of water
3 reabsorption of water

C *A nephron consists of the **Bowman's capsule**, **convoluted tubules**, the **loop of Henlé** and the **collecting duct**.*

> **2** Name the part of a nephron in which these events take place:
> **a** filtration
> **b** selective reabsorption of glucose
> **c** osmoregulation. ?
>
> **3** Name two substances that are filtered from the blood into the nephron, and two that stay in the blood.

This is how a nephron works:
- Blood flows along the renal artery and into a network of capillaries called a **glomerulus**, which runs inside the Bowman's capsule of the nephron.
- The capsule has tiny holes that let really small molecules, such as water, urea and glucose, through into the nephron. Big molecules like proteins, and blood cells stay in the blood. This process is called **filtration**.
- The fluid flows along inside the nephron. Some substances are absorbed back through the walls of the nephron into the blood. Only useful substances that the body needs return to the blood, such as glucose, so this is called **selective reabsorption**. Water is also reabsorbed depending on how much the body needs. This is called **osmoregulation**.
- At the end of the nephron the remaining fluid flows into the ureter. The fluid contains excess water that the body doesn't need, plus urea and other substances. It is now called urine.

Controlling water content

As well as getting rid of urea, the kidneys help to control the water content of the blood. The kidneys are controlled by the **pituitary gland**, which secretes several hormones. One of these, **ADH** (antidiuretic hormone), helps to control the water content of the blood.

The control of water content is a good example of a mechanism called **negative feedback**. This is where a change in a factor leads to the opposite change happening to keep things fairly constant, even if their tendency is to keep changing.

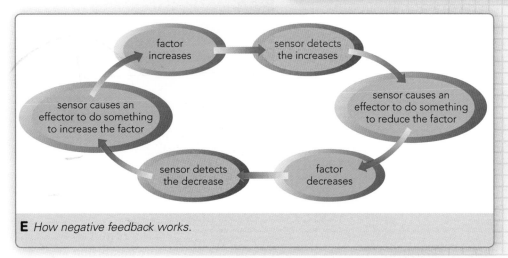

The brain senses there is not enough water in the blood.

The pituitary gland secretes more ADH.

The ADH causes the kidneys to reabsorb more water.

A small volume of concentrated urine is produced.

The brain senses there is too much water in the blood.

The pituitary gland secretes less ADH.

This makes the kidneys reabsorb less water.

A large volume of dilute urine is produced.

pituitary gland

D *ADH and the control of water content.*

factor increases

sensor detects the increases

sensor causes an effector to do something to reduce the factor

factor decreases

sensor detects the decrease

sensor causes an effector to do something to increase the factor

E *How negative feedback works.*

Skills spotlight

H The negative feedback diagram is a model of feedback control. Draw a similar diagram, but instead of using the words 'sensor', 'effector' and 'factor', use words that describe how the water content of the blood is controlled, and explain how this helps us to understand the control of ADH production.

H 4 What is ADH, where is it produced and where does it have an effect?

H 5 Explain in your own words what 'negative feedback' means.

6 Explain why urine contains water but not glucose. You should refer to the way that a nephron works in your answer.

ResultsPlus
Watch Out!

Students find explaining the action of ADH hard because of the "anti" bit. Diuresis is the production of lots of dilute urine. ADH stops this by causing reabsorption of water from urine.

Learning Outcomes

1.5 Describe the structure of a nephron including:
  a glomerulus and Bowman's capsule **b** convoluted tubule **c** loop of Henlé **d** collecting duct

1.6 Explain how the structure of the nephron is related to its function in filtering the blood and forming urine (osmoregulation), including:
  a filtration in the glomerulus and Bowman's capsule **b** selective reabsorption of glucose
  c reabsorption of water (osmoregulation) **d** removal of excess water in urine

H **1.7** Demonstrate an understanding of the role of ADH (produced by the pituitary gland) in regulating the water content of the blood

H **1.8** Demonstrate an understanding of how ADH production is controlled by a negative feedback mechanism

HSW **3** Describe how phenomena are explained using scientific models

>>>>>>>>>>>>>>>>> Some perfumes and aftershaves contain pheromones – what are pheromones?

The menstrual cycle

How is a woman's menstrual cycle controlled?

There's an idea that we produce chemicals called pheromones that make us attractive to the opposite sex. It's thought that, in men, they may vary according to the time of day. In women, they may vary according to the menstrual cycle.

A *The perfume (called Realm) contains pheromones that are meant to be attractive to the opposite sex.*

1 On which day of the cycle does ovulation take place?

2 Women may release pheromones that make them particularly attractive to men when they have egg cells ready to be fertilised. On which days of the cycle would you expect these pheromones to be produced?

Between the ages of about 12 and 50 (the ages vary in different women) most women have a **menstrual cycle** that lasts for roughly 4 weeks. During the cycle an egg cell is released from an ovary. This is called **ovulation**. The lining of the **uterus** thickens to receive the egg cell. After a few weeks the uterus lining breaks down and is lost with the egg in **menstruation**. Figure B shows what happens during the cycle.

Oestrogen and **progesterone** are hormones that are secreted by the ovaries and control the menstrual cycle.

The menstrual cycle stops if an egg cell is fertilised. When that happens, the thickened lining of the uterus stays in place, so the embryo can embed into it and begin to develop. Missing a normal menstrual period is usually the first clue that a woman may be pregnant.

3 Explain why menstruation doesn't take place if fertilisation happens.

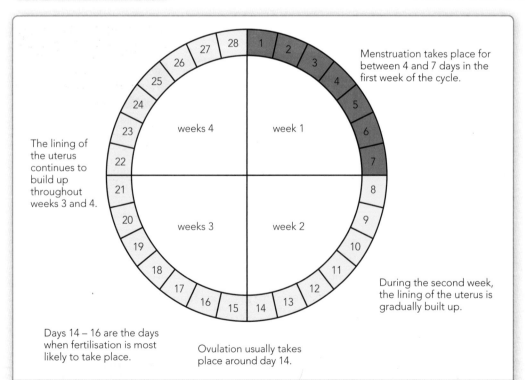

Menstruation takes place for between 4 and 7 days in the first week of the cycle.

The lining of the uterus continues to build up throughout weeks 3 and 4.

During the second week, the lining of the uterus is gradually built up.

Days 14 – 16 are the days when fertilisation is most likely to take place.

Ovulation usually takes place around day 14.

B *What happens during one menstrual cycle.*

Hormones and the menstrual cycle

Oestrogen and progesterone are not the only hormones that control the menstrual cycle. **FSH** (follicle-stimulating hormone) and **LH** (luteinising hormone) are hormones secreted by the **pituitary gland** that also play a part. The release of these hormones is controlled by the levels of oestrogen (which increase as the egg **follicle** matures) and progesterone (which is secreted by the follicle after it releases the egg and becomes the **corpus luteum**). Figure C shows how the pituitary gland, ovaries and uterus interact to make the menstrual cycle happen.

If fertilisation occurs, the corpus luteum continues to secrete progesterone so that levels of the hormone remain high.

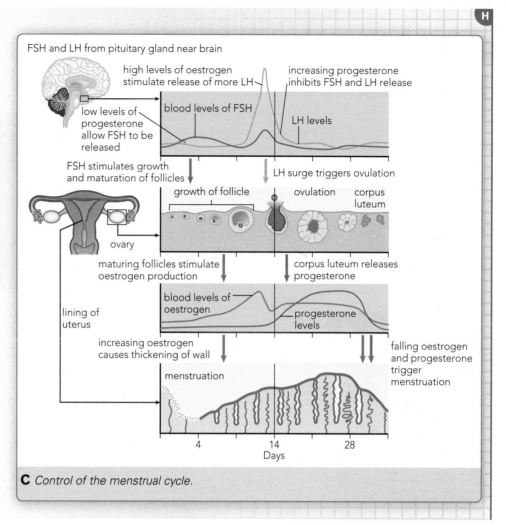

C Control of the menstrual cycle.

In the figure: FSH and LH from pituitary gland near brain; high levels of oestrogen stimulate release of more LH; increasing progesterone inhibits FSH and LH release; low levels of progesterone allow FSH to be released; blood levels of FSH; LH levels; FSH stimulates growth and maturation of follicles; LH surge triggers ovulation; growth of follicle; ovulation; corpus luteum; ovary; maturing follicles stimulate oestrogen production; corpus luteum releases progesterone; lining of uterus; blood levels of oestrogen; progesterone levels; increasing oestrogen causes thickening of wall; falling oestrogen and progesterone trigger menstruation; menstruation; Days 4, 14, 28

H **4** On which day of the cycle does the LH surge occur?

H **5** Suggest how the fall in progesterone in the 4th week of the cycle can make the whole cycle start again from the beginning.

H **6** If an egg cell is fertilised, the corpus luteum carries on secreting progesterone – it doesn't break down. Explain why that stops menstruation happening.

7 A woman wants to know on which day in June ovulation is likely to happen. Her menstrual period happened between June 2nd and 7th. Explain to her how she can work out the answer to her question.

Skills spotlight

Use the negative feedback model on page 41 to draw a diagram that explains the feedback control of the menstrual cycle by hormones.

Learning Outcomes

1.9 Recall that the menstrual cycle is controlled by the hormones oestrogen and progesterone

1.10 Describe the stages of the menstrual cycle including menstruation, uterus lining thickening and ovulation

1.11 Explain why the uterus lining is maintained if fertilisation occurs

H **1.12** Demonstrate an understanding of how oestrogen, progesterone, FSH and LH control the menstrual cycle

H **1.13** Demonstrate an understanding of how the menstrual cycle is controlled by a negative feedback mechanism

HSW **3** Describe how phenomena are explained using scientific models

How can a woman have another woman's baby?

Fertilisation

What happens at fertilisation?

When the eggs of this tiny poison frog hatch, the male carries each tadpole to its own private pool. He calls to the female, who responds by laying a new egg in the pool. But this egg doesn't grow into a tadpole – it's just for the first tadpole to eat.

A *Watched by the male, this female poison frog is laying a 'food egg'.*

Egg cells and sperm cells

Egg cells and sperm cells are **gametes** (**sex cells**). They are highly specialised for their very important functions.

Watch Out!

Students sometimes forget that the large amount of cytoplasm in the egg is needed to supply the nutrients for the cell divisions when it becomes a zygote at fertilisation.

1 Describe three ways in which a sperm differs from an egg. For each difference explain its importance.

2 a What does 'haploid' mean?
b Why are egg cells and sperm cells haploid?

3 Look at the information about tree frogs at the top of this page. Why wouldn't it work if the male frog tried to feed the tadpole by shedding sperm into the tadpole's pool?

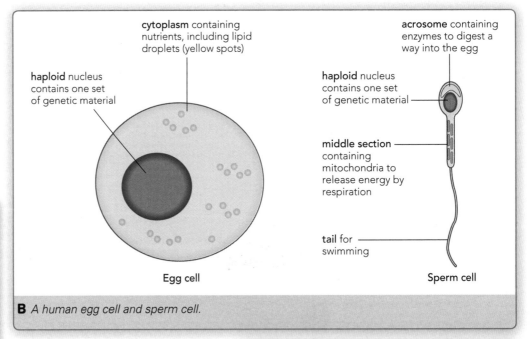

cytoplasm containing nutrients, including lipid droplets (yellow spots)

haploid nucleus contains one set of genetic material

acrosome containing enzymes to digest a way into the egg

haploid nucleus contains one set of genetic material

middle section containing mitochondria to release energy by respiration

tail for swimming

Egg cell

Sperm cell

B *A human egg cell and sperm cell.*

During **fertilisation**, a sperm cell burrows into an egg cell. The sperm cell nucleus enters the egg cell and at this point the membrane around the egg cell quickly changes so that no more sperm cell nuclei can enter. The two nuclei fuse and the resulting cell is called a zygote. The zygote is **diploid** (has two sets of chromosomes) and divides repeatedly to form an embryo, which embeds into the uterus lining to grow and develop.

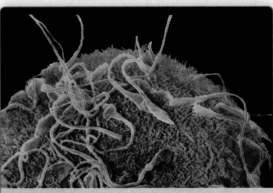

C *Hundreds of sperm (coloured yellow in this photo) compete to be the first to get into the egg.*

Infertility treatment

Many couples who would love to have children are not able to. There are many reasons why a couple may be **infertile**, and it is important to find out what the problem is before a solution can be tried.

- **IVF:** This stands for *in vitro* **fertilisation**. Some of the woman's egg cells are taken from her ovaries and fertilised in a dish with her partner's sperm cells. One or two embryos are then put into her uterus to develop. IVF babies are born early more often than naturally conceived babies, which may cause problems at birth or in development later.
- **Egg donation:** If the woman's ovaries aren't producing eggs, then eggs can be taken from another woman who agrees to donate some. She will be given hormones to make her ovaries release the eggs. Then IVF is carried out using sperm from the first woman's partner. A few women who donate eggs react badly to the high levels of hormones used to collect them.
- **Surrogate mothers:** If the woman isn't able to grow an embryo in her uterus, then her partner's sperm may be used to fertilise one of her eggs, or another woman's eggs. A fertilised egg is then placed in another woman's uterus to develop. She is the surrogate mother, and she gives birth to the baby. Handing the baby over to the couple may cause problems if the surrogate mother has developed a strong bond with the baby and does not want to give it up.
- **Hormones:** Giving a woman extra hormones may help her ovaries to produce more eggs, but this increases the risk of her having more than one baby at the same time. The babies tend to be born earlier than usual, increasing the risk of problems at birth or later. Some women react badly to this hormone treatment.

D *Sperm cells being added to egg cells during IVF.*

4 Explain the difference between IVF and the use of a surrogate mother.

5 Sometimes a couple are not able to have a baby because the man's sperm do not swim very well. Which of the types of infertility treatment described here would you recommend they should try? Explain your recommendation.

6 Summarise the advantages and risks of different treatments for infertility.

Skills spotlight

In the UK, couples can have IVF treatment through the NHS, at no cost to themselves. It is estimated that one IVF treatment costs the NHS between £2500 and £3000. Suggest why some people are against this.

1.14 Explain how the structure of an egg is adapted to its function:
  a cytoplasm to provide nutrients
  b haploid nucleus containing one set of the genetic material
  c immediately after fertilisation the cell membrane around the egg changes to block entry of other sperm

1.15 Explain how the structure of a sperm cell is adapted to its function, including:
  a acrosome containing enzymes
  b haploid nucleus containing one set of the genetic material
  c middle section containing mitochondria
  d tail for motility

1.16 Demonstrate an understanding of the advantages and disadvantages of infertility treatments, including:
  a donation of eggs
  b *in vitro* fertilisation
  c use of surrogate mothers
  d use of hormones

HSW 3 Describe the benefits, drawbacks and risks of using new scientific and technological developments

>>>>>>>>>>>>>>>>>>>>>> Why are there roughly equal numbers of girl and boy babies born?

B3.10 Sex determination

What makes a person male or female?

Santhi Soundarajan has lived all her life as a woman. Santhi is a talented athlete. Tests in 2006 showed that she has a Y chromosome, but her body is not sensitive to male hormones so she has developed as a female.

A *Santhi (on the left) won a silver medal in the 800 m at the 2006 Asian Games but her medal was withdrawn after a chromosome test.*

X and Y

Humans have 46 chromosomes in each of their body cells. Two of these determine what gender a person is, so they are called the **sex chromosomes**.

Women have two X chromosomes, XX. Men have one X and one Y chromosome, XY.

> **1** Which gamete determines the sex of a baby – the sperm cell or the egg cell?

Offspring genotypes and phenotypes			
		possible female gametes	
		X	X
possible male gametes	X	XX female	XX female
	Y	XY male	XY male

Parents' phenotypes: male — female
Parents' genotypes: XY — XX
Gametes: X and Y — all X

B *Sex inheritance*

The **Punnett square** in Figure B shows how the sex chromosomes are inherited. Remember that the **phenotype** is what an individual looks like, and the **genotype** shows the genetic material of the individual.

The diagram explains why there is an equal chance that a baby will be a boy or a girl.

Sex-linked inheritance

Most of our chromosomes come in matching pairs. The two chromosomes in a pair have the same genes in the same places. So we have two copies of each gene, which may be different **alleles**.

However, the X chromosome is much bigger than the Y chromosome. There are many more genes on the X chromosome than there are on the Y chromosome. This means that males will only have one copy of most of the genes on the X chromosome.

One gene found only on the X chromosome codes for a substance that helps blood to clot properly. The normal allele, H, allows the blood to clot. The **recessive** allele, h, prevents normal clotting and causes a disease called **haemophilia**. Haemophilia is an example of a **sex-linked genetic disorder**.

Table C shows genotypes and phenotypes for this gene. We include the X and Y chromosomes and the alleles, when writing these genotypes.

genotype	phenotype
$X^H X^H$	female, normal blood clotting
$X^H X^h$	female, normal blood clotting (but she is a **carrier** of the h allele)
$X^h X^h$	foetus does not usually develop
$X^H Y$	male, normal blood clotting
$X^h Y$	male, haemophilia

C *Phenotypes and genotypes for the haemophilia gene*

Gametes	X^H	X^h
X^H	$X^H X^H$ female, normal clotting	$X^H X^h$ female, normal clotting (carrier)
Y	$X^H Y$ male, normal clotting	$X^h Y$ male haemophilia

D *Inheritance of haemophilia*

We can work out how these alleles are inherited in the same way as with normal genes. The only difference is that we must show the chromosomes that the genes are on. The genetic diagram in Figure D shows the possible children that a man who doesn't have haemophilia, and a woman who is a carrier, could have.

Each time this couple have a child, the probability that it will be a boy with haemophilia is 1 in 4. You can write this as a ratio (1:3) or as a percentage (25%).

The gene for **red-green colour blindness** is also on the X chromosome. The normal allele of this gene gives normal colour vision, but there is a recessive allele that means a person cannot distinguish red from green.

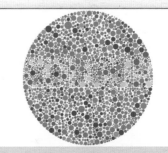

E *About 10% of men cannot distinguish the word in this image, but almost all women can.*

2 Suggest a definition for the term 'sex-linked genetic disorder'.

3 Draw a genetic diagram to show the possible genotypes and phenotypes of children born to a haemophiliac man and a woman who is a carrier for this condition.

4 Explain how two people, both with normal colour vision, can have a child who is red-green colour blind. Include a genetic diagram as part of your answer.

5 A couple have two boys and are expecting their third child. Explain why their chance of having another boy is still equal to having a girl.

Maths skills

The **probability** of an event is how likely it is the event will occur. In Figure D, 2 out of the 4 outcomes are female with normal clotting. So the probability this couple will have a female, normal clotting child is 2 in 4. It can be written as a simplified ratio (1:1), percentage (50%) or number (0.5).

Learning Outcomes

1.17 Recall that the sex of a person is controlled by one pair of chromosomes, XX in a female and XY in a male

1.18 Explain how the sex of offspring is determined at fertilisation, using a genetic diagram

1.19 Explain (using probabilities, ratios and percentages) how sex-linked genetic disorders are inherited, including:
  a haemophilia
  b colour blindness

HSW 3 Describe how phenomena are explained using scientific theories and ideas

B3.11 Courtship and parenting

Why do animals have courtship rituals?

Advertisers know they can catch our attention with references to sex. Sometimes it's really obvious, but sometimes it is more subtle. Why is this such a successful approach?

A Does this advert grab your attention?

> 1 Describe a behaviour that happens in response to an external stimulus.

Behaviour

We can define the term **behaviour** as the ways in which an animal responds to external stimuli (things that are happening outside it) or internal stimuli (things that are happening inside its body). For example, you might respond to treading on a sharp object by pulling your foot away, or to feeling sleepy by going to bed.

Choosing a mate

For an animal that reproduces sexually, choosing a mate is a very important behaviour. A mate that is healthy and well adapted to its environment is of good **reproductive quality**. It is more likely to have healthy offspring than a mate that is struggling to survive.

Elaborate **courtship behaviour** helps with choosing a mate. This often involves the male displaying to females. He is advertising that he is a high-quality choice. This is why male birds are often brightly coloured. The female is more usually well camouflaged, so that she can care for her young without being spotted by a predator.

B Male birds of paradise have fantastic plumage and amazing dances that they use to attract females.

> 2 Explain what is meant by the term 'courtship behaviour'.
>
> 3 Describe four different mating strategies in animals.

Mating strategies

Some animal species (e.g. swans) mate for life with the same partner. Only if their partner dies will they look for another mate. Other animals will pair up for a breeding season (e.g. robins) but find new mates in the following season. Pairs of animals in these relationships usually raise their offspring together.

In some animal species, groups of females all breed with one 'dominant' male. Sometimes these groups form each breeding season (e.g. in deer) but more often they remain together over the years, with the dominant male being replaced every so often (e.g. in some apes and lions). The males in these groups don't usually help with rearing the offspring.

Caring for young

Many animals look after their young until they have grown and developed enough to look after themselves. Female mammals feed their young on milk and teach them how to find food and avoid predators. Many birds keep their young in a nest, sitting on them to keep them warm and bringing them food, until the young are able to fly. This increases the chances that their offspring will survive, and that the parents' genes will carry on into future generations.

An evolutionary strategy is any process that affects how a species changes over time and spreads. Parental care helps to ensure that plenty of offspring survive. The more offspring there are, the more likely that there will be offspring adapted to changes in conditions and so the species can evolve and spread. Parental care can therefore be a successful evolutionary strategy.

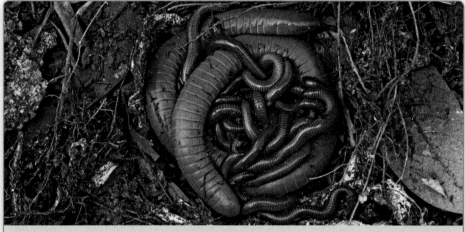

C *This blue worm-like animal is a kind of amphibian. The young are cared for by their mother, and feed on the outer layers of her skin.*

D *Many parents will protect their young from danger even at risk to their own safety.*

4 Give one example of how a named animal cares for its young.

5 Risking your own life to save the lives of your offspring is a good evolutionary strategy. Explain this in terms of passing genes on to future generations.

Skills spotlight

How would a scientist find out if swans mate for life? What resources would be needed and how would these resources be used?

Learning Outcomes

2.1 Describe that sexual reproduction requires the finding and selection of a suitable mate, and can involve courtship behaviours that advertise an individual's quality

2.2 Describe how animals have different mating techniques, including:
a a mate for life *b* several mates over a lifetime *c* a mate for a breeding season *d* several mates over one breeding season

2.3 Describe that some animals, in particular birds and mammals, have developed special behaviours for rearing their young

2.4 Demonstrate an understanding of why parental care can be a successful evolutionary strategy, including:
a increased chance of survival of offspring
b increased chance of parental genes being passed on by the offspring

2.5 Explain how, within the animal kingdom, parental care may involve risks to the parents

HSW *5* Plan to test a scientific idea, answer a scientific question, or solve a scientific problem by choosing appropriate resources

Why are some behaviours hardwired into our brains?

What sorts of behaviours do very young animals show?

A newborn baby can already do quite a lot of things. For example, if you've been holding the baby's head and then stop supporting it, the baby throws its arms out and curls its fingers up. This is called the startle reflex.

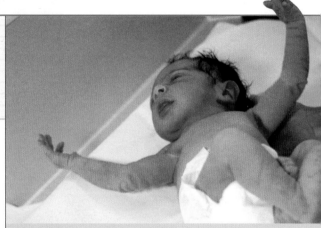

A *Testing a baby's startle reflex.*

Innate behaviour

The startle reflex is an example of an **innate** reflex. A **reflex** is an automatic response to a stimulus. 'Innate' means 'inborn'. Innate behaviour is something that we don't have to learn. It is 'hardwired' into our brains.

All animals have some sort of innate behaviour. Some of it is very simple, like the human baby's startle reflex. Some of it is quite complicated, such as a dragonfly nymph crawling out of the water, going through a set of complicated manoeuvres to shed its skin, and then flying off as though it had been flying all its life.

Innate behaviour increases the chances of an animal surviving and is controlled by genes. Animals with useful innate behaviour patterns are more likely to survive, reproduce and pass on their genes than animals without this behaviour.

> **?**
>
> **1** What is meant by 'innate behaviour'?
>
> **2** Suggest two examples of human innate behaviour.
>
> **3** Suggest an example of innate behaviour in another animal and describe how it helps the animal to survive.

B *Newborn mammals instinctively know where to look for milk.*

C *Hungry young herring gulls innately peck at the red spot on a parent's beak.*

Tinbergen and herring gulls

Niko Tinbergen (1907–1988) was one of the first people to make scientific studies of innate behaviour. He founded the science of **ethology** – the study of animal behaviour.

One of his investigations in the 1940s involved innate behaviour in birds called herring gulls. He noticed that the chicks pecked at their parents' beaks, to make the parent regurgitate food from its stomach for the chick.

An adult's beak has a red spot on it. Tinbergen made cardboard models of gulls' heads, using different colours for the spot on the beak, and presented the cardboard models to young gull chicks to see if they pecked at the spots. Figure D shows some of his results.

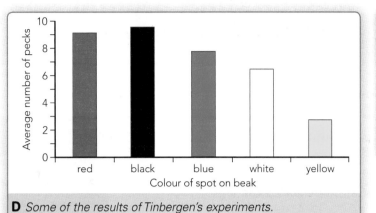

D *Some of the results of Tinbergen's experiments.*

Skills spotlight

Summarise the results of Tinbergen's experiment, shown in Figure D, and use these results to draw a conclusion.

Imprinting

In the 1930s, another ethologist, Konrad Lorenz (1903–1989), was studying the behaviour of young animals. People knew that goslings (young geese) and ducklings learned a new behaviour just after they hatched. In the wild, the first thing they would see would be their mother, and they immediately learned to stay close to her. This is useful behaviour, as it ensures that the young birds are protected and can learn from their mother how to find food.

Lorenz found that when the birds hatched in an incubator, they became attached to whatever they first saw and interacted with. This could be a wooden cube, or even Lorenz himself.

Lorenz called this behaviour **imprinting**. It is a kind of simple **learning**. We can define learning as a change in behaviour as a result of experience. Imprinting only happens during a very short 'window' of time, very early in the animal's life. But it lasts well into adulthood.

E *Lorenz followed by goslings who had imprinted on him as though he were their mother.*

4 Describe what imprinting is, and give one example.

5 Explain how imprinting differs from innate behaviour.

6 Describe how the work of one named ethologist has contributed to our understanding of animal behaviour.

Results Plus
Watch Out!

When explaining the term 'imprinting' students often only describe it as a type of learning and forget that it happens very early in the development of an individual.

Learning Outcomes

2.6 Describe the different behaviours exhibited by animals, including:
a innate behaviour b imprinting

2.12 Demonstrate an understanding of the work of ethologists, including:
a Tinbergen, innate behaviour in gulls b Lorenz, imprinting in geese

HSW 11 Present information, develop an argument and draw a conclusion, using scientific, technical and mathematical language, and ICT tools

>>>>>>>>>>>>>>>>>>>>>>>>> How much do animals think about what they do?

B3.13 Investigating animal behaviour using choice chambers

Do woodlice choose where to live?

If you take a torch and look at a lawn after dark on a damp evening you will probably see worms on the surface. However, if you stamp your foot sharply the worms rapidly disappear into their burrows. This behaviour often saves their lives.

Woodlice are invertebrates. You can find them under rotting logs and in dark, damp places. This is where they feed. They are also hidden from other animals which might eat them. They use innate behaviour to help them to find and stay in these damp, hidden places. Innate behaviour is inborn – the animals don't need to learn how to do it.

A *Worms burrow slowly through the soil but they can move very fast when they need too.*

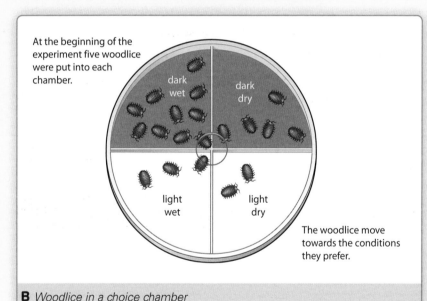

At the beginning of the experiment five woodlice were put into each chamber.

dark wet

dark dry

light wet

light dry

The woodlice move towards the conditions they prefer.

B *Woodlice in a choice chamber*

One way of investigating animal behaviour is to use **choice chambers**. This is a piece of equipment with different sections or chambers in it. The chambers have different conditions (such as dry or damp) and the animal can choose where it wants to be. Different types of choice chambers can be used to investigate innate behaviour in animals such as woodlice and also conscious choices in animals such as rats.

Your task

You are going to plan an investigation that will allow you to find out about innate animal behaviour. You are going to use woodlice and choice chambers to investigate whether the animals choose particular conditions.

 Learning Outcomes

2.8 Investigate animal behaviour using choice chambers

ResultsPlus
Build Better Answers

When planning an investigation like this, one of the skills you will be assessed on is your ability to *identify risks*. There are 4 marks available for this skill. Here are two extracts taken from two different pieces of work.

Student extract 1 — A basic response for this skill

This is a good start because the student has indentified a possible risk in the investigation.

> I think that the woodlice could carry germs. I think that I should wash my hands when I have finished

The student has also explained what they should do to deal with the risk.

In this investigation it is not just the students that need to be kept safe from harm but also the woodlice.

Student extract 2 — A good response for this skill

The student has realised that the woodlice need to be looked after as well as the students.

> I think that there is a risk from handling the woodlice because they could carry germs. I also think that the drying agent could irritate my skin. I should wash my hands after handling both the woodlice and the drying agent. I also need to make sure that the woodlice do not come to any harm. This means that they need to be handled carefully, not exposed to the choice chamber for too long and I need to make sure that they are returned to their environment when the investigation is over.

The student has made some sensible suggestions about how the welfare of the woodlice can be managed.

 ResultsPlus

To access 2 marks
- Identify a relevant risk which is specific to the task.
- Suggest a way (or ways) to manage the risk.

To access 4 marks
- Identify most of the relevant risks which are specific to the task.
- The method reflects how risks need to be managed.

How are animals trained?

esearch shows that most people don't really notice the ads that appear on web pages. We just lose interest in them. This is called banner blindness. People who sell advertising would like to find ways that they can prevent banner blindness, and make us actually notice their ads.

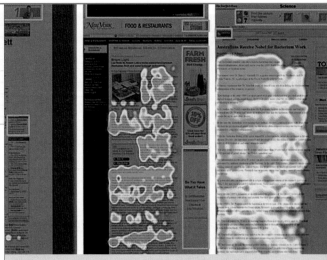

A *Eye-scan studies show banner blindness. Advertisers often use flashing or moving images to try to get people to look at their adverts.*

Habituation

Although innate behaviour helps animals to respond appropriately to a particular stimulus from birth, they also need to learn to adapt their behaviour to different circumstances. One simple kind of learning is 'switching off' from a repeated stimulus. This is called **habituation**.

gill

B *The sea hare has delicate gills that it uses for gas exchange.*

The sea hare, a kind of marine slug, has a gill that sticks out from its back. If a sea hare is touched suddenly it withdraws the gill. This response helps to stop predators damaging its gill. However, if you keep on touching the sea hare but don't hurt it, it eventually stops withdrawing its gill.

Classical conditioning

Dogs produce saliva when they smell food. This is an innate response. In the 1930s, Ivan Pavlov (1849–1936) investigated whether dogs could learn to respond to other stimuli in the same way.

Pavlov rang a bell just before giving food to a dog. The dog pricked up its ears when it heard the bell, but it didn't salivate until it was given the food. After repeating this several times, the dog produced saliva when it heard the bell. It had learned to associate the sound of the bell with the food.

This kind of learning is known as **classical conditioning**. It starts with an innate reflex action but then the animal learns to respond to a new stimulus in the same way.

Operant conditioning

Another simple kind of learning is called **operant conditioning**. It occurs when an animal discovers that a particular kind of behaviour can make something good happen – or something bad not happen. For example, a rat in a cage may just happen to press a bar when it is exploring, and discovers that an unpleasant bright light switches off. After this happens a few times, it associates the behaviour with the reward. Eventually, it will carry out the action on purpose.

Training animals

Operant conditioning begins with a chance behaviour, which produces a reward. The reward reinforces the behaviour. We use this to **train** animals.

When a sniffer dog is being trained, it is given an object with a smell to sniff. Then it is presented with several objects with various smells. When it indicates the one with the original smell the dog is rewarded. After many repeats, the dog learns to search for that particular smell.

> **1** Give one example of each of these kinds of learning: habituation, classical conditioning, operant conditioning.
>
> **2** Suggest how habituation is useful to an animal.
>
> **3** Explain what is meant by the term 'classical conditioning'.

C *When a police horse is repeatedly exposed to smoke and finds that nothing bad happens to it, it learns not to be afraid of it.*

D *This dolphin has been trained to locate mines so that they can be cleared.*

4 Describe how rewards are used when training a sniffer dog.

5 Wild dolphins will jump high out of the water. How could you use operant conditioning to train a dolphin to jump when you hold your arms up?

6 Look at Figure D. Discuss whether it is acceptable to train dolphins to do dangerous jobs like this.

7 Explain how operant conditioning differs from classical conditioning using particular examples in your answer.

Skills spotlight

Use the theory of operant conditioning to explain why training works.

Learning Outcomes

2.6 Describe the different behaviours exhibited by animals, including:
  c habituation **d** classical conditioning **e** operant conditioning

2.7 Explain that humans can make use of conditioning when training captive animals for specific purposes, including:
  a sniffer dogs **b** police horses **c** dolphins

HSW **3** Describe how phenomena are explained using scientific theories and ideas

Why do glow-worms glow?

B3.15 Animal communication

How and why do animals communicate?

Glow-worms are not worms at all, but flightless female insects. They switch on their lights on summer nights. You may find one if you look carefully on grassy slopes or hedge banks in southern England. They look like little green LEDs.

A The lights produced by female glow-worms attract males, which have wings and can fly.

Communication signals

Organisms use different methods to **communicate**.

relaxed

aggressive

fearful

very aggressive

B Cats use body language and facial expressions to communicate their mood.

1 Give three examples each of visual, sound and chemical communication between animals.

2 Suggest why it is an advantage to a cat to communicate its mood through body language.

3 Suggest why male moths use chemical rather than visual signals to find females.

- **Visual signals** A female glow-worm's light tells males where to find her. Courtship behaviour also uses visual signals. Mammals often use gestures, facial expressions and **body language** to communicate their mood.
- **Sound** Many birds keep others out of their territory by singing. Male grasshoppers rub their hind legs against their wing-cases to make a high-pitched sound that attracts females.
- **Chemical substances** Many animals produce **pheromones** – hormone-like substances that diffuse into the air and influence the behaviour of others.

C The antennae of this male moth have extremely sensitive receptors that can detect pheromones from females over a kilometre away.

Social behaviour

Communication is especially important when animals live and interact in close groups, such as wasps, meerkats, chimpanzees, gorillas and humans. Behaviour between members of the same species is called **social behaviour**.

Social behaviour can improve survival chances. Different individuals in the group can take on different tasks, such as watching for predators or searching for new food sources. And groups may also have a better chance of defending a territory if they communicate and work together.

The American zoologist Dian Fossey (1932–1985) studied social behaviour in mountain gorillas in Rwanda, in the 1960s to 1980s. She found that, by imitating their behaviour towards each other, she was partly accepted into the group. She discovered that the groups of gorillas had complex family relationships and that, contrary to what had previously been believed, they were not violent. She was able to work out the meanings of many of their calls, and was the first person to begin to understand how gorilla society worked.

D *Despite having to live in very difficult and unsafe conditions, Dian Fossey spent long periods sitting close to the gorillas, observing them carefully and recording their behaviour.*

The British researcher Jane Goodall (1934–) carried out similar research on chimpanzees, which she began in Tanzania in the 1960s. Until then, we knew very little about how chimps live in the wild. Jane lived closely with chimpanzees and, like Dian Fossey, recorded their behaviour and the ways in which they interacted with one another. She was the first person to learn that chimpanzees make and use tools to help them to obtain food. She also discovered that they hunt together as a group.

Fossey's and Goodall's work helps us to understand the complex societies and uses of communication in gorillas and chimps. Their work has given us insights into our own behaviour.

> 4 What are the advantages of living in social groups.
>
> 5 Explain how Jane Goodall's studies added to our knowledge of chimpanzees.
>
> 6 The mountain gorillas of Rwanda are endangered. Explain how Dian Fossey studied them and why her observations and conclusions are important.

Skills spotlight

Fossey's work has been criticised by many scientists who study animal behaviour, because she did not do controlled experiments but simply recorded what she observed as the gorillas behaved naturally. Suggest why Fossey decided to collect data in the way she did.

Learning Outcomes

2.9 Describe how some animal behaviour requires communication

2.10 Explain how animals use a variety of types of signals to communicate, including:
  a sound signals
  b chemical signals (pheromones)
  c visual signals (gestures, body language, facial expression)

2.12 Demonstrate an understanding of the work of ethologists, including:
  c Fossey, social behaviour in gorillas
  d Goodall, social behaviour in chimpanzees

HSW *1* Explain how scientific data is collected and analysed

How and why do plants communicate?

Scientists in South Korea say they have found genes in plants that can 'hear'. They claim that playing classical music to rice plants makes the genes more active so the plants grow better.

A *The idea of playing music to plants to help them grow first gained popularity in the 1970s.*

Communicating with animals

Many plants rely on insects to transport pollen from one flower to another.

Their flowers have evolved brightly coloured chemicals in the petals that attract insects to them. They also produce chemical scents that spread out into the air. Insects find the flower by moving in the direction where the concentration of the chemical is greatest.

B *The shining white petals and strong scent of this flower indicate to the bee that there is nectar there.*

Some plants produce brightly coloured fruit. Animals, such as birds, recognise that this means the fruits are ready for eating. Inside the fruits, the seeds are ready for dispersal. The seeds may be carried a long way from the parent plant in the animal's gut before they are released in the animal's waste, and can start growing.

Plants often produce chemicals that harm insects, to provide protection against being eaten. The Labrador tea plant of northern Europe produces chemicals in its leaves that are poisonous to insects. These chemicals diffuse out into the air, so the insects don't even land on the plant's leaves.

Communicating with other plants

Some plants send signals to other plants. The leaves of some *Acacia* trees in Africa produce distasteful, poisonous chemicals to deter herbivores. As this takes a lot of energy, they only do it when they are attacked.

When an insect attack occurs, the leaves also produce a gas called ethene. This diffuses through the air to nearby *Acacia* trees. These trees pick up the warning and start to make the distasteful chemicals even before the herbivores start to eat them.

> ?
>
> 1 How do plants use chemicals to attract insects?
>
> 2 Describe three different reasons why plants might communicate with animals.

Co-evolution of plants and animals

Evolution is the change in a species over time. **Co-evolution** is where two species change together over time. Flower **pollination** by insects is one example. Insects that recognise the signals of flower scent and colour have a survival advantage, because they are more likely to find food. Plants with flowers that attract more insects have a survival advantage, because they are more likely to be pollinated. So, as one species changes, the individuals of the other species that are best suited to those changes are more likely to survive. This happens over and over again and so the two species co-evolve.

Co-evolution also occurs in **plant chemical defence**. Several plant species that grow in the dry grasslands of Australia make poison in their leaves. Grey kangaroos can eat leaves that contain quite high levels of poison. In places where there are few kangaroos, the plants don't waste energy making the poison.

C This orchid flower looks and smells like a female wasp and is irresistible to male wasps. The wasp receives a packet of pollen when he tries to mate with the flower, which he then carries to the next flower.

D Grey kangaroos are able to eat the leaves of bushes that contain a poison called fluoroacetate.

Skills spotlight

Suggest how scientists came up with the idea that *Acacia* plants communicate when herbivores attack.

H **3** Explain how the orchid and the wasp each benefit from their co-evolution.

H **4** Explain why bushes in Australia that make poisons only produce them in their leaves.

H **5** Suggest how co-evolution may have led to increasing levels of fluoroacetate in the leaves of some bushes in Australia.

H **6** Fossils suggest that plants with large flowers may have appeared on Earth at about the same time as bees and wasps. Suggest how co-evolution could explain this.

7 Describe some of the similarities between the ways in which plants and animals communicate with one another. You should refer to particular examples in your answer.

Learning Outcomes

2.11 Describe how plants can communicate using chemicals, including,
  a with animals (particularly insects)
  b with other plants

H *2.13* Demonstrate an understanding of how plants and animals have co-evolved, including:
  a flower structure and insect behaviour in pollination
  b plant defence and animal metabolism

HSW *2* Describe the importance of creative thought in the development of hypotheses and theories

Evidence for human evolution

::: What can bones and tools tell us about human evolution?

Scientists think that humans have changed over time. However, they cannot agree as to how humans will change in the future, although some interesting ideas have been put forward. How would you like humans to change?

A *A possible future for humans*

Fossil evidence

Many different fossils that are similar to, but not exactly like, modern humans have been discovered.

Scientists decided that the fossil bones of a 4.4 million-year-old, human-like, female animal were from an extinct species. They gave it the binomial name *Ardipithecus ramidus*, or **Ardi** for short.

1 Describe two differences between Ardi and a modern human.

Ardi was about 120 cm tall, and would have weighed about 50 kg. Her leg bones show that she walked upright, more like a human than an ape. But she had very long arms, and her big toes would have been able to grasp branches. Her brain was small, about 350 cm^3, similar to a chimpanzee. (A human brain is about 1500 cm^3.)

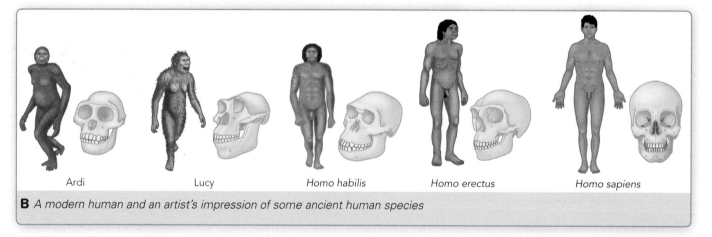

| Ardi | Lucy | *Homo habilis* | *Homo erectus* | *Homo sapiens* |

B *A modern human and an artist's impression of some ancient human species*

2 How was Lucy
a similar to and
b different from a modern human?

3 Using Figure B, identify trends in the evolution of body form in humans.

The fossilised bones of a female from another human-like species were called *Australopithecus afarensis* and nicknamed **Lucy**. She lived about 3.2 million years ago and was only about 1.07 m tall. She had long arms, and her bones suggest she didn't walk completely upright, more like a chimpanzee than a human. Her brain volume was about 400 cm^3.

In the 1960s, British scientists Mary Leakey (1913–96) and Louis Leakey (1903–72) found fossils of a more recent human-like species. They decided it was closely related to modern humans and so gave it the same first word for its binomial name. It is called *Homo habilis*, which translates as 'handy man'. (Modern humans are *Homo sapiens*.)

Fossils of this species are between 2.4 and 1.4 million years old. They walked upright, and were quite short with long arms. Their brains were between 500 and 600 cm³.

The fossil of another close relative of modern humans, *Homo erectus*, was found by Richard Leakey (1944–) in 1984. This almost-complete skeleton showed it was a tall (1.79 m) but strongly-built species with a brain volume of about 850 cm³.

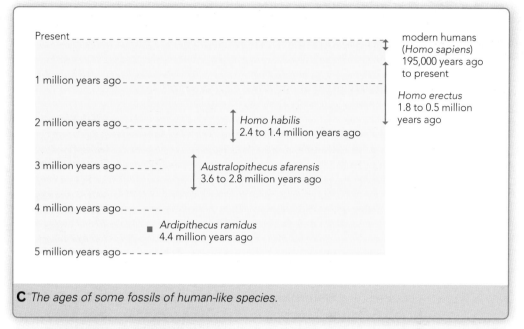

Present ⸺⸺⸺⸺⸺⸺⸺⸺⸺⸺⸺⸺⸺⸺⸺⸺⸺ modern humans (*Homo sapiens*) 195,000 years ago to present

1 million years ago ⸺⸺⸺⸺⸺⸺⸺⸺⸺⸺ *Homo erectus* 1.8 to 0.5 million years ago

2 million years ago ⸺⸺⸺⸺⸺⸺⸺⸺ *Homo habilis* 2.4 to 1.4 million years ago

3 million years ago ⸺⸺⸺⸺ *Australopithecus afarensis* 3.6 to 2.8 million years ago

4 million years ago ⸺⸺⸺ *Ardipithecus ramidus* 4.4 million years ago

5 million years ago ⸺⸺⸺

C *The ages of some fossils of human-like species.*

Stone tools

No tools were found with Ardi or Lucy, but tools have been found with *Homo habilis* and *Homo erectus* fossils. Stone tools cannot be dated directly, but we can date the layers of rock or sediment they are found in. So we assume that the tool is the same age as that layer of rock or sediment.

D *The stone tool on the left is about 2 million years old. The one on the right is about 13 000 years old.*

The oldest stone tools so far discovered were not found with fossil bones, and are at least 2.6 million years old. They are very simple, but would have helped with skinning an animal or cutting up meat. Tools found in more recent rock are more sophisticated.

4 a Using Figure D, describe how stone tools developed over time.
b Suggest what evidence this gives us for the differences between human-like species.

5 Some scientists suggest that the evolutionary line to *Homo sapiens* included both *Homo habilis* and *Homo erectus*. Discuss arguments for and against this idea.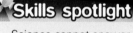

Skills spotlight

Science cannot answer all of our questions. One explanation for the appearance of more sophisticated tools is that larger or more complex brains were evolving. Suggest another hypothesis to explain why stone tools became better.

Learning Outcomes

2.14 Describe the evidence for human evolution, based on fossils, including:
  a Ardi from 4.4 million years ago **b** Lucy from 3.2 million years ago **c** Leakey's discovery of fossils from 1.6 million years ago

2.15 Describe the evidence for human evolution based on stone tools, including:
  a the development of stone tools over time **b** how these can be dated from their environment

HSW **4** Identify questions that science cannot currently answer, and explain why these questions cannot be answered

How did humans spread across the world?

What do you build your home out of when it is too cold for trees to grow, there's not enough snow for an igloo, and your tools aren't strong enough to shape rocks? Over 12 000 years ago people in the cold of northern Europe used woolly mammoth bones and deer hide.

A *A dwelling made of mammoth bones and tusks, it would have been covered with hide.*

Climate change and human behaviour

We think modern *Homo sapiens* first evolved in Africa about 200 000 years ago, but may not have spread out of Africa until before about 60 000 years ago.

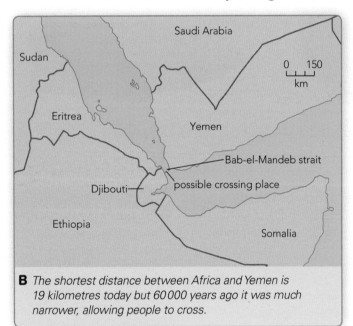

B *The shortest distance between Africa and Yemen is 19 kilometres today but 60 000 years ago it was much narrower, allowing people to cross.*

An Ice Age is a time of very cold periods called 'glacials' and warmer 'interglacials'. Around 60 000 years ago in a glacial period a lot of water was locked up in ice and sea levels were much lower. It would have been easier to cross from Africa to Yemen.

These people would move to hunt and gather food. As they spread through Asia and Europe during the interglacial, they adapted their tools, clothing, homes and equipment to suit new environments.

About 25 000 years ago, another cold period produced a land bridge between Siberia and North America. We think that humans then spread from Asia into North America. About 11 000 years ago, the climate became more stable, and it is around then that we see the first signs of people settling down in the same place and starting to grow crops.

1 Suggest which African people moved out into Asia around 60 000 years ago.

2 Explain why people started to settle down around 11 000 years ago.

Mitochondrial DNA

H

In each cell there are many tiny organelles called **mitochondria** in which energy is released from food. Mitochondria have their own DNA.

Each person begins life as a zygote. The **nuclear DNA** in the zygote comes from both the mother and father. However, all the mitochondria come from the cytoplasm of the egg cell, so the **mitochondrial DNA** (mtDNA) only comes from the mother.

All DNA changes over time due to mutations. However, mtDNA mutates around 100 to 1000 times faster than nuclear DNA. This means that over the past 50 000 years many more mutations have happened in the mtDNA.

After death, tissues start to decay and the chemicals in cells break down, including DNA. The longer the time since death, the greater the decay. However, scientists have been able to extract cells from fossils that are several tens of thousands of years old. As each cell contains many mitochondria but only one nucleus, there is likely to be a greater abundance of mtDNA in the sample than nuclear DNA. There is also a greater chance that it will be in a good enough condition to identify the genetic sequence. This makes mtDNA often more useful than nuclear DNA for tracking evolution using fossil material.

H

ResultsPlus
Watch Out!

Don't confuse mtDNA with mRNA.

H 3 Describe two differences between mtDNA and nuclear DNA.

mtDNA detective work

Studies of mutations in mtDNA in people from all over the world suggest that all of us have mtDNA that has evolved from the mtDNA of a woman in Africa, between 130 000 and 200 000 years ago. She has been called 'mitochondrial Eve' or '**African Eve**'. This doesn't mean she was the only woman living then, but she is the only one where there is an unbroken female–female line all the way down from her generation to ours.

The evidence also shows which people are most closely related to others. This suggests how humans spread out of Africa and populated the rest of the world.

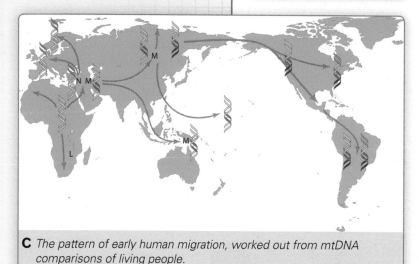

C *The pattern of early human migration, worked out from mtDNA comparisons of living people.*

H 4 The human population of Africa around 130 000 years ago was probably several thousand. Explain what we mean by 'African Eve'.

H 5 Use Figure C to explain how mtDNA suggests that we all evolved from one group of humans who left Africa.

6 Explain how and why humans migrated out of Africa to spread all over the world.

Skills spotlight

Results of sequencing mtDNA in many different people have been added to online databases, such as *Mitomap*, so that other researchers can use it. Suggest one advantage and one disadvantage of pooling and sharing data in this way.

Learning Outcomes

H 2.16 Describe why mitochondrial DNA provides evidence for the African Eve theory for non-Africans, including:
   a its inheritance down the family line   b its high mutation rate

H 2.17 Demonstrate an understanding of why mitochondrial DNA may be more useful than nuclear DNA for tracking human migration and evolution, including:
   a mitochondrial DNA is less likely to have degraded over time   b mitochondrial DNA is more abundant

2.18 Demonstrate an understanding of the impact of climate change on human behaviour, including:
   a the effect of the Ice Age   b human migration

HSW 12 Describe the benefits, drawbacks and risks of using new scientific and technological developments

What is biotechnology?

The century, or hundred-year, egg is an ingredient that may have been used in Chinese recipes for over 600 years. An egg is wrapped in a mixture of clay, salt, lime and rice shell. Despite the name, it only takes weeks or months for the chemicals in the wrapping to change the proteins and fats in the egg white and yolk.

A *The dark yolk of a century egg smells strongly of sulfur and ammonia, and the 'white' is fairly tasteless.*

> **1** Suggest the advantages of turning milk into yogurt.
>
> **2** In cheese manufacture, what is the biomolecule in milk, and what changes it?

When humans were making their long migrations, hundreds of thousands of years ago, they would have wanted to carry long-lasting food with them. Probably even the earliest humans would have hung up strips of meat to dry. Later, they discovered that milk could be kept for much longer by allowing it to turn into yoghurt or cheese.

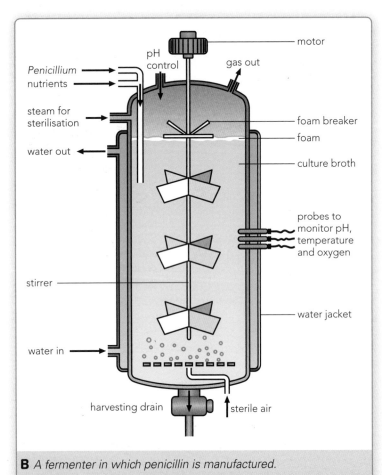

B *A fermenter in which penicillin is manufactured.*

Today, we know that most of these changes to food are caused by microorganisms – bacteria and microscopic fungi. The microorganisms produce enzymes that change molecules in the original substance into different molecules. For example, bacteria act on a protein called casein in milk when it turns to cheese.

Today, we call processes like this **biotechnology**. We can describe biotechnology as the alteration of natural **biomolecules** using science and engineering to provide goods and services. (A biomolecule is a substance made by living organisms.) We don't just use biotechnology to make food, but to make all sorts of different substances that we use in many different ways, such as making medicines.

Fermenters

Modern biotechnology often involves big steel vessels, called **fermenters**, in which microorganisms are grown. Inside the fermenter the microorganisms are provided with exactly the right conditions to encourage them to grow and produce the substances we require. For example, the fungus *Penicillium* is used to produce the antibiotic penicillin.

Before the microorganism is put into the fermenter it's essential to kill any other microorganisms already in there, as they might grow instead. The fermenter is **sterilised** using high-pressure steam. Everything that is added to the fermenter is first sterilised to prevent microorganisms getting into the culture. These are called **aseptic precautions**.

Inside the fermenter, optimal conditions for the microorganism are supplied, so that it produces as much product as possible in the shortest time. These conditions include:

- **nutrients**, including sources of carbohydrates and nitrogen, such as sugar and ammonium ions
- an **optimum temperature**, so the enzymes in the microorganism can work at a fast rate but don't get denatured
- the **optimum pH**, also to allow the enzymes to work efficiently
- oxygen, provided by bubbling sterile air into the fermenter, so the microorganism can respire aerobically
- **agitation**, produced by a stirrer, to mix the oxygen and nutrients into all of the liquid.

C Wearing overalls, gloves and a face mask help prevent microorganisms getting into the fermenter.

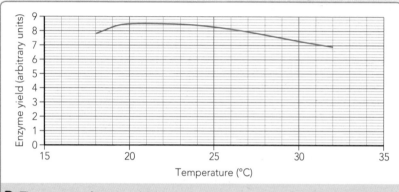

D The amount of enzyme (yield) produced by microorganisms in a fermenter at different temperatures.

3 The diagram of the fermenter shows a pipe where steam can be introduced. Suggest when this would this be used, and why.

4 Explain why the fermenter has a probe to measure the pH.

5 What is the optimum temperature for the microorganism used to produce the graph in Figure D? Explain your answer.

6 Respiration by microorganisms in a fermenter produces carbon dioxide and heat. Explain why these have to be removed, and describe how the design of the fermenter allows this to happen.

Skills spotlight

Biotechnology companies are always working to improve their products, or the yield they get. Imagine that a new variety of the fungus *Penicillium* has been discovered. How could you find its optimum temperature in order to produce the maximum amount of penicillin in the shortest time?

Learning Outcomes

3.1 Describe biotechnology as the alteration of natural biomolecules using science and engineering to provide goods and services

3.2 Describe a fermenter as a vessel used to cultivate microorganisms for the production of biomolecules on a large scale

3.3 Explain the need to supply suitable conditions in fermenters and the effect they have on growth, including:
  a aseptic precautions *b* nutrients *c* optimum temperature *d* pH *e* oxygenation *f* agitation

HSW **5** Plan to test a scientific idea, answer a scientific question, or solve a scientific problem by controlling relevant variables

What's the connection between yeast, saliva and honey?

B3.20 Factors affecting growth in yeast

How do different factors (such as pH) affect the growth of yeast?

Bees have many different species of yeasts growing in their salivary glands, in their intestines and in their 'honey stomachs'. Scientists think that a healthy growth of these yeasts may play an important part in the process of turning nectar into honey.

A *The honey made by bees helps the whole hive survive the winter.*

Yeasts are widely used in biotechnology for making bread and alcoholic drinks such as beer and wine. Yeasts can also be grown on an industrial scale in fermenters to produce enzymes and medicines such as penicillin. Conditions in these fermenters are carefully controlled so that the yeast grows as quickly as possible. The factors that are controlled in the fermenters include the pH of the culture. If the pH is too acidic or too alkaline, the yeast enzymes do not function properly. The yeast does not respire and grow. It may die.

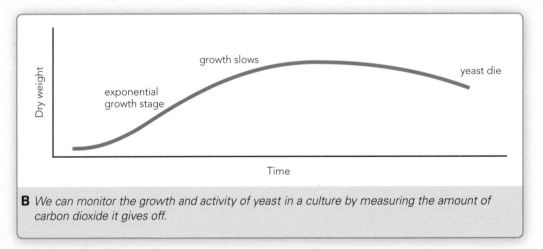

B *We can monitor the growth and activity of yeast in a culture by measuring the amount of carbon dioxide it gives off.*

Your task

You are going to plan an investigation that will allow you to find out how pH affects the growth of yeast.

Learning Outcomes

3.4 Investigate the effect of factors on the growth of yeast, including pH

Build Better Answers

When planning an investigation like this, one of the skills you will be assessed on is your ability to *process evidence*. There are 4 marks available for this skill. Here are two extracts focusing on this skill. Other skills that you need for the practical assessment are dealt with in other lessons.

Student extract 1 — A basic response for this skill

> I have counted how many bubbles were released in one minute for each of the yeast mixtures. I have taken more than one set of results for each pH so I am going to calculate the mean number of bubbles produced in one minute for each pH. When I have done this I will put the information in a table.

This student has used a calculation which is a good way to process evidence.

The student should describe how they are going to calculate the mean or should show how they have carried out the calculation.

It would be better to plot a graph here so that the patterns in the results could be seen clearly.

Student extract 2 — A good response for this skill

> I have counted how many bubbles were released in one minute for each of the yeast mixtures. I have taken more than one set of results for each pH so I am going to calculate the mean number of bubbles produced in one minute for each pH. I will do this by adding the number of bubbles together for each pH and then dividing by the number of readings. When I have done this I will put the information in a line graph.

A line graph or a bar chart is a good idea because it makes it easier to see any trends in the data.

Here the student has clearly described how to carry out the calculation – although they could just show the working out.

ResultsPlus

To access 2 marks
- Attempt to process all collected evidence, using appropriate mathematical skills
- Attempt to present the processed evidence in a way appropriate for the topic

To access 4 marks
- Process all collected evidence in a way that is appropriate to the task, using appropriate mathematical skills
- Present the processed evidence in a way that allows conclusions to be drawn

How do we use microorganisms in our food?

For a time in the 1950s, it really was thought that biotechnology might mean the food of the future could be a plate of tablets. That will never happen because people enjoy their food too much.

1 Explain what we mean by mycoprotein.

2 Describe two differences between the methods used to produce mycoprotein and penicillin.

In the early 1960s, scientists were looking for cheap sources of protein for people in parts of the world where food was in short supply. They tried cultivating various kinds of microorganisms, including single-celled plants, microscopic fungi and bacteria.

A *Not everyone's idea of a nice meal!*

Only one of these foods was successful – and you can still buy it today. It is called **mycoprotein**, and is made from a fungus called *Fusarium*. It is sold as Quorn™. Figure B shows a fermenter in which mycoprotein is produced.

Fusarium is made up of tiny fibres called hyphae. There is no stirrer in the fermenter because this would tangle and break the fibres.

The hyphae are collected and heat-treated to remove a bitter-tasting substance that they contain. They are dried and pressed to form a fibrous substance, which has a similar texture to meat.

Food from microorganisms has advantages over growing crops and keeping animals:
- Microorganism populations can double in number in as little as 20 minutes. This is much faster than crops or animals can grow.
- Microorganisms are easy to handle and manipulate. They can be grown in fermenters, rather than taking up space in fields or buildings.
- Microorganisms can be grown in any part of the world, no matter how hot, cold, dry or wet it is outside.
- Microorganisms can often be grown using waste materials from other processes as their food source. *Fusarium* is grown on waste material produced when flour is made from wheat grains.

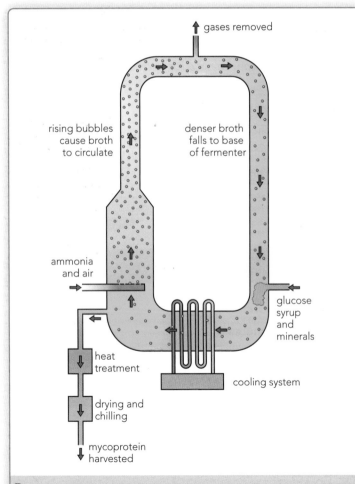

B *A fermenter used for growing mycoprotein. The fermenters are huge – about 40 m tall.*

Mycoprotein as a food source

Mycoprotein is an excellent food source from a health point of view. Saturated fat is a risk factor in heart disease; mycoprotein contains no saturated fat but meat does.

The high fibre content of mycoprotein slows the rate at which glucose is absorbed from food. This stops blood glucose concentration rising rapidly after a meal. This, in turn, means that insulin isn't secreted so quickly or in such large amounts. Glucose and insulin surges are thought to contribute to the risk of developing type II diabetes, so it's possible that eating mycoprotein could reduce this risk.

C *An alga called* Spirulina *is grown in warm, shallow ponds to produce food in some parts of Asia, Africa and Central America.*

Nutrient		Mass in 100g of mycoprotein (g)	Mass in 100g of minced beef (g)
Protein		48	19
Fat:	total	12	16
	saturated	0	6
Carbohydrate		12	0
Dietary fibre		25	0

D *Comparison of the nutrient content of mycoprotein and minced beef.*

Maths skills

The guideline daily amount (GDA) of protein is approximately 55g for men. Using Figure D we can work out the **percentage** of this GDA that 100g of mycoprotein will provide:

$$\frac{48}{55} \times 100 = 87\% \text{ (to 2 significant figures) of the GDA}$$

3 List four advantages of growing microorganisms such as *Fusarium* for food, rather than growing crops.

4 a Use the data in the table to explain why eating mycoprotein instead of beef could reduce the risk of developing heart disease.
b Outline three other ways in which eating mycoprotein is likely to be better for a person's health than eating meat.

5 Describe how *Fusarium* is used to produce mycoprotein.

Skills spotlight

Dried *Spirulina* is about 65% protein, more than 35 times the protein content of maize. Its growth rate is seven times faster than maize. It would grow well in many African countries where maize is the staple food. Suggest some reasons why *Spirulina* is not more widely grown. Consider social and economic factors.

Learning Outcomes

3.5 Explain the advantages of using microorganisms for food production, including:
 a rapid population growth
 b ease of manipulation
 c production independent of climate
 d use of waste products from other industrial processes

3.6 Describe how mycoprotein is manufactured, including the role of the fungus *Fusarium* sp.

3.7 Explain the advantages of using mycoprotein as a food source

HSW **13** Describe the social, economic and environmental effects of decisions about the uses of science and technology

How was yoghurt first made?

B3.22 Investigating the effect of different factors on yogurt making

⁞⁞⁞ How do different factors affect yogurt making?

Over the years yogurt has been used to help keep both animals and people clean, as a hair shampoo and as a medicine to cure problems from diarrhoea to thrush. People think that yogurt was first made thousands of years ago when milk was carried in goat skin bags. Yogurt can be made from the milk of cows, sheep, goats, camels and even water buffalo. It is also used in many different ways as a food – it can be found as a drink, in sweet and savoury dishes and even salted and dried to preserve it.

Yogurt is made from milk by bacteria such as *Lactobacillus bulgaricus*. The bacteria live on the sugars in the milk. They convert **lactose** (milk sugar) into **lactic acid** as they respire anaerobically. A variety of factors affect yogurt making, such as the type of bacteria used, the type of milk used, the levels of nutrients in the milk, the temperature of the mixture of milk and bacteria and the pH. These factors can affect both the speed at which yogurt is made from milk, and also the type of yogurt that is produced.

A *Jameed – a form of dried, solid goat's milk yogurt.*

Your task

You are going to plan an investigation that will allow you to find out how one particular factor affects yogurt making.

Learning ⊕utcomes

3.8 Describe how bacteria are used in the production of yogurt from milk by the conversion of lactose to lactic acid
3.9 Investigate the effect of different factors on yogurt making

Build Better Answers

When planning an investigation like this, one of the skills you will be assessed on is your ability to *plan and select suitable controls*. There are 6 marks available for this skill. Here are two examples of the sort of responses that may be made in this part of a Controlled Assessment.

Student extract 1 — A basic response for this skill

There are more variables which need to be added to this list.

> I think that I need to use the same amount of yoghurt each time and the same amount of milk. I will also keep the water bath at the same temperature.

It is also important to say how the variables are going to be controlled.

Student extract 2 — A good response for this skill

The student has also explained how they are going to control each variable.

> I will control the following variables in my experiment: the amount of each type of milk, the amount of yogurt, the temperature of the water bath, the starting temperature of the milk and the method of measuring pH. I will measure out the same amount of milk each time using a measuring cylinder. This will mean that there is the same amount of milk for the yogurt to work on. I will use a syringe to measure out the yogurt and this will mean that there will be roughly the same number of bacteria in each mixture. I will keep all the mixtures at the same temperature by using a water bath. This will help to provide the best conditions for the bacteria to grow and change lactose sugar into lactic acid. I will measure pH using a universal indicator solution each time. This will allow me to keep track of the pH in the same way each time. I will make sure that the milk is put into the water bath for five minutes before it is mixed with the yoghurt. This will mean that the milk will be at the same temperature as the water bath and will provide a warm environment for the bacteria to grow.

The student has provided a list of all the variables to be controlled.

In order to access the highest marks the student has also explained why it is important to control each of the variables.

To access 2 marks
- Identify one appropriate variable to control.
- Describe how this variable can be controlled.

To access 6 marks
- Identify a range of variables appropriate to control.
- Give an appropriate explanation of how to control these variables.

How are enzymes made and used in industry?

Meat contains fibres and these can be tough. One way of making meat more tender is to beat it to break up the fibres. A less energetic way is to add enzymes. Pineapple juice is sometimes added to meat recipes because it contains enzymes that break down protein fibres.

A *Gammon with pineapple is a popular meal, but it was invented to make the meat more tender.*

Enzymes for sweets

Enzymes are proteins, produced by living organisms, that act as catalysts.

One enzyme that is widely used in food manufacture is **invertase**. Invertase is produced by cultivating a yeast called **Saccharomyces cerevisae** in fermenters.

B *These sweets are made with a hard centre of sucrose and invertase before covering them in chocolate. Over the next 2 weeks the invertase changes the centre to a softer mix of glucose and fructose.*

The sugar that we get from sugarcane and sugar-beet is mostly sucrose. Invertase converts sucrose to glucose and fructose. (An alternative name for invertase is **sucrase**.)

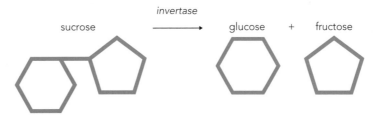

The mixture of glucose and fructose is sweeter than the original sucrose, so less is needed to make sweet foods. It is also good for making soft-centred sweets.

Enzymes for washing powders

Washing powders contain detergents that cannot remove some kinds of stains. Therefore many washing powders also contain enzymes, including **proteases** and **lipases**. Proteases break down proteins, such as haemoglobin in blood stains. Lipases break down fats, such as grease.

Enzymes for cheese-making

Cheese is made from milk. Traditionally, an enzyme from calves' stomachs, called **chymosin**, is added to the milk. It affects the protein in the milk, making the milk separate into curds (a semi-solid mix of protein and fat) and liquid whey. The curds are pressed to produce cheese.

?

1 What is invertase used for?

2 State one advantage of using washing powders that contain enzymes.

3 It is generally recommended that washing powders containing enzymes should be used at lower temperatures than other types of washing powder. Suggest why.

In the 1980s, scientists found a way of making chymosin using bacteria. They took the calf gene for chymosin and put it into the bacteria, which then produced chymosin. This is called **genetic modification**. Today, most chymosin is made from genetically modified yeast. It's much easier and cheaper to produce large quantities of very pure chymosin in this way rather than to get it from calves. It also makes a lot of cheese suitable for vegetarians.

Genetically modified organisms

Making a genetically modified organism uses **recombinant DNA technology**. This means that different pieces of DNA are 'recombined' in a new way. One of the first examples of this technology was the production of bacteria that contained the human gene for making **insulin**. Figure D shows how this was done.

C Chymosin is added to milk to make the solid fat and protein (curds) separate out from the liquid whey.

1 DNA from a human cell is cut into pieces using enzymes called **restriction enzymes**. These make staggered cuts across the double-stranded DNA, leaving a few unpaired bases at each end, called **sticky ends**.

2 Bacteria cells contain small circles of DNA called **plasmids**. The same restiction enzymes are used to cut plasmids open, leaving sticky ends with matching sets of unpaired bases.

3 The pieces of DNA containing the insulin gene are mixed with the plasmids. The bases in the sticky ends pair up. An enzyme called DNA **ligase** is added, linking the DNA back into a continuous circle.

4 The recombinant plasmids are inserted into bacteria. The bacteria can now be grown in huge fermenters, where they make human insulin.

D Producing genetically modified bacteria to make human insulin.

Skills spotlight

Suggest some benefits of making cheese using chymosin from genetically modified organisms, rather than chymosin from calves.

(?) 4 Explain how chymosin is used in cheese-making.

ResultsPlus
Watch Out!

Students often forget to explain that in genetic modification the new gene has come from a different organism and if it is from a different species then it is transgenic.

(H) 5 Outline the role of each of these enzymes in recombinant DNA technology: **(?)**
a restriction enzymes b DNA ligase.

6 Describe how invertase is produced, and explain why it is used to make sweets.

Learning Outcomes

3.10 Describe the use of enzyme technology including:
   a chymosin, produced by genetically modified microorganisms, used in the manufacture of vegetarian cheese
   b invertase (sucrase) produced by *Saccharomyces cerevisiae* (yeast), used in the manufacture of sweets
   c enzymes used in washing powders

(H) 3.13 Explain recombinant DNA technology using insulin as an example, including:
   a restriction enzymes b ligase c sticky ends

HSW **12** Describe the benefits, drawbacks and risks of using new scientific and technological developments

Millions of people around the world can't digest milk properly – why not?

B3.24 Are immobilised enzymes less affected by temperature?

:::: What are immobilised enzymes?

Human babies all around the world can digest milk. They produce the enzyme **lactase**, which breaks down the milk sugar, lactose, into glucose. However as people get older they often stop making this enzyme and become lactose intolerant. If lactose is not digested it passes into the large intestine and causes a build up of gases which can cause cramps and bloating. People who are lactose intolerant may feel very uncomfortable and even have diarrhoea if they drink milk. 34% of adults in England don't make lactase. However, the number of people in a population who are lactose intolerant seems to vary around the world. Only 17% of the cattle herding people of the Southern Sudan are lactose intolerant, while 99% of adults from Thailand make no lactase!

A Milk is an important part of the diet in Southern Sudan – and most people can digest lactose even when they are adults.

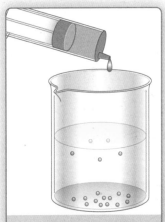

B By mixing an enzyme with sodium alginate you can make beads of immobilised (or trapped) enzymes.

Enzymes are widely used in biotechnology. They are usually **immobilised** – which means trapped on or in an inert material. This means that they can be used time after time. For example, lactase can be immobilised and used to break down the lactose found in milk to make lactose-free milk. This is useful for people who are lactose intolerant and also as a food for cats which do not make the lactase enzyme.

You can make immobilised enzymes quite simply by mixing an enzyme with sodium alginate solution. When you add drops of this solution to calcium chloride solution, you will get insoluble beads of calcium alginate containing the enzyme immobilised in the bead.

Your task

You are going to plan an investigation that will allow you to find out how immobilising an enzyme can change the way it is affected by temperature.

3.12 Investigate the use of immobilised lactase to produce lactose-free milk

ResultsPlus
Build Better Answers

When planning an investigation like this, one of the skills you will be assessed on is your ability to *find and use secondary evidence*. There are 2 marks available for this skill. Here are two extracts focusing on this skill. Other skills that you need for the practical assessment are dealt with in other lessons.

Student extract 1 | **A basic response for this skill**

The student has found a website and noted it down correctly.

> I looked on the internet and I found lots of different websites. One was called www.glutenintolerant.org and explained why some people cannot digest gluten in flour. The second gave me some information about how immobilised enzymes are made.

In this case the website does sound relevant but there is no reference for it so no-one else could look it up.

The website is not relevant to this practical which is looking at lactose intolerance.

Student extract 2 | **A good response for this skill**

It is a good idea to use books as well as the Internet.

This is the correct way to reference a textbook.

> I found a website which explained how immobilised enzymes are made and the sorts of things they are used for. It also talked about the effect of temperature on immobilised enzymes. The web site was part of company website called www.enzymes.com and I think that the information was relevant and reliable because the company makes immobilised enzymes.
> I also found a practical in a textbook called 'Biotechnology for all' by A Scientist published by Sciencebooks, 2009. It gave a way of testing if milk contained glucose or lactose. I think that it was a reliable resource because it had been tested by lots of other scientists.

The student has evaluated the information from the website which is a good way to access the higher marks.

ResultsPlus

To access 1 mark

Collect and record secondary evidence relevant to the hypothesis in a way that is appropriate for the topic.

To access 2 marks

- Collect and record secondary evidence relevant to the hypothesis in a way that is appropriate for the topic.
- Comment on the quality of the sources of secondary evidence

B3.25 Enzymes and food production

 How can enzymes be used to make apple juice?

Young herring gulls peck at a special spot on the base of their parent's beak. This makes the parent bird regurgitate food which has been partially digested in the gut. It sounds a bit revolting – but the baby food we buy in jars has also been partly digested by enzymes ready for us to give our babies!

Enzyme technology is important in the production of many different types of food and drink. Enzymes are used to produce things as varied as vegetarian cheeses, sweets, baby foods and many different types of fruit juice. They speed up the production of these foods and make them much cheaper for us to buy. Enzymes such as cellulose and pectinase are used in the manufacture of fruit juice. Pectinase separates the plant cells from each other, and cellulase breaks down the cellulose cell walls. This lets us extract much more juice from the cells. Cellulase is produced by the microorganisms which are found in the digestive system of cows. It is the enzyme which makes it possible for cows to digest the cell walls of grass.

A Predigested food is easier for the chicks to digest.

Your task

You are going to plan an investigation that will allow you to find out how enzymes affect the production of apple juice from apples.

Learning Outcomes

3.12 Investigate the use of enzymes in food production

Build Better Answers

When planning an investigation like this, one of the skills you will be assessed on is your ability to *develop a hypothesis*. There are 4 marks available for this skill. Here are two extracts focusing on this skill. Other skills that you need for the practical assessment are dealt with in other lessons.

Student extract 1 — A basic response for this skill

To access the higher marks the student would have to say how the amount of juice will change – will it increase or decrease?

I think that if you add an enzyme to a chopped up apple the amount of juice coming out of the apple will change. I think this because I know that enzymes are used to speed up reactions.

This is a clear hypothesis and would be easy to test

The pupil has also given a reason for the hypothesis.

Student extract 2 — A good response for this skill

This is a clear and detailed hypothesis.

I think that adding pectinase and cellulase enzymes to a chopped up apple will increase the volume of juice extracted by the greatest amount. I think that this will happen because the enzymes will help to digest the apple and this will allow more juice to flow out. I know that enzymes can be used in digestion reactions to break large molecules up into smaller molecules so it may be that the enzymes are able to break down the cell walls of the apple cells and allow the juice to be extracted.

The student has used their scientific information to explain why they think the hypothesis is true.

 ResultsPlus

To access 2 marks
- Provide a hypothesis that is appropriate for most of the task.
- Partially justify the hypothesis.

To access 4 marks
- Provide a hypothesis that is appropriate for the full scope of the task, based on relevant scientific ideas.
- Justify the hypothesis fully using relevant scientific ideas.

:::: **Can we feed everyone in the future?**

Scientists are trying all sorts of ways to make new foods and fuels, and they get ideas from some strange places. The foam nests of the Tungara frog inspired some scientists to make bubbles containing a mix of enzymes that could create sugars using energy from the Sun (just like plants but more efficient).

A *Tungara frogs lay their eggs in a mass of foam that protects them from the environment.*

1 Explain what is meant by 'global food security'.

2 You have one variety of maize that is resistant to attack by rust fungus, and another that grows well in dry conditions. Describe how selective breeding could produce a variety that has both of these features.

3 Describe the different strategies that are used together to control pests of raspberries.

Breeding plants

As the human population continues to grow, people in many parts of the world do not get enough food. The World Health Organization calls this the '**global food security crisis**'; we won't have enough food for everyone. New varieties of crops with higher yields are being produced to provide more food.

Most new plant varieties are produced by **conventional breeding** programmes. For example, to produce a very high-yielding wheat variety, one high-yielding wheat variety is crossed with another. All the resulting seeds are sown and allowed to grow into adult plants. From these, the individuals producing the most grain are selected and bred together. This is repeated for at least 20 generations, eventually producing a high-yielding variety that is named and sold.

Pest management strategies

Each year, huge amounts of crops are lost to pests such as insects and fungal diseases. Resistant plants can be developed, but the best way of combating pests is often to use a system called **integrated pest management** (IPM). This uses several different pest control strategies at the same time, as shown in Figure B.

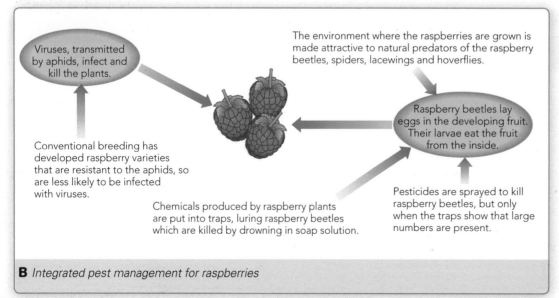

Viruses, transmitted by aphids, infect and kill the plants.

The environment where the raspberries are grown is made attractive to natural predators of the raspberry beetles, spiders, lacewings and hoverflies.

Raspberry beetles lay eggs in the developing fruit. Their larvae eat the fruit from the inside.

Conventional breeding has developed raspberry varieties that are resistant to the aphids, so are less likely to be infected with viruses.

Chemicals produced by raspberry plants are put into traps, luring raspberry beetles which are killed by drowning in soap solution.

Pesticides are sprayed to kill raspberry beetles, but only when the traps show that large numbers are present.

B *Integrated pest management for raspberries*

Crops like raspberries stay in the same field for many years. However, for annual crops a different crop can be planted in the same field each year in a 3- or 4-year cycle, such as potatoes, oats, beans and cabbages. This is called **crop rotation** and helps prevent the build-up of soil pests for each crop.

Biofuels

Our increasing population also needs more energy for industry, transport and other uses. Yet almost everyone agrees we need to reduce our use of fossil fuels. One possible replacement for them is **biofuels**. These are fuels that are made by, or from, living organisms, including plants such as maize or oil palms.

Biofuels are **renewable**; it doesn't take long to produce them and we can keep growing the plants from which they are produced year after year. They are also said to be 'carbon neutral'. This means that the carbon dioxide released into the air when they are burned balances out the carbon dioxide that the growing plants removed from the air for photosynthesis. However, the plants take up land that could be used for growing food.

C *Elephant grass is increasingly being grown in the UK for use as a fuel in power stations.*

D *In Indonesia, large areas of rainforest and other land areas are being planted with oil palm trees to make biofuel because this will generate more income than growing crops.*

4 Explain why biofuels are renewable sources of energy.

5 Describe some advantages and disadvantages of growing biofuels.

6 The oil palm plantations in Indonesia are owned by companies, not local people. Explain why the local people could be badly affected by the plantations.

Skills spotlight

Describe the impact of rainforest destruction to plant oil palm trees for biofuel on atmospheric carbon, and discuss whether this biofuel can be considered 'carbon neutral'.

Learning Outcomes

3.14 Demonstrate an understanding of the impact of human population growth on global food security

3.18 Explain how increased food production for humans includes:
a conventional plant breeding programmes b pest management strategies

3.19 Demonstrate an understanding of the advantages and disadvantages of replacing fossil fuels with biofuels, including the facts that biofuels are renewable and that their production uses carbon dioxide but that growing the crops to make them requires land and may affect the availability of land for growing food

HSW *12* Describe the benefits, drawbacks and risks of using new scientific and technological developments

>>>>>>>>>>>>>>>>>>>>>>>>> How could you make Christmas trees that don't need lights?

.·:·: Can genetically modified crops feed the world?

Jack O'Lantern mushrooms glow in the dark. If the gene for the glowing pigment in the fungus were transferred into Christmas trees, we could have glow-in-the dark decorations without using electricity.

A These mushrooms naturally glow in the dark.

Genetically modified maize, soya and cotton are widely grown in both developed and developing countries. Many of these have a gene that makes them resistant to a herbicide. This means crops are not damaged by the chemical but the weeds growing with them are killed.

B These purple GM tomatoes may help to treat cancer.

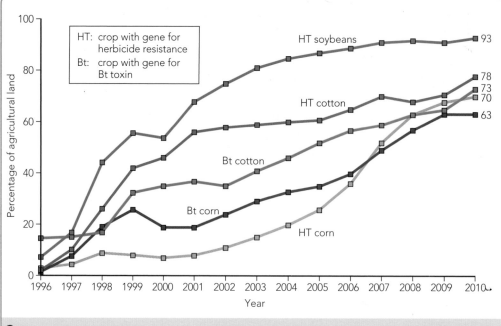

C The percentage of GM crops compared with non-GM grown in the US has increased rapidly.

?

1 a Why were tomatoes engineered to produce flavonoids? **b** Where in the world are these tomatoes most likely to be grown? Explain your reasoning.

2 Look at Figure C. Suggest a reason for the trend in the uptake of Bt corn.

3 Explain why plants from the US GM seed gave a smaller yield than normal crop plants grown in India.

In 2008, a new purple GM variety of tomato was developed. It contains snapdragon genes that produce extra pigments called **flavonoids**. Tests have shown that it helps mice with cancer to live longer, and this might be useful for humans. This tomato will probably be too expensive for people in developing countries to grow or buy.

GM crop seeds produced in developed countries are more expensive than normal seeds. In India, many farmers borrowed money to buy GM seed because they believed they would give a better crop yield than normal plants. However, many found that the GM plants produced less food because they were not adapted to the Indian soil and climate. The farmers then had even less money.

Making GM plants

A **transgenic** organism contains genes transferred from another organism. Transgenic plants are often produced using a bacterium called **Agrobacterium tumefaciens**.

The gene for the required characteristic is inserted into *Agrobacterium tumefaciens*, which is then allowed to infect plants. This introduces the required gene into the plant cells. So the *A. tumefaciens* acts as a go-between or **vector**.

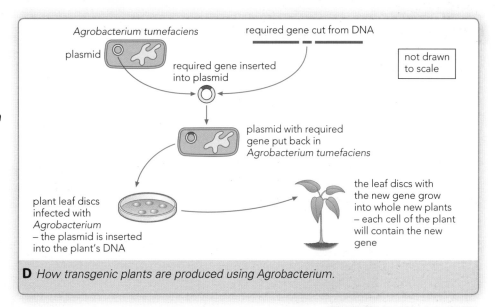

D How transgenic plants are produced using Agrobacterium.

Advantages and disadvantages of Bt crops

Bacillus thuringiensis is a bacterium that is normally found in soil. It produces **Bt toxin** when eaten by insects, which is poisonous.

The gene for Bt toxin has been identified in the bacterium and transferred into crop plants using *Agrobacterium*. When insects eat the plant cells, the cells release Bt toxin, which kills the insects. This means less insecticide has to be sprayed onto the crop, reducing damage to the environment. Higher yields should be produced, as less of the crop is lost to the pests.

However, there are worries that the toxin could kill other, harmless, insects such as butterflies and bees. The Bt gene might also spread into closely related wild plant species if pollen from a Bt crop is transferred to a related wild plant and leads to a fertilisation of that plant.

Another problem is that many insect populations have evolved resistance to the Bt toxin, so they can live and breed on the Bt plants.

H 5 List two advantages and two disadvantages of growing Bt crops.

H 6 Explain why the spread of the Bt gene to wild plants would be a problem.

7 Using numbered steps, describe how the Bt gene was put into soybean plants.

4 Explain how plants can be genetically modified using *Agrobacterium tumefaciens*.

ResultsPlus
Watch Out!

When describing the production of GM plants students often forget to mention that the new gene is in the plasmid of the *A. tumefaciens*.

Skills spotlight

Around two thirds of food products on sale in British supermarkets contain soya. Suggest who would benefit, and why they would benefit, if GM soya was allowed in UK food products.

Learning Outcomes

3.15 Explain how *Agrobacterium tumefaciens* is used as a vector in creating transgenic plants

H 3.16 Demonstrate an understanding of the advantages and disadvantages of introducing genes for insect resistance from *Bacillus thuringiensis* into crop plants

3.17 Demonstrate an understanding of the costs and benefits of genetic modification of crop plants in the context of developed and developing countries, including the introduction of flavonoids in the purple tomato

3.18 Explain how increased food production for humans includes: **c** genetic modification

HSW 12 Describe the benefits, drawbacks and risks of using new scientific and technological developments

These questions are indicative of the type of questions used in the exam. Refer to page 6 for information on the grades.

Animal behaviour

1. As soon as a new brood of ducklings is born they follow their mother around.
Ducklings will do this with the first animal they see after breaking out of their egg.

(a) (i) This type of behaviour is known as
   A habituation
   B imprinting
   C classical conditioning
   D operant conditioning   (1)

   (ii) Describe the benefits to the ducklings of this type of behaviour.   (2)

(b) (i) Explain why parenting is likely to be a successful evolutionary strategy. (2)

   (ii) Use one of the words from the box to complete the sentence on animal behaviour.

   | innate   habituated   imprinted   conditioned |

   The ability to suckle milk from the moment a mammal is born is known
   as _____ behaviour.   (1)

(c) The police train animals including dogs and horses to seek out drugs or control riots.
   Describe the training methods used by the police to make sure the animals carry out
   the required behaviour.   (6)

Fertilisation

2. The diagram shows the sperm and egg cell (ovum) and the sperm and ovum combined at fertilisation.

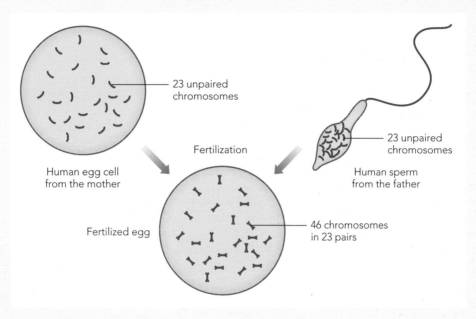

(a) (i) Sperm cells determine gender.
Sperm cells contain

    A   Y chromosomes only for gender
    B   X chromosomes only for gender
    C   both X and Y chromosomes in each sperm cell
    D   either X or Y chromosomes in each sperm cell   (1)

  (ii) Complete the Punnett square to show how the gender of a child is inherited
from the parents.

	X	X
X		
Y		

(2)

  (iii) What is the percentage chance that the offspring of a single fertilisation will be female?   (1)

(b) Describe how the structure of an egg cell (ovum) is related to it's function.   (3)

(c) Many couples are unable to have children due to problems with infertility.
Suggest one ethical reason why some people may be concerned about the use
of fertility treatment.   (1)

(d) Explain how hormones can be used in fertility treatment.   (2)

Using fermenters for food production

3. The diagram shows a fermenter commonly used for the production of mycoprotein.

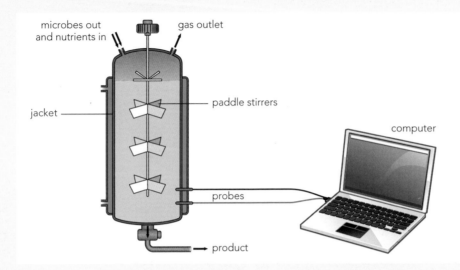

(a) (i) Suggest why steam is used to sterilise the fermenter rather than a chemical disinfectant. (1)

(ii) Use the diagram to describe how temperature is controlled in the fermenter. (2)

(iii) Mycoprotein production has many advantages over the production of protein from animal sources. Name one advantage of this type of protein production. (1)

(b) Air entering the fermenter is filtered to stop other microbes entering. Suggest what may happen to the amount of mycoprotein produced if other microbes did enter the fermenter. Give a reason for your answer. (2)

(c) The table shows a comparison of the major food groups found in mycoprotein and in beef.

	Percentage of dry mass	
Food type	Mycoprotein	Beef
protein	45–50	65–70
fat	5–10	35–40
mineral salts	3–4	3–4
fibre	25–30	none

Explain the advantages of using mycoprotein in the human diet rather than beef. (4)

Human evolution

4. There are two main hypotheses regarding human evolution. The two main hypotheses agree that *Homo erectus* evolved in Africa and spread to the rest of the world around 1–2 million years ago.

> Hypothesis 1
> This suggests that modern humans evolved from archaic forms (such as *Homo erectus* which existed) concurrently in different regions of the world.

> Hypothesis 2
> This proposes that modern humans evolved once in Africa between 100–200 thousand years ago, modern humans subsequently colonised the rest of the world without genetic mixing.

(a) (i) Scientists have been made aware of the second hypothesis through:

      A   Darwin's theory of evolution
      B   the fossil theory
      C   the multi-regional theory
      D   the African Eve theory   (1)

(ii) Mitochondrial DNA evidence points towards hypothesis 2 being more likely, with the dates where the sequences all join as being 171,500 years ago. Suggest differences you would expect to find in mitochondrial DNA if hypothesis 1 were to be accepted.   (2)

(b) Describe **two** other methods that scientists use as evidence for developing the theory of human evolution?   (2)

(c) Explain why mitochondrial DNA provides a good source of evidence for human evolution.   (4)

Enzymes

5. Around 5% of adults in the UK suffer from a condition known as lactose intolerance. These people lack an enzyme that breaks down lactose, a sugar found in milk.

   (a) (i) Name the enzyme that breaks down lactose. (1)

   (ii) The breakdown of lactose is an enzyme-catalysed reaction. Write a word equation to show this reaction. (2)

   (iii) One advantage of using immobilised enzymes is that the

       A   enzymes are destroyed quickly preventing contamination of the product
       B   enzymes and products are easily separated from each other
       C   reaction is slower and can be controlled more easily
       D   substrate cannot easily reach the enzymes resulting in less product (1)

   (b) The enzymes found in biological washing powders are free-moving once they are dissolved in water. These enzymes break down food stains in clothing. Explain how these enzymes help to remove stains from clothing. (3)

   (c) Two experiments were carried out to find the effects of temperature on chymotrypsin, a digestive enzyme that breaks down protein. One experiment was carried out using immobilised chymotrypsin and the other using free-moving chymotrypsin in solution. The graph shows the results of the experiment.

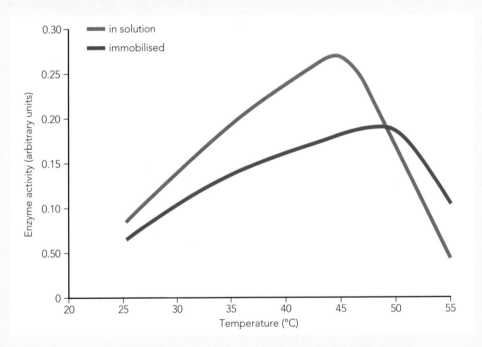

Explain why the reaction using the enzyme in solution produced more product than the immobilised enzyme between 25 °C and 48 °C (3)

Immunisation

6. In 2007 the Government announced a new routine immunisation of all school girls aged 12–13 years. The immunisation is designed to help protect the girls from cervical cancer caused by the human papilloma virus (HPV).

   (a) (i) Describe how immunisation against HPV can protect girls from some types of cervical cancer. (2)

   (ii) The HPV vaccine is given in three doses over six months. Explain why girls may not be fully protected against cervical cancer if they received just one dose of the vaccine. (2)

   (iii) Sketch a graph to show the levels of antibodies in the blood after each dose of the HPV vaccine. On the graph indicate where the 1st, 2nd and 3rd dose of the vaccine were given. (2)

   (b) Explain how monoclonal antibodies can be used in locating cancer cells in the body and in the treatment of cancer. (6)

Biofuels

7. The following article recently appeared on a website.

   > 'Biofuels are much more environment-friendly than any other known form of fuels and are a perfect replacement for oil products like petrol and diesel. This is because biofuels are easily renewable and are very inexpensive to produce'.

   Source: http://www.biofuelswatch.com/biofuels-pros-and-cons

   (a) (i) State what is meant by a biofuel, using a named example. (2)

   (ii) Why are biofuels often described as renewable? (1)

   (iii) Explain why the use of biofuels are said to be 'more environmentally-friendly' than any other known types of fuel. (3)

   (b) Some people are concerned about the impact that the production of biofuels will have on the environment. Discuss the disadvantages of producing biofuels. (3)

Kidney dialysis

8. Kidney dialysis is needed when the kidney fails to function correctly.
The diagram shows the processes involved during kidney dialysis.

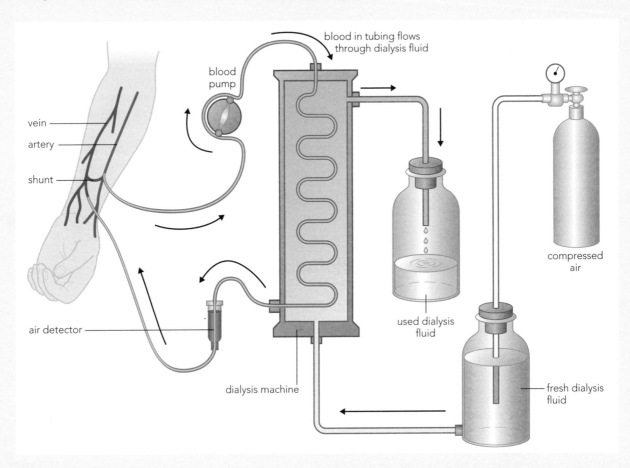

(a) What substance, formed by the breakdown of amino acids, is removed during dialysis?

    A   water
    B   protein
    C   urea
    D   carbon dioxide   (1)

(ii) The dialysis machine is completing the job of ultrafiltration of the blood.
What structures in the nephron carries out ultrafiltration?

    A   loop of Henle and collecting duct
    B   collecting duct and convoluted tubule
    C   convoluted tubule and glomerulus
    D   glomerulus and Bowman's capsule   (1)

(b) During dialysis the used fluid is collected. Describe what happens to fluids that leave the kidney but are not reabsorbed by the blood. (3)

(c) Name one substance, other than water, that can be selectively reabsorbed in the kidney. (1)

(d) The diagram below shows a negative feedback loop.

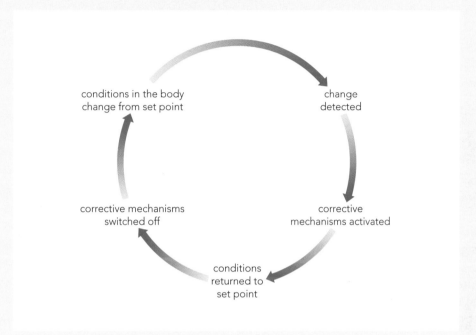

Explain how antidiuretic hormone (ADH) controls water levels in the body using a negative feedback mechanism similar to the one in the diagram. (6)

Genetic modification

9. Read the article about genetic modification of soya beans.

> ### Soya bean plants can be killed by selective weedkiller.
>
> Scientists have transferred a gene from a bacterium into soya bean plants to create a genetically modified variety. This new variety of soya beans is resistant to selective weedkiller.

(a) (i) What proteins are needed to remove the required gene from the bacterium?

     A ligase enzymes
     B restriction enzymes
     C chymosin enzymes
     D *Agrobacterium tumefaciens* (1)

(ii) Explain how the crop yield of soya bean will change as a result of the introduction of this gene. (3)

(iii) Many pressure groups are worried about the impact of genetically-modified crops on natural ecosystems. Describe how the introduction of genetically-modified crops may impact on natural ecosystems. (2)

(b) *Bacillus thuringiensis* produces a protein that is toxic to insects. Describe the processes that a scientist must take to genetically modify the soya plant to contain the protein from *Bacillus thuringiensis*. (6)

Inheriting information

10. In July 1978 the world's first test tube baby, Louise Brown, was born in the UK. Now, more than 12,000 IVF babies are born each year in the UK and many thousands more worldwide.

(a) *In vitro* fertilisation (IVF) involves

    A   replacing the nucleus of an egg cell with the nucleus from a body cell
    B   using hormones to encourage egg development in the ovaries
    C   implantation of an egg cell followed by fertilisation by a sperm cell
    D   fertilisation of an embryo outside of the uterus using sperm cells   (1)

(b) (i) The diagram shows a human sperm cell.

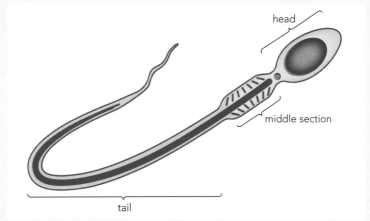

    Describe how the structure of the sperm is adapted to carry out its function.   (2)

  (ii) Each human sperm cell contains one of two types of sex chromosome each of which is responsible for determining the sex of a baby. Use a genetic diagram to help explain how the chromosomes in the sperm cell determine the sex of a baby.   (3)

(c) Haemophilia is a sex-linked genetic disorder that affects the ability of the blood to clot. Explain why male offspring are more likely to suffer from haemophilia than females whereas females are more likely to be carriers of the disorder. You may use a genetic diagram to help with your explanation.   (6)

ResultsPlus
Build Better Answers

Here are three student answers to the following question. Read the answers together with the examiner comments around and after them.

| Question | Courtship | | Grade | D–A* |

The picture shows a male peacock attracting a female during courtship.

Explain how the peacock uses various methods of communication during courtship to advertise his quality as a potential mate.

Student answer 1 — Extract typical of a level ① answer

A good attempt at an answer but it needs to say that this display attracts the mate not just that they see him.

The pecock has a large tail and he raises it so the girl peacock can see him. He does this so he can mate with the girl peacock and have babies. If the girl peacock likes him they get together.

The peacock wants to mate so that he can pass his genes onto the next generation – try to add as much detail as possible.

Examiner summary
This answer has just enough detail to achieve a level 1 mark. It identifies that courtship behaviour happens prior to mating and that the male peacock is trying to impress the female. To achieve a higher level, mention other methods of communication that the male peacock could do, e.g. making sound signals or gestures such as strutting in front of the female.

Student answer 2 — Extract typical of a level ② answer

A good description which you can improve by adding a few more details such as other ways in which he may communicate with the female.

The peacock has raised his tail feathers so he looks better to the female. He is hoping she will find him atractive and want to mate with him. The longer the feathers the more attractive he will be to the female. He can communicate as well by making sounds to call her. He does this so he can have offspring with his genes in.

This is a good start but try to think why else he may do this. If he has a very heavy tail this will show that he is strong enough to lift it and is therefore a good mate.

A good point to make but you need to actually say the peacock wants to pass his genes on.

Examiner summary
Overall the answer includes a fair description but there is little detail in the description of the various methods of communication. The peacock is showing his longer tail feathers to let the female know that he is a strong fit male and she will choose him because he has characteristics she wants in her offspring. The peacock can call out which is another method of advertising that he is available as a mate. To improve the answer include appropriate methods of non-verbal communication such as strutting back and forth to show off the tail and how strong he is.

Student answer 3 — Extract typical of a level ③ answer

Good – this is the main reason for this type of courtship behaviour, i.e. to let the female know that he is the fittest and therefore most attractive.

> The peacock is exhibiting courtship behaviour in order to attract the female to him. By showing off his tail feathers he shows her that he is very strong as the tail feathers are big and heavy and he can still manage to raise them. This will make the female think he has good strong genes to pass onto his offspring so they will be more likely to survive. The peacock may use other forms of communication such as calling to attract her attention or to frighten off other potential males around. The peacock can also use non-verbal communication techniques such as strutting or parading in front of the female to further attract her.

Courtship behaviour is all about the male passing his genes on so this is a clear explanation.

A good example of extending the answer to include other knowledge that you have.

Examiner summary

This is a very good answer written in a coherent manner with each part of the question addressed effectively. The student has noted that the question asks about the quality as a potential mate and also that it is not just the picture that needs to be referred to as a form of communication.

 ResultsPlus

Move from level ① to level ②

To move from level 1 to 2 more scientific facts are needed and the answer should be constructed so that you show off the knowledge you have. Avoid just making general statements but link the question to scientific knowledge. Do not just state 'so the peacock can be seen' but why he would want to be seen. The question is about courting behaviour so make sure there is some reference in the answer to courting behaviour.

Move from level ② to level ③

The key to moving from level 2 to 3 is in the detail and making sure you address every part of the question. You should include all the information you have about courting behaviour and why the peacock would have such extreme forms of courting behaviour. Try to think beyond the basic and apply the other scientific knowledge you have. You have knowledge about how genes are passed on so use this in the answer to the question.

Here are three student answers to the following question. Read the answers together with the examiner comments around and after them.

Question	Menstrual cycle	Grade	D–A*

The diagram shows feedback mechanisms present in the menstrual cycle.

Use the diagram to help explain how the four hormones control the menstrual cycle

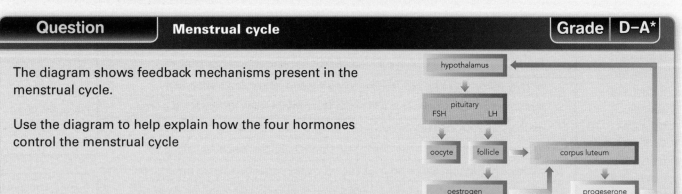

Student answer 1 — Extract typical of a level ① answer

You need to use the diagram here. A lot of information on the names of hormones is given so use it to make your answer better.

The cycle is every month and is controled by hormones. estrogen and the other hormones make you produce eggs. FSH can be used in fertility treatment and makes lots of eggs in the ovary.

Make sure you spell scientific terms correctly, especially when they are given in the question.

Make sure you name all the hormones here that are mentioned in the diagram.

Be careful not to give information that does not answer the question.

Examiner summary

This is a very basic and vague answer to the question. There is no evidence that the diagram has been used, which is a specific part of the question. The answer has been expanded by trying to add other information but this does not gain any extra credit even though it is correct as it does not answer the question.

Student answer 2 — Extract typical of a level ② answer

To get a better mark you must describe how the hormones control each of these parts of the menstrual cycle not just mention them.

The menstrual cycle is a 28-day cycle and it involves the hormones oestrogen, progesterone, FSH and LH. These hormones cause changes during the cycle including ovulation and menstruation. If progesterone stays high then you might be pregnant, if progesterone is low you have a period. FSH and LH are made in the pituitary, oestrogen is made in the follicle and progesterone in the corpus luteum.

Well done, this is a good use of the diagram to help you answer the question.

Examiner summary

The answer uses the diagram for information but does not include all the details that would be expected of a level 3 answer. One of the roles of progesterone is correctly outlined but the interaction between the hormones is not explored as effectively as possible. The answer needs to include further details of the inhibition of FSH and LH by progesterone, or details of the roles of the other hormones.

Student answer 3 — Extract typical of a level ③ answer

Though the mark could be improved by discussing the feedback mechanisms further and the role of LH, there is enough information here to gain level 3.

The diagram shows evidence of a negative feedback mechanism. FSH, made in the pituitary, causes the oocyte to develop in the follicles and stimulates oestrogen production. Oestrogen helps to build up the lining of the uterus. Progesterone is produced by the corpus luteum and high levels of progesterone stop menstruation from happening. Menstruation occurs when levels of oestrogen and progesterone drop.

An excellent statement which describes the whole diagram.

A good level of detail to inform what is happening and effective use of the diagram.

Examiner summary

This is a clear and detailed answer which describes the role of the hormones in the menstrual cycle in a clear and coherent way. It recognises the need to use the diagram in the answer and describes the roles of the various hormones. There could be more detail given here, such as the role of LH or how the corpus luteum is formed, but there is sufficient information on this lengthy and complicated topic to achieve a level 3.

 Results**Plus**

Move from level ① to level ②

The answer should refer to the diagram as this was given to help answer the question more effectively. To move to level 2, give interpretations wherever possible and only include information you are sure is correct. In this case you could move up to level 2 by describing the information given, including mentioning the hormones involved and where they act.

Move from level ② to level ③

To move up to level 3, give more scientific detail. You must be able to interpret the diagram and also use your own scientific knowledge about the hormones that control the menstrual cycle. You should recognise that there is a feedback mechanism involved in this. There is the chance here to describe one of the processes in depth such as menstruation and ovulation, which will help you achieve a better mark.

Here are three student answers to the following question. Read the answers together with the examiner comments around and after them.

Question	Population size	Grade	D–A*

The graph shows how the population of yeast grown in a fermenter changes with time.

Use the graph to help you explain the changes in the size of the yeast population at Stage 1, Stage 2, Stage 3 and Stage 4.

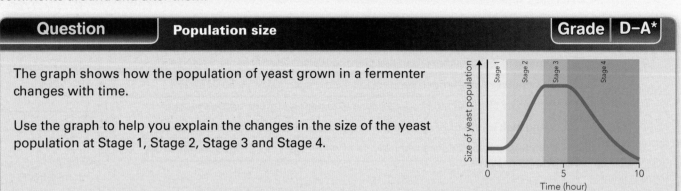

Student answer 1 — Extract typical of a level ① answer

Spell terms correctly, especially if they are given in the question.

The yeest doesn't grow at first and then grows really quickly in the fist stage and then it starts to die in stage 3. It starts to die as it has used all the food. The food has run out in stage 4 and all the yeest are dead.

Avoid using 'it' here as it is vague, 'population size' is clearer.

The first and second stages have been confused here and it is wrong to suggest that the yeast does not grow at first. Remember that the question asks about the size of the population not the growth of individual yeast cells.

This answer correctly states that the lack of food could be a factor that determines the size of the yeast population. However, not all of the yeast are dead as the answer suggests and some will still reproduce to keep the population stable.

Examiner summary

This answer gives very simple, brief information but has some spelling errors and does not explain all the stages of the growth curve correctly. To improve the answer you must make it clear that it is the population size that is being discussed and not just yeast or 'it'.

Student answer 2 — Extract typical of a level ② answer

The differences between the stages are identified although the scientific information given is not always correct. Refer to population size and not yeast.

In Stage 1 there are only a few yeast but they grow quickly in stage 2 so by day 3 there are lots. They grow quickly as there is lots of food and they use the food to get bigger. In stage 3 the yeast start to die as they compete for food and there isn't enough for them all to survive. The yeast then start to die in stage 4 as the food has gone. In the earlier stages there is no contamination but later they might also be contaminated by waste or other microorganisms could be in the container using the food.

Good – this gives a factor that explains the yeast population growth and that the yeast compete for food. This is good use of science, although it does imply that all of the yeast die, which is incorrect.

The yeast do start to die during stage 4 but the graph actually declines as more die than reproduce.

This is good as it gives other factors that may affect the yeast population.

Examiner summary

This answer is presented clearly and in a logical order. Scientific terminology is used to help explain the shape of the graph. Although it is not correct in all areas, the information given shows a fair understanding of the factors affecting the population size.

Student answer 3   **Extract typical of a level ③ answer**

This clearly recognises that there is no change in the population size during Stage 1 although it does not give any detail about why.

You should mention that some yeast are still reproducing although not as quickly as they are dying, and therefore there is a drop in the overall population size.

The yeast population remains stable during stage 1 so there is no change in size. In Stage 2 it uses the nutrients to grow so the population size increases as the yeast reproduce. The fermenter provides the ideal conditions for the yeast to grow such as temperature and oxygen so it can grow rapidly. In Stage 3 the population size doesn't change which means that some yeast die and some reproduce. This is because of intraspecific competition for resources like food and space. The population size decreases in Stage 4. This means that the yeast are dying which is because there is no food left in the fermenter. It might also be because there is interspecific competition with other microbes which respire and use up oxygen in the fermenter. The microbes might produce waste that is poisonous to the yeast or the yeast might be killed from the alcohol or carbon dioxide they produce during fermentation.

This is good as it uses scientific information to explain the shape of the graph during Stage 3.

Good - these are some factors that influence population growth during Stage 3 and makes good use of scientific terminology.

This shows a good understanding of the science underlying the factors affecting population growth. It is good to discuss interspecific competition and the build up of waste, which could reduce the size of the yeast population.

Examiner summary

This is a clear level 3 answer that shows a good understanding of the factors that affect the size of the yeast population. It is an ordered account of the scientific principles underlying most stages of the growth curve with good detail and use of scientific terminology, e.g. intraspecific, to further explain what the graph shows.

 ResultsPlus

Move from level ❶ to level ❷

To move to level 2, try to set out your answer so that each stage of the graph is discussed in order, from Stage 1 to Stage 4. Think carefully about what the shape of the graph is telling you about the population size and use scientific information and terminology in your response that explains why the population size changes, as shown by the graph.

Move from level ❷ to level ❸

To move to level 3 you need to identify further factors that may affect the population size of yeast and describe the effect of these factors on the yeast population. Use your understanding of these factors to clearly explain each stage of the graph.

ResultsPlus
Build Better Answers

Here are three student answers to the following question. Read the answers together with the examiner comments around and after them.

Question	Recombinant DNA Technology	Grade	D–A*

In 1982, insulin became the first recombinant DNA (rDNA) drug on the market. Since this time it has been used to treat thousands of patients with diabetes.

Describe how human insulin can be produced using rDNA technology.

Student answer 1   Extract typical of a level ① answer

Good - this identifies that bacteria can be used to produce large amounts of insulin and correctly names fermentation as the process where insulin is produced. Be careful to spell scientific words correctly.

> Insulin is a hormone that treats diabetes. It can be produced by bacteria that produce it in large amounts in fermentation. The bacteria have DNA for insulin which tells them to produce insulin for humans. The insulin is safe for use in humans as it is made by bacteria quickly.

The answer shows some understanding of why the bacteria produce insulin i.e. that they contain the appropriate DNA.

This could be improved with a description of how bacteria produce insulin quickly.

Examiner summary

The answer correctly identifies some details associated with the production of insulin using rDNA technology although the information given is limited to simple ideas. To move to level 2, include further details of some of the procedures used in rDNA technology, e.g. removal of the insulin gene from the human genome and the use of plasmids.

Student answer 2   Extract typical of a level ② answer

This shows some understanding of the use of enzymes in recombinant DNA technology, but the information about plasmids is incorrect: plasmids do not produce the insulin gene – they contain the gene that makes insulin.

> The human insulin gene is cut out and inserted into bacteria. Bacteria have plasmids that produce the insulin gene once it is put into them. Enzymes are used to cut the gene out of humans. The bacteria multiply very quickly and they produce lots of insulin in a short time. The insulin doesn't cause side effects in people as it is made from humans and not cattle so there is much less chance of rejection.

This correctly states that the insulin gene is extracted from humans but has missed out a stage by implying that it is inserted directly into bacterial cells.

This part correctly gives the benefits of using insulin produced by bacteria although this information will not gain you more marks as it does not answer the question.

Examiner summary

This answer shows an understanding of some of the recombinant DNA technology processes as the use of enzymes is mentioned. It could be improved by covereing their full role in 'cutting' and 'sticking'. A level 3 response should provide a full account of how human insulin can be produced using bacteria, stating the full role of enzymes and plasmids.

Student answer 3 | **Extract typical of a level ③ answer**

This part is thorough and covers all of the initial stages involved in preparing the DNA for insertion into the plasmid.

First of the all the human insulin gene is identified and cut out using a restriction enzyme. The same restriction enzyme is used to cut out a section from a plasmid. The human gene is then stuck into a plasmid and ligase is used for this. Sticky ends help the human gene to stick into the plasmid by complimentary base pairing. The plasmid is inserted into a bacteria and this is grown in a fermenter in optimum conditions such as the correct temperature. Aseptic conditions are needed in the fermenter for maximum growth of the bacteria and to get as much insulin as possible. The insulin is extracted from the fermenter and purified.

This is a good way to round off the response, and marks will be gained for mentioning the final extraction and purification to obtain insulin for human use.

All the stages in the production of insulin have been included here and given in the correct order, with the correct roles for specific enzymes identified.

Examiner summary

This is a good level 3 response that details the stages of insulin production in a clear and logical manner. The information covers most aspects of human insulin production by bacteria, from identification of the human gene to purification of insulin using good scientific terminology.

 ResultsPlus

Move from level ❶ to level ❷

To move to level 2, your answer needs to describe the steps involved in transforming bacteria using the human insulin gene. Think about what needs to be done to the bacteria to make it produce human insulin. Add more detail to the information you have given, using more scientific terminology. Make sure that your spelling of scientific words is correct.

Move from level ❷ to level ❸

To move to level 3, you will need to cover more detail in the steps that you have given, and give more steps, including the use of plasmids and enzymes in transforming bacteria. Try to set out your answer so that each step of the process is covered in a logical manner, from the identification of the human gene at the start to the extraction of insulin from the fermenter.

Results Plus
Exam question report

A computer was programmed to model the effects of changing global temperatures on endangered animals. It was found that as the global temperature increased more species became extinct. Why was a computer used to model this rather then experimental evidence?

A computers are more accurate   **B** computers give results faster   **C** experimental evidence cannot be proven   **D** experimental evidence is less reliable

Answer: The correct answer is B.

How students answered

| 0 marks | 1 mark |

More than half of students got this wrong. Many students find questions about computer modelling difficult.

You need to memorise the advantages and disadvantages given in the table to make sure you can answer questions like this correctly.

Results Plus

In 1859 rabbits were introduced to Australia for hunting. The rabbit population grew very quickly and they became serious pests.

a) Sometimes, the population of rabbits in a small area gets so large that it will suddenly 'crash'. A crash is when large numbers of the rabbits die so that the number of rabbits falls dramatically. Suggest what may cause a crash to happen. (1)

▲ **Correct answer:** The rabbits had eaten all of the food so they starved (other correct answers include drought, disease or increase in predators).

■ Many students lost this mark because they just said something like 'The amount of food', which doesn't give enough detail to gain the mark.

b) By 1900, Australian sheep farmers were very worried about the large rabbit population. Explain how rabbits could affect sheep. (2)

▲ **Correct answer:** The rabbits and sheep eat the same food, so they are competing for food. This means the sheep do no get enough food, and do not produce enough meat.

● A lot of students lost a mark by just saying that the rabbits eat the same food as the sheep, without explaining what effect this would have on the sheep.

Results Plus
Exam question report

Bio-butanol is a new fuel that the producers intend to market. Bio-butanol has a higher energy content per litre than bio-ethanol. An advantage of bio-butanol compared to bio-ethanol is:

A it is produced from renewable resources   **B** under the same conditions a car will use less fuel   **C** it can be used instead of petrol   **D** it produces different waste products

Answer: The answer is B.

How students answered

About two-thirds of students got this wrong. Only about one-third of students gave the correct answer. Statements A an C are correct, but they aren't advantages of bio-butanol *compared* to bio-ethanol, as they apply to bio-ethanol as well.

ResultsPlus
Exam question report

Corn is genetically modified by inserting foreign genes into its genome. This is carried out using:

A plasmids and enzynes **B** plasmids and hormones **C** hormones and enzymes **D** hormones, plasmids and enzymes

Answer: The correct answer here is A.

How students answered

Most students got this one wrong. Even if you can't remember what plasmids are, the key thing to know is that hormones are *not* involved. Hormones are chemical messengers in animals and plants, and are not used in genetic engineering.

ResultsPlus
Exam question report

The table shows two diseases. Which row of the table shows genetic diseases only?

	haemophilia	sickle-cell anaemia		haemophilia	sickle-cell anaemia
A	yes	yes	C	no	yes
B	yes	no	D	no	no

Answer: The correct answer is A.

How students answered

0 marks

Most students couldn't identify that both of these diseases are genetic diseases.

1 mark

Only about a third of students realised that both diseases were genetic.

ResultsPlus

Why are drugs tested before they are given to humans? (1)

Any of the following would be acceptable:
- The drug may be toxic or harmful.
- The drugs may cause side-effects.
- To check that they work.

Some students used 'dangerous' or 'unsafe' in their answers. If you use these words, you need to explain what they mean otherwise you won't get the mark.

ResultsPlus
Exam question report

What is the name given to disease-causing organisms?

A foreign bodies **B** microbes **C** pathogens **D** viruses

Answer: The correct answer is C.

How students answered

Over half of students got this wrong. Remember that the word 'microbes' means all small organisms, not all of which cause disease, so B isn't the correct answer.

Chemistry 3
Chemistry in action

These giant crystals are found in a cave in Mexico. They are made from a calcium compound that was dissolved in the water in the cave. As the water evaporated, over thousands of years, the crystals grew.

Calcium compounds are common in our water, and in this unit you will find out about some of the problems they can cause. You will also learn about how analytical chemists check to see what is in our water. Apart from calcium compounds, there may also be other chemical substances in water supplies (e.g. fertilisers, soaps) and you will find out about some of the problems that these substances can cause as well as how they are made.

Learning Outcomes

Throughout the unit you will be asked to:

0.1 Recall the formulae of elements and simple compounds in the unit

0.2 Represent chemical reactions by word equations and simple balanced equations

0.3 Write balanced chemical equations including the use of state symbols (s), (l), (g) and (aq) for a wide range of reactions in this unit

0.4 Write balanced ionic equations for a wide range of reactions in this unit and those in unit C2, specification point 2.15

0.5 Assess practical work for risks and suggest suitable precautions for a range of practical scenarios for reactions in this unit

0.6 Demonstrate an understanding that hazard symbols used on containers:
  a indicate the dangers associated with the contents
  b inform people about safe-working procedures with these substances in the laboratory

Water testing

How do we know our water is safe to drink?

In 2007, a warning was issued about a brand of bottled water. The water was found to contain dangerous levels of arsenic. The water was recalled and fortunately there were no reports of any illness.

A How could you tell if this water contained a poison?

Our food, and many other products, are checked for purity and safety by chemists. There are two main types of chemical **analysis**. **Qualitative analysis**, which investigates the kind of substances present in a sample, and **quantitative analysis**, which measures the *amount* of each substance present.

B Analytical chemists check the purity of our drinking water.

Water often contains dissolved **ionic compounds**, which are made up of **cations** (positive ions) and **anions** (negative ions). To identify an unknown ionic compound, an analyst carries out tests for each ion. Both the anion and cation need to be identified to identify the compound.

The ion tests must give a positive result with only one type of ion. If a test gave the same positive result with two or more different ions, you would not be sure which of those ions was in the compound. **Flame tests** can be used to detect some metal cations.

1 What are the two main types of analysis?

2 Why must we have a unique test for each ion?

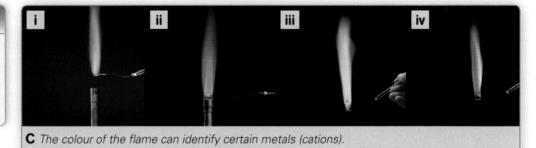

i   ii   iii   iv

C The colour of the flame can identify certain metals (cations).

3 a Explain why flame tests are a 'qualitative' method of analysis.
b Name the elements that produce the flame colours (i) to (iv) in Figure C.

Element	Symbol	Flame colour
calcium	Ca^{2+}	brick red
sodium	Na^+	yellow
potassium	K^+	lilac
copper	Cu^{2+}	green/blue

D Flame test colours

To test for other cations, a few drops of sodium hydroxide solution are added to a solution of the unknown substance. This works because many metal hydroxides are insoluble, so a **precipitation reaction** can occur. The **precipitate** formed can identify the ion present.

Cation	Symbol	Effect of adding sodium hydroxide solution
aluminium	$Al^{3+}(aq)$	white precipitate
calcium	$Ca^{2+}(aq)$	white precipitate
copper(II)	$Cu^{2+}(aq)$	pale blue precipitate
iron(II)	$Fe^{2+}(aq)$	green precipitate
iron(III)	$Fe^{3+}(aq)$	brown (rust) precipitate

E *The colour of the solid formed by precipitation can identify the cation present.*

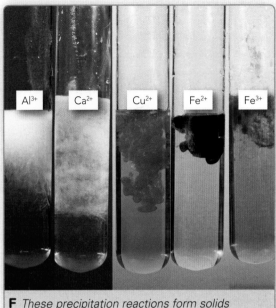

F *These precipitation reactions form solids (precipitates) that have different colours.*

Both aluminium ions (Al^{3+}) and calcium ions (Ca^{2+}) form a white precipitate. They can be distinguished by adding excess sodium hydroxide. In excess sodium hydroxide, the calcium ion precipitate is unchanged, but the aluminium ion precipitate redissolves to form a colourless solution.

The precipitate will be a solid hydroxide of the cation. For example, if the compound was copper(II) sulfate, the precipitate would be copper(II) hydroxide. The balanced and word equations for this reaction are given below:

$$CuSO_4(aq) \quad + \quad 2NaOH(aq) \quad \rightarrow \quad Cu(OH)_2(s) \quad + \quad Na_2SO_4(aq)$$

copper(II) sulfate	+	sodium hydroxide	$\rightarrow$	copper(II) hydroxide	+	sodium sulfate

4 Which ions could be present if the precipitate formed with sodium hydroxide is: **a** brown **b** white?

5 Name the precipitate formed when sodium hydroxide reacts with:
a aluminium nitrate solution **b** calcium nitrate solution.

6 Magnesium ions (Mg^{2+}) form a white precipitate when added to sodium hydroxide solution. Explain why this cannot be used as a test for magnesium ions.

7 Analytical chemists could be asked to investigate:
a the levels of salt in food products
b the source of pollution in a river.
In each case state if the analysis will be mainly quantitative or qualitative, and explain your choice.

Skills spotlight

When scientists collect and analyse scientific data, qualitative tests are always carried out before quantitative tests. Explain why.

ResultsPlus
Watch Out!

Many students mix up the terms *qualitative* and *quantitative*. Remember – quantitative is about quantity, the amount of substance present and is likely to include a number whereas qualitative will be a description in words.

Learning Outcomes

1.1 Demonstrate an understanding that analysis may be qualitative or quantitative

1.2 Explain why the test for any ion must be unique

1.3 Describe tests to show the presence of the following ions in solids or solutions as appropriate:
a Al^{3+}, Ca^{2+}, Cu^{2+}, Fe^{2+}, Fe^{3+} using sodium hydroxide solution

HSW **10** Using both qualitative and quantitative approaches

Chlorine is a poison – so why is it added to our drinking water?

How is our water supply made safe to drink?

Health experts recommend that we drink lots of water each day and we are fortunate enough to have a clean and safe water supply in Britain. The water is filtered to remove solid particles, chemically treated to eliminate other impurities and chlorinated to kill bacteria.

A *A water supply chlorinator. Chlorine is used to kill bacteria in water. The chlorine is later converted to chloride ions to make the water taste better.*

Chlorine is an example of a halogen (group 7). The concentrations of chloride ions and other halide ions in our water are monitored by chemists.

Halogen	Formula	Halide ion
fluorine	F_2	F^-
chlorine	Cl_2	Cl^-
bromine	Br_2	Br^-
iodine	I_2	I^-

B *Halogens and their halide ions*

1 What is a halide ion?

2 What is the name of the ion the chlorine atom forms?

The halide ions – chloride, bromide and iodide – can be identified using silver nitrate solution acidified with dilute nitric acid. A different coloured silver halide precipitate forms in each case.

C *Testing for halide ions*

Halide ion	Precipitate with silver ions
chloride (Cl^-)	white
bromide (Br^-)	cream
iodide (I^-)	yellow

D *Testing for halide ions*

The equations for the reaction between sodium chloride and silver nitrate solutions are:

$$AgNO_3(aq) \quad + \quad NaCl(aq) \quad \rightarrow \quad AgCl(s) \quad + \quad NaNO_3(aq)$$

silver nitrate + sodium chloride → silver chloride + sodium nitrate

(white precipitate)

Because the ions in *solution* can move about independently, they can be separated in the equation:

$$Ag^+(aq) + NO_3^-(aq) + Na^+(aq) + Cl^-(aq) \rightarrow AgCl(s) + Na^+(aq) + NO_3^-(aq)$$

This shows that the $Na^+(aq)$ and $NO_3^-(aq)$ ions are not changed in the reaction. Removing them gives us the **ionic equation** for the reaction:

$$Ag^+(aq) + Cl^-(aq) \rightarrow AgCl(s)$$

Ammonium ions in water

Many fertilisers used by gardeners and farmers contain ammonium ions (NH_4^+). If these ions get into our rivers and lakes they can harm water life.

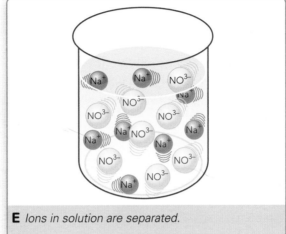

E *Ions in solution are separated.*

Analysts test for ammonium ions by warming the unknown substance with sodium hydroxide solution. If ammonium ions are present, a smelly alkaline gas is given off. The gas, ammonia, can be detected by its distinctive smell and because it turns damp red **litmus** paper blue.

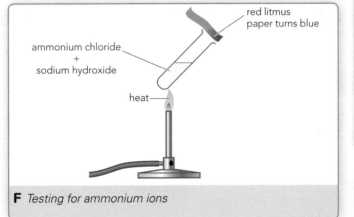

F *Testing for ammonium ions*

5 Using as few words as possible, describe the tests you would use to show that a white powder was ammonium chloride.

6 Write an ionic equation for the reaction between copper(II) sulfate and sodium hydroxide shown on page 105.

7 The balanced equation for the reaction between sodium hydroxide and ammonium chloride solutions is:
$$NaOH(aq) + NH_4Cl(aq) \rightarrow NH_3(g) + NaCl(aq) + H_2O(l)$$
Write the ionic equation for this reaction, and name the ions that don't take part.

---

3 Name the precipitate formed when acidified silver nitrate solution is added to: **a** sodium bromide solution **b** lithium iodide solution.

4 **a** Write the word equation, balanced equation and ionic equation for the reaction in question 3a.
b Which ions do not take part in this reaction?

Skills spotlight

Scientists plan experiments to test ideas and to solve problems. How could you test that tap water contains dissolved solids?

ResultsPlus
Watch Out!

When balancing equations, remember to count all the atoms in a formula. For example $2FeCl_3$ contains two Fe^{3+} ions and *six* Cl^- ions. Students often forget to multiply the number molecules (in this case two) by the number of ions (3 for chlorine) to give a total of six chlorine ions.

Learning Outcomes

1.3 Describe tests to show the presence of the following ions in solids or solutions as appropriate:
  b NH_4^+ using sodium hydroxide solution, warming and testing for the ammonia gas produced
  c Cl^-, Br^-, I^- using dilute nitric acid and silver nitrate solution

HSW **5** Planning to test a scientific idea, answer a scientific question or solve a scientific problem

C3.3 Ion identification

```
•···•
```
How can forensic chemists solve crimes?

Dr. John Walker was a tall, handsome 45-year-old man. Fit and active, he was a keen golfer and still regularly played senior league rugby. Dr Walker was the local GP and was well respected in the area, if not always liked. Dr. John Walker was also dead.

A *A police artist drew the crime scene but can chemistry solve the crime?*

So what caused Dr Walker's death? Was there poison in his drink? Did he take his own life? He certainly had access to suitable poisons. Or was he murdered? His wife had cause and opportunity. Or was it his secretary? Rejected by him in her youth, she had the oldest motive of all. Or was it the gardener? Bullied and underpaid, he had easy access to toxic garden chemicals.

Test carried out using ...	Ions identified
flame test	Na^+, K^+, Ca^{2+}, Cu^{2+}
dilute acid and lime water	CO_3^{2-}
dilute hydrochloric acid and barium chloride solution	SO_4^{2-}
silver nitrate solution and dilute nitric acid	Cl^-, Br^-, I^-
sodium hydroxide solution and heat	Al^{3+}, Ca^{2+}, Cu^{2+}, Fe^{2+}, Fe^{3+}, NH_4^+

E *Some of the tests that a forensic chemist might perform on unknown substances.*

To help solve this mystery, evidence was collected from the suspected crime scene and the main suspects:
• the half drunk glass of water
• the white powder that was scattered on the garage floor
• a solid, found in the boot of Dr Walker's secretary's car
• crystals from a bottle, covered in Mrs Walker's fingerprints
• a substance, found at the back of the gardener's shed.
All of these were collected and taken to the forensic chemistry laboratory for further investigation. The first step in any investigation like this is always to identify the substances collected from the crime scene.

Your task

You are going to plan an investigation that will allow you to identify the ions in unknown substances.

Learning Outcomes

1.3 Describe tests to show the presence of the following ions in solids or solutions as appropriate:
  a Al^{3+}, Ca^{2+}, Cu^{2+}, Fe^{2+}, Fe^{3+} using sodium hydroxide solution **b** NH_4^+ using sodium hydroxide solution, warming and testing for the ammonia gas produced **c** Cl^-, Br^-, I^- using dilute nitric acid and silver nitrate solution
1.4 *Identify the ions in unknown salts, using the tests above and in unit C2, specification point 2.15*

Build Better Answers

When planning an investigation like this, one of the skills you will be assessed on is your ability to *plan an investigation*. There are 4 marks available for this skill. Here are two extracts focusing on this skill. Other skills that you need for the practical assessment are dealt with in other lessons.

Student extract 1 — A basic response for this skill

The additional tests, which are needed to confirm certain results, have not been described.

> I am going to carry out the following tests on the unknowns.
> 1 Flame tests.
> 2 Sodium hydroxide test.
> 3 Adding hydrochloric acid and testing gases with limewater test.
> 4 Adding barium chloride and looking for precipitates test.

This answer is incomplete because the student has not described most of the observations, which need to be made.

The tests have been put in a logical order but other tests could have been carried out. For example the test for Cl^-, Br^- and I^- is missing.

Student extract 2 — A good response for this skill

The additional tests and observations have also been described

> I am going to carry out the following tests and observations.
> 1 Flame tests, observing the colours of flames produced.
> 2 The sodium hydroxide test, observing the colours of the precipitates formed and carrying out further tests where a white precipitate or no precipitate is formed, These tests would involve adding more sodium hydroxide, heating and testing gases produced.
> 3 Testing with hydrochloric acid and identifying any gas produced.
> 4 The barium chloride test, noting the effect of hydrochloric acid on any precipitates.
> 5 Testing with acidified silver nitrate solution and noting colours of precipitates formed.
> These tests should distinguish what chemicals are in the unknown substances. This will test my hypothesis.

The student has described what has to be observed in these tests.

This answer is a good one because it describes all the available tests, additional tests and the observations that have to be made.

ResultsPlus

To access 2 marks
- Plan a method which is logically ordered to produce results
- Choose a range of data/observations that would test the hypothesis

To access 4 marks
- Plan a method which is logically ordered to produce results and include an explanation of why it would test the hypothesis
- Choose a range of data/observations that would test the hypothesis and explain why the range was chosen

What do analytical chemists actually do?

In 1988 an accident occurred in Camelford, North Cornwall. A driver poured 20 tonnes of aluminium sulfate into the wrong tank at the water works. Hundreds of people drank the contaminated water, but it wasn't until reports of 'funny' tasting tea that chemists found it contained very high levels of aluminium. Scientists found evidence that the water caused problems such as memory loss in people who drank it.

A *The Camelford water works*

B *Analytical chemists check the purity of water.*

A safe water supply is essential to our health. However, our drinking water is not *pure* because it always contains dissolved substances. Some come from the rocks through and over which it flows, and others from the chemicals used in water treatment. Analytical chemists, employed by the water authorities, check the **purity** of our water against government standards. These set maximum limits for chemicals and microorganisms and make sure that our water looks good, tastes good and is safe to drink as well.

As well as chlorine, several other chemicals are used in water treatment. For example, aluminium salts are used to remove small particles of solids. Sodium fluoride is also added in some areas because it has been shown to reduce tooth decay. Some scientists are concerned about the use of these chemicals. For example, high levels of aluminium have been linked to Alzheimer's disease and damage to the digestive system.

1 Why does the government set standards for water purity?

2 Where do the dissolved substances in our drinking water come from?

3 Why are analytical chemists employed in the water industry?

4 How would you test for aluminium in drinking water?

C *At a drinking water purification plant, aluminium salts are used in these tanks, where they help to stick small dirt particles together to form clumps that can be removed more easily.*

Chemical analysis in medicine

Analytical chemists working in medical laboratories test patients' blood for aluminium, iron, sodium and other dissolved substances. This helps doctors to identify illnesses. For example, low levels of iron in the blood are an indicator of anaemia and high levels of sodium ions have been linked to high blood pressure and kidney disease.

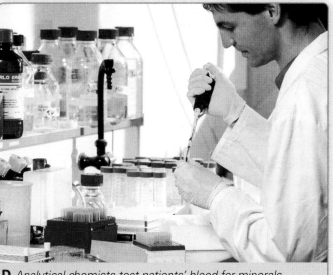

D Analytical chemists test patients' blood for minerals.

Chemists are also often involved in medical research. For example, analytical investigations have shown a link between high levels of aluminium and Alzheimer's disease. This disease causes damage to the brain, which can lead to memory loss and changes in behaviour. To see if there was a link between aluminium levels and Alzheimer's, researchers would have to measure blood aluminium levels in a considerable number of patients and monitor their mental health over many years.

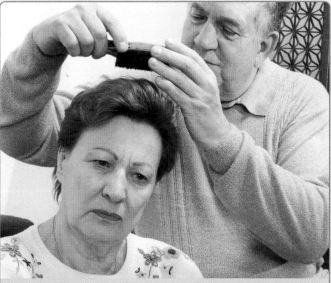

E Jean suffers from Alzheimer's disease. She can no longer remember how to dress herself properly and needs constant care.

5 What *symptom* would alert hospital doctors to order blood tests for sodium ions?

Skills spotlight

Scientific developments can have benefits, drawbacks and risks. What are some of the benefits, drawbacks and risks of adding chemicals to our drinking water?

ResultsPlus
Watch Out!

Students often describe liquids as pure and forget that if they are solutions they will have a solvent and at least one solute. Remember that many liquids (like blood) are never pure because they will always contain more than one substance. Water can be pure but usually isn't because it contains dissolved substances.

6 Why are analytical chemists employed in hospitals?

7 Some scientists believe there is a link between high fluoride levels and certain kinds of cancer. What data would researchers need to collect to test this hypothesis, and how would they use it?

Learning Outcomes

1.5 Demonstrate an understanding that these tests form the basis for testing by chemists: **a** working in the water industry to check the purity of drinking water **b** for the presence of substances in the blood

HSW 12 The use of contemporary science and technological developments and their benefits, drawbacks and risks

>>>>>>>>>>>>>>>>>>>>>>>>> How does where you live affect how easy it is to wash with soap?

What is the effect of having solutes in tap water?

At Old Mother Shipton's Cave in North Yorkshire, the water contains high concentrations of magnesium and calcium compounds. When the water evaporates, it leaves these compounds behind turning items hung there to 'stone'.

A *The Petrifying Well at Old Mother Shipton's Cave*

1 a What is a mineral?
b State the names of two ions that are often found in minerals.

In some parts of Britain, the water supply is taken from water that has passed through and over rocks. The water has dissolved some of the compounds (minerals) in the rocks to form **solutions**. Minerals containing calcium and magnesium ions make the water **hard**.

B *Rainwater that falls on areas of chalk and limestone in Britain dissolves minerals as it passes through the rocks and produces hard tap water.*

Skills spotlight

Scientists use symbols to make things clearer. The little minus sign in the units for concentration means 'per' and is used instead of a slash (/) because lots of slashes are confusing in complex calculations. Write out two examples of units for speed and two examples for concentration using the little minus signs.

The amount of a **solute** dissolved in a stated volume of a solution is called its **concentration**. Units of concentration are often 'milligrams or grams per cubic decimetre', usually written as '$mg\,dm^{-3}$, or '$g\,dm^{-3}$', where the little minus sign means 'per'. $1\,dm^3$ is the same volume as 1 litre or $1000\,cm^3$.

You can calculate the concentration of a solution in $g\,dm^{-3}$ using this equation:

$$\text{concentration} = \frac{\text{amount of solute in g}}{\text{volume of solution in } dm^3}$$

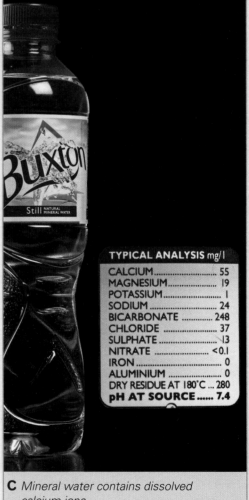

TYPICAL ANALYSIS mg/l	
CALCIUM	55
MAGNESIUM	19
POTASSIUM	1
SODIUM	24
BICARBONATE	248
CHLORIDE	37
SULPHATE	13
NITRATE	<0.1
IRON	0
ALUMINIUM	0
DRY RESIDUE AT 180°C	280
pH AT SOURCE	7.4

C *Mineral water contains dissolved calcium ions.*

e.g.

If 1 dm³ of a water sample contains 0.5 g of dissolved sodium chloride, the concentration of sodium chloride is 0.5 g dm⁻³.

Problems with hard water

If you try to wash with soap in hard water, you will find it is difficult to make a lather. Soap bubbles do not form until you have used up a lot of soap. This is because the calcium ions and magnesium ions in the water combine with the soap to make an **insoluble** precipitate, which forms a **scum** on the surface of the water. You have to precipitate all the calcium ions and magnesium ions in the water as scum before the soap can form a lather. The harder the water, the more soap is needed, and the more scum is formed. This means that in hard water areas some soap is wasted and the scum has to be removed in water treatment works.

Results Plus
Watch Out!

Many students lose marks in calculations by giving incorrect units. When calculating a concentration, make sure the mass is in g and divide this by the volume, which should be in dm³, to give g dm⁻³.

D You can compare the hardness of water by seeing how much of a soap solution is needed to form a lather.

2 What is the concentration of calcium ions in a sample of water that has:
a 0.4 g of calcium ions dissolved in 2 dm³ of the water
b 0.25 g of calcium ions dissolved in 5 dm³ of the water?

3 A 500 cm³ bottle of mineral water contains 0.2 g of magnesium ions dissolved in the water. What is the concentration of magnesium ions in g dm⁻³?

4 Look at Figure D. Both samples of water had the same amount of soap added. Which sample of water needs the most soap solution to produce a lather?

5 Name two ions that cause water to be hard.

6 Discuss two problems of living in an area that has hard water.

Learning Outcomes

2.1 Calculate the concentration of solutions in g dm⁻³

2.2 Demonstrate an understanding that some areas of the country have dissolved calcium or magnesium ions in their tap water and that the presence of these ions makes water hard

2.3 Describe problems caused by hard water, including: **a** it does not easily form a lather with soap
b it reacts with soap to form a precipitate ('scum'), which causes soap to be wasted

HSW **11** Present information using scientific conventions and symbols

Why does heating hard water cause problems?

Central heating boilers, washing machines, kettles and dishwashers can become furred up with a white solid called 'limescale' in some regions of Britain. This forms when tap water is heated and it can waste energy and block pipes.

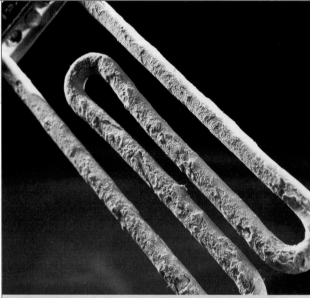

A *The limescale on this heating element from a washing machine makes the machine much less efficient.*

Different types of hardness

Some types of hard water produce a precipitate of limescale when heated. The dissolved calcium or magnesium compounds that make the water hard, decompose to form insoluble compounds (limescale). Removing the soluble calcium and magnesium ions from the water means that the water will now form a lather with soap easily. Since heating 'softens' this type of hard water it is called **temporary hardness**.

$$\text{calcium hydrogencarbonate} \rightarrow \text{calcium carbonate} + \text{carbon dioxide} + \text{water}$$
$$Ca(HCO_3)_2(aq) \rightarrow CaCO_3(s) + CO_2(g) + H_2O(l)$$

Other types of hard water do not lose their hardness when they are heated, so the water still forms a scum with soap – this is called **permanent hardness**. The dissolved calcium and magnesium compounds in this type of hard water do not decompose when they are heated.

Removing hardness

Removing water hardness is called 'softening' hard water. Hard water wastes soap and produces scum that must be rinsed off. So the hardness is sometimes removed before the water is used. Boiling temporary hard water removes the calcium and magnesium ions from the water leaving softened water behind. This method does not work with permanent hard water and a different method is needed to remove all the calcium and magnesium ions. One way of doing this is to use an **ion exchange column**. This method will work on temporary hard water as well.

An ion exchange column is packed with tiny plastic beads made of a special 'resin' (a type of polymer). When hard water is passed through the column, positively charged calcium or magnesium ions in the water swap places with positively charged sodium ions that are weakly attached to the resin. The sodium ions take the place of the calcium and magnesium ions in the water, and the water is softened.

1 A sample of hard water is not affected by boiling. Will it form a lather with soap easily after boiling? Explain your answer.

2 Describe the difference between permanent hard water and temporary hard water.

Eventually all the sodium ions in the column will have been exchanged for calcium or magnesium ions, so the ion exchange column no longer works. Passing a concentrated sodium chloride solution (brine) through the column flushes the calcium and magnesium ions out, exchanging them for sodium ions – so the column can be used again.

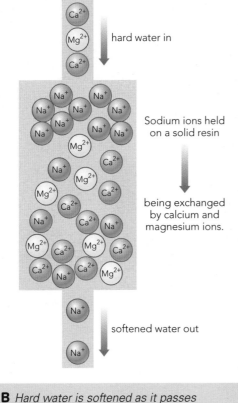

hard water in

Sodium ions held on a solid resin

being exchanged by calcium and magnesium ions.

softened water out

B *Hard water is softened as it passes through an ion exchange column.*

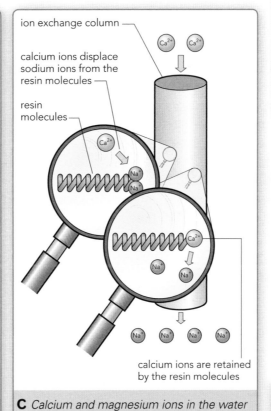

ion exchange column

calcium ions displace sodium ions from the resin molecules

resin molecules

calcium ions are retained by the resin molecules

C *Calcium and magnesium ions in the water take the place of sodium ions attached to an ion exchange resin.*

ResultsPlus
Watch Out!

Be careful not to lose marks in exams by suggesting that homes supplied with hard water could soften water used for washing by boiling it first. This will not work on permanently hard water.

D *Dishwashers have built-in water softeners to prevent the build-up of limescale. Owners must add salt regularly to recharge the resin in the ion-exchange system.*

3 Why is it desirable for a house owner to treat their water if the area they live in has temporary hard water?

4 After an ion exchange column has been used for some time, the water coming out of it remains hard. Explain why this happens, and what can be done to correct it.

5 Why does ion exchange soften all types of water, while boiling removes only temporary hardness?

6 State a method that can be used to soften all types of hard water. Explain how it works.

Learning Outcomes

2.4 Describe hard water as either temporary or permanent, and describe how boiling removes temporary hardness but not permanent hardness

2.5 Explain how hard water can be softened by removing dissolved calcium and/or magnesium ions and that this can be done by:
a boiling (for temporary hard water only) **b** using an ion exchange resin

HSW **12** Describe the benefits, drawbacks and risks of using new scientific and technological developments

C3.7 Finding the mass of solute in a solution

> ⋯ What happens when the solvent evaporates from a solution?

Stalactites and stalagmites form some of the most dramatic sights found in caves. They are formed when water containing calcium compounds seeps through the roof of a cave. As the drop starts to form some of the water evaporates and the calcium compounds crystallise. Very slowly the solid grows into a stalactite. Drops of water fall to the floor of the cave where the same process takes place but the crystals grow upwards to form a stalagmite.

The speed that the stalactites and stalagmites grow depends on a number of factors such as the temperature in the cave, and the concentration of the calcium salts in the solution.

A solution is made up of a solute and a **solvent**. If the solvent is evaporated away completely only the solute will be left. Thus the concentration of a solution can be found by measuring the mass of solute left when all the solvent has been evaporated from a known mass of the solution.

A Stalactites hold tight to the roof of a cave while stalagmites grow up from the ground.

B The Bonneville salt flats in the USA formed when the water evaporated from seawater leaving the salt behind.

Your task

You are going to plan an investigation to determine how the mass of a solute varies with the concentration of a solution.

Learning Outcomes

2.6 Evaporate a solution to dryness to determine the mass of solute in a given mass of solution

ResultsPlus
Build Better Answers

When planning an investigation like this, one of the skills you will be assessed on is your ability to *evaluate the method*. There are 6 marks available for this skill. Here are two extracts focusing on this skill. Other skills that you need for the practical assessment are dealt with in other lessons.

Student extract 1 | **A basic response for this skill**

> I turned the Bunsen burner off because the solution was spitting but I didn't know if it was ready. It would have been better to carry on heating on a lower flame until the salt was dry.

This is a good suggestion about how to fix the problem.

This is a good start because it explains a weakness in the method.

The student has not explained why it is important that the salt is dry.

Student extract 2 | **A good response for this skill**

> The first time I did the experiment the solution spat just before it boiled dry. This meant that the mass of solute was reduced I didn't know if all the water had been evaporated so the mass of the solute I calculated may have been higher than it should have been. I repeated the experiment but reduced the size of the flame so that the water evaporated more slowly. After I weighed the evaporating dish and the salt, I re-heated it and re-weighed it until the mass was the same each time. I repeated the experiment three times to get a mean for the mass of solute in 1 dm³ of solution.

A good suggestion is made about how to fix the problem.

The is a good answer because the effect of the problem is noted.

The method is a strong one because care is taken to produce reliable results.

 ## ResultsPlus

To access 2 marks

- Identify a strength or weakness in the method
- Suggest how to improve the method and justify the comments you make.

To access 6 marks

- Describe strengths and weaknesses in the method and relate them to the quality of the evidence collected
- Suggest how to improve the method, justifying comments made by relating them to the hypothesis and explaining how better quality evidence could be produced.

Particles and moles

  How are moles used in calculations involving atoms?

All substances are made of particles. This diamond is made up of about 20 000 000 000 000 000 000 000 particles (carbon atoms).

A *Diamonds are made of carbon atoms.*

1 Look at the relative atomic masses of the elements in the periodic table. What is the mass of an Avogadro's number of:
a hydrogen atoms
b oxygen atoms
c calcium atoms?

The amount of a substance can be measured in terms of numbers of atoms or mass. The mass of an element equal to its **relative atomic mass** in grams always contains 6.02×10^{23} atoms. This number is called **Avogadro's number**. The relative atomic mass of magnesium is 24 – so a piece of magnesium with Avogadro's number of magnesium atoms has a mass of 24 g.

The amount of a substance can also be measured in **moles**. One mole of a substance is the amount that contains an Avogadro's number of a named particle. For example, 12 g of carbon is 1 mole of carbon atoms. 1 mole of iron atoms has a mass of 56 g.

We can use the same idea with molecules and compounds. The **relative formula mass** of water, H_2O, is the sum of the relative atomic masses of all the atoms in the formula of water – i.e. $1 + 1 + 16 = 18$. 18 g of water contains Avogadro's number of water molecules, so 1 mole of water molecules has a mass of 18 g.

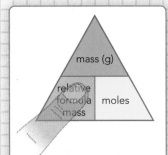

B *To rearrange equations with a formula triangle, cover up the quantity you want to calculate and what you can see gives you the rest of the equation.*

You can calculate the number of moles of any substance using one of these equations:

$$\text{number of moles of an element} = \frac{\text{mass of element in grams}}{\text{relative atomic mass}}$$

$$\text{number of moles of a compound} = \frac{\text{mass of compound in grams}}{\text{relative formula mass}}$$

C *Clockwise from top left – 1 mole each of iron(III) chloride, copper sulfate, potassium iodide, cobalt nitrate, potassium manganate(VII) and sodium chloride.*

ResultsPlus
Watch Out!

Make sure you note what kind of particle is mentioned in a question. For example, the mass of 1 mole of oxygen atoms is 16 g, but 1 mole of oxygen molecules (O_2) is 32 g.

2 What is the mass of an Avogadro's number of: **a** oxygen molecules, O_2 **b** carbon dioxide molecules, CO_2?

3 What is the mass of 1 mole of: **a** copper atoms, Cu **b** sodium hydroxide, NaOH?

4 Calculate the number of moles of: **a** calcium atoms in 80 g of calcium **b** sulfur dioxide molecules (SO_2) in 6.4 g of sulfur dioxide.

H

Solutions

The concentration of a solution is often given as the number of moles of solute dissolved to make $1\,dm^3$ of solution. The unit is $mol\,dm^{-3}$.
You can work out the concentration of a solution using this equation:

$$\text{concentration in } mol\,dm^{-3} = \frac{\text{number of moles of solute}}{\text{volume of solution in } dm^3}$$

e.g.

What is the concentration in $mol\,dm^{-3}$ of a sodium hydroxide (NaOH) solution with a concentration of $4\,g\,dm^{-3}$?

relative formular mass of NaOH:

$$23 \quad + \quad 16 \quad + \quad 1 \quad = \quad 40$$

amount of NaOH in moles: $= \dfrac{4}{40}$

$$= 0.1 \text{ moles.}$$

$$\text{concentration: } = 0.1\,mol\,dm^{-3}$$

If the concentration of a solution of sodium hydroxide is $1.2\,mol\,dm^{-3}$, how many grams of the solute are in $250\,cm^3$ of solution?

amount of NaOH in $250\,cm^3 = 1.2 \quad \times \quad 0.25$

$$= 0.3 \text{ moles.}$$

$$\begin{array}{c}\text{Mass of compound in} \\ \text{grams}\end{array} = \begin{array}{c}\text{number of} \\ \text{moles}\end{array} \times \begin{array}{c}\text{relative formula} \\ \text{mass}\end{array} = 0.3 \times 40$$

$$= 12\,g$$

?

6 Some seawater contains $30\,g$ of sodium chloride in every $1\,dm^3$.
  Calculate the concentration of sodium chloride in the seawater in $mol\,dm^{-3}$.

7 A solution of ammonia in water has a concentration of $2\,mol\,dm^{-3}$.
a How many moles of ammonia are in $1\,dm^3$ of the solution?
b What is the relative formula mass of ammonia, NH_3? (Use the periodic table on p.264)
c What is the concentration of ammonia in $g\,dm^{-3}$?

8 Copper sulfate, with a *relative formula mass* of 159.5, is dissolved in water to produce a solution with a *concentration* of $0.5\,mol\,dm^{-3}$. Explain the terms in italics and calculate the mass of copper sulfate dissolved in $500\,cm^3$ of the solution.

Maths skills

Avogadro's number is usually written in **standard form**.
6.02×10^{23} is actually 602,000,000,000,000, 000,000,000 (that's 21 zeros after the 2). The decimal point has been moved 23 places to the right.

?

5 What is the mass of:
a 3 moles of potassium atoms, K
b 0.5 moles of calcium carbonate, $CaCO_3$?

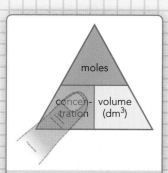

D *Formula triangle for working out concentrations*

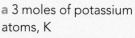

Skills spotlight

Suggest reasons why concentration in $mol\,dm^{-3}$ is more useful to chemists than $g\,dm^{-3}$.

Learning Outcomes

H **2.7** Demonstrate an understanding that the amount of a substance can be measured in grams, numbers of particles or number of moles of particles

H **2.8** Convert masses of a substance into moles of particles of the substance and vice versa

H **2.9** Convert concentration in $g\,dm^{-3}$ into $mol\,dm^{-3}$ and vice versa

HSW **11** Present information using scientific conventions and symbols

How can we use bases to make salts that are soluble in water?

Copper sulfate solution is used for removing algae from water, treating wood, keeping the hulls of boats clear of barnacles, as the electrolyte for copper-plating other metals and in a simple test of anaemia for blood donors.

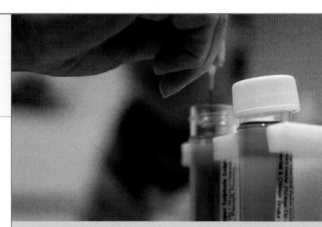

A Copper sulfate is used as part of a blood test for anaemia.

Making copper sulfate

A **base** is a substance that can react with an acid in a neutralisation reaction to form water and a **salt**. Copper sulfate is an example of a **soluble** salt. It can be made by reacting sulfuric acid and copper oxide.

copper oxide + sulfuric acid → copper sulfate + water

$$CuO(s) + H_2SO_4(aq) \rightarrow CuSO_4(aq) + H_2O(l)$$

1 Why should the acid be warmed?

2 Why should the copper oxide be added a little at a time?

Copper oxide reacts with sulfuric acid, but does not dissolve in water. If copper oxide is added a little at a time to warm dilute sulfuric acid it will react and form a blue solution of copper sulfate. When all the sulfuric acid has been used up, the next bit of base that is added has nothing to react with. The copper oxide is now in **excess**. It remains as a solid and makes the mixture cloudy. Excess reactant (the copper oxide) is added to make sure that all the acid is used up.

3 How can you be fairly sure that the copper sulfate solution does not contain inpurities?

4 Explain why adding excess base is useful when preparing a soluble salt.

5 Why should a dilute salt solution be heated before allowing it to crystallise?

Solids can be separated from liquids by **filtration**. The mixture of copper sulfate solution and solid copper oxide is poured into a folded piece of filter paper in a filter funnel. The **filtrate** is collected – it should be a clear blue liquid. It contains only the salt (copper sulfate) and water. The excess copper oxide remains in the filter paper. It can be washed with water, dried and reused.

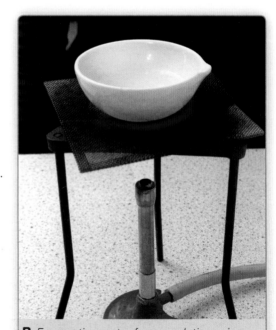

B Evaporating water from a solution using a tripod and Bunsen burner.

The copper sulfate will start to **crystallise** as the water in the solution evaporates. If the solution is dilute, it can be heated until most of the water has evaporated. When crystals of the salt start to appear then the solution is removed from the source of heat and more crystals will appear as it cools. Evaporating slowly to dryness results in the largest crystals.

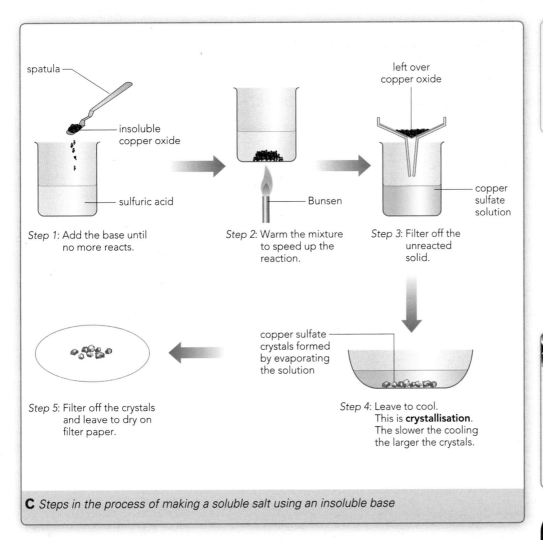

Step 1: Add the base until no more reacts.

Step 2: Warm the mixture to speed up the reaction.

Step 3: Filter off the unreacted solid.

Step 4: Leave to cool. This is **crystallisation**. The slower the cooling the larger the crystals.

Step 5: Filter off the crystals and leave to dry on filter paper.

copper sulfate crystals formed by evaporating the solution

C *Steps in the process of making a soluble salt using an insoluble base*

6 Why does the salt go through the filter paper, while the excess copper oxide remains in the filter?

Skills spotlight

You are asked to prepare a soluble salt starting from a named acid. Name the items of equipment needed and explain why they are used.

Results Plus
Watch Out!

When choosing a separation method, students often use filtration and forget that this only works if one of the products is insoluble. Check on the solubility of both the base and the salt before you choose this method and don't write about just the solubility of the salt.

7 Copper carbonate is an insoluble, green solid that reacts with sulfuric acid to form copper sulfate, water and carbon dioxide gas. What signs would tell you that all the acid has been used up?

8 Zinc sulfate ($ZnSO_4$) is a soluble salt. It can be made by reacting the insoluble base zinc oxide (ZnO) with sulfuric acid (H_2SO_4).
a Write a word equation for the reaction.
b Write a balanced equation with state symbols.

9 Describe how a sample of pure, solid zinc sulfate could be made – include the steps you would take to make sure the zinc sulfate is pure.

Learning Outcomes

2.10 Demonstrate an understanding that if soluble salts are prepared from an acid and an insoluble reactant:
  a excess of the reactant can be added to ensure that all the acid is used up
  b the excess reactant can be removed by filtration
  c the solution remaining is only salt and water

HSW 5 Plan to test a scientific idea, answer a scientific question or solve a scientific problem by choosing appropriate resources

How can we make a soluble salt from soluble reactants?

Pure ammonium nitrate is used as fertiliser and to make instant coolpacks for strained joints.

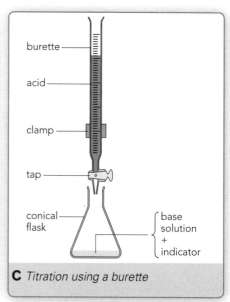

A

1 Sodium hydroxide is a soluble base. It reacts with hydrochloric acid to form sodium chloride and water. Explain why it is difficult to prepare pure sodium chloride using this reaction.

Ammonium nitrate is a soluble salt made by reacting ammonia with nitric acid. Both reactants are soluble. The product must not be contaminated by excess ammonia or excess nitric acid. We must know exactly how much ammonia is needed to react with the nitric acid.

Titrations

To prepare soluble salts using a soluble base, an **indicator** must be used. The indicator is added to a solution of the base, then the acid is added a measured amount at a time. The indicator changes colour when sufficient acid has been added to neutralise the base. So the indicator needs to be one colour in an acidic solution and another colour in a neutral solution. A **pipette** is used to measure a fixed volume of soluble base solution. A **burette** allows acid to be added drop by drop, and the volume added to be measured.

B A titration taking place

burette ——
acid ——
clamp ——
tap ——
conical flask ——
base solution + indicator

C Titration using a burette

2 Methyl orange is an acid/base indicator. It is red in acid solutions and yellow in alkaline solutions. What colour change would you see in a titration in which hydrochloric acid is added to sodium hydroxide solution?

This method of carrying out reactions is called **titration**. It is repeated at least three times to find the mean volume of acid needed to just react with a measured volume of base solution with no excess acid left over.

To make a pure solution of the salt without any indicator in it, the titration is repeated without the indicator by adding the calculated mean volume of acid to the fixed volume of base solution. All the acid will react with the base and only the salt and water will be left. The salt can be obtained by evaporation or crystallisation.

Neutralisation with soluble bases

When an acid dissolves in water it forms **hydrogen ions, H⁺(aq)**.
For example:

$$HCl(aq) \rightarrow H^+(aq) + Cl^-(aq)$$

When a soluble base is dissolved in water it forms **hydroxide ions, OH⁻(aq)**.
For example:

$$NaOH(aq) \rightarrow Na^+(aq) + OH^-(aq)$$

If solutions of an acid and base are mixed together, the hydrogen ions and the hydroxide ions combine to form water molecules. This occurs in a neutralisation reaction:

$$H^+(aq) + OH^-(aq) \rightarrow H_2O(l)$$

The other ions from the acid and base stay in the solution as ions of the dissolved salt.

Skills spotlight

How could you check if a base was soluble in order to choose which method to use to make a soluble salt?

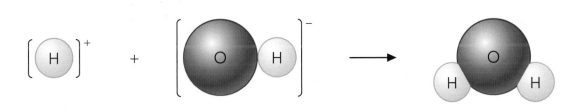

D *Hydrogen ions and hydroxide ions combine to form water molecules.*

3 Which of the following substances will form hydrogen ions in solution?
a sulfuric acid b sodium hydroxide c citric acid d calcium hydroxide

4 Sodium sulfate is used to stop bubbles forming in glass when it is manufactured. The sodium sulfate must be pure. Sodium hydroxide is a soluble base used to make sodium sulfate, which is a soluble salt. Name the other reactant needed and explain why a titration must be used to produce a salt that is not contaminated by excess reactants.

5 Why is water a product of all neutralisation reactions?

6 Potassium nitrate, KNO_3, is a soluble salt. Suggest, with reasons, the names of an acid and a soluble base that could be used to make potassium nitrate, and describe how titration could be used to produce a pure sample of the salt.

ResultsPlus
Watch Out!

Many students lose marks by just using the word hydrogen and not making it clear that this is an atom, ion or molecule of hydrogen. Write hydrogen ions in solution as H⁺(aq).

Learning Outcomes

2.11 Demonstrate an understanding that if soluble salts are prepared from an acid and a soluble reactant: **a** titration must be used to determine the exact amount of the soluble reactant that reacts with an acid **b** the acid and the soluble reactant can then be mixed in the correct proportions **c** the solution remaining after reaction is only salt and water

2.12 Describe an acid–base titration as a neutralisation reaction where hydrogen ions (H⁺) from the acid react with hydroxide ions (OH⁻) from the base

HSW **5** Plan to test a scientific idea, answer a scientific question or solve a scientific problem by choosing appropriate resources

>>>>>>>>>>>>>>>>>>>>>>>> How can we find how much acid and alkali is needed to make a salt?

C3.11 Acid/alkali titrations

How can titration solve a crime?

Fake medicines can be bought on the Internet – just like fake designer clothes. Criminals produce drugs and package them to look as though they are the well-known brands. Investigators trying to track down the fakes need to know how much of the drug is present in the tablets. Some drugs, such as aspirin, are acids. The investigators can use acid/alkali titrations to work out if the amount of drug present in the fake is more or less than in the correct tablets.

A The campaign was run by Pfizer

An acid/alkali titration is the controlled reaction that takes place when a measured amount of an acid reacts with a measured amount of an alkali. An **alkali** is a base which dissolves in water. The reaction can be followed using an indicator, which gives a clear colour change when **neutralisation** occurs. Neutralisation happens when the amounts of the hydrogen ions (H^+) from the acid is equal to the number of hydroxide ions (OH^-) from the alkali. Volumes of solutions can be measured accurately using pipettes and burettes.

B Carrying out a titration using pipettes and burettes.

Your task

You are going to plan an investigation that will allow you to find out how the preparation of a salt in a neutralisation reaction depends on the concentration and volume of the acid and alkali.

Learning Outcomes

2.13 Describe how to carry out simple acid-base titrations using burette, pipette and suitable acid-base indicators
2.14 Carry out an acid-base titration to prepare a salt from a soluble base

When planning an investigation like this, one of the skills you will be assessed on is your ability to *collect and record primary data*. There are 4 marks available for this skill. Here are two extracts focusing on this skill. Other skills that you need for the practical assessment are dealt with in other lessons.

Student extract 1 | A basic response for this skill

There is a large enough range of values to see the pattern

Volume of sodium hydroxide used	10	15	20	25	30
volume of hydrochloric acid used at neutralization	10.3	15.4	20.7	22.4	30.9

The results are given to one decimal place.

The student has not given any units.

Student extract 2 | A good response for this skill

This results table has all the correct headings and units as well as containing repeat results.

The burette does not actually have to be filled before each titration but the starting volume must be recorded.

Concentration of hydrochloric acid (mol dm³)	0.1							
Concentration of sodium hydroxide (mol dm³)	0.1							
Volume of sodium hydroxide used (cm³)	10	10	15	15	20	20	25	25
Burette reading at end	10.3	10.2	14.9	15.0	20.7	20.4	22.4	24.6
Burette reading at start	0	0	0	0	0	0	0	0
Volume of hydrochloric acid used at neutralisation (cm³)	10.3	10.2	14.9	15.0	20.7	20.4	22.4	24.6

Although these concentrations were provided by the teacher it is important to note them down.

ResultsPlus

To access 2 marks

- Collect a suitable range of data and record some appropriately for example in a simple table or list.

To access 4 marks

- Collect a suitable range of data and record it all appropriately for example in a table, and record further/repeat data.

What information can be found from the results of titrations?

Vinegar is produced with the same concentration of acid day after day, bottle after bottle. An analyst does titrations to check the concentration of acid and make sure that every bottle meets the required standard.

A

ResultsPlus
Watch Out!

Many students lose marks by forgetting to give the units of their answer – so 0.002 mol, not just 0.002. Also make sure that all volumes in cm^3 are converted to dm^3, by dividing by 1000.

The volumes of the solutions in a titration can be used to calculate the concentration of one of the solutions, if the concentration of the other solution is known. Remember that:

$$\text{concentration of a solution (mol dm}^{-3}) = \frac{\text{number of moles of solute (mol)}}{\text{volume of solution (dm}^3)}$$

e.g.

25.00 cm^3 of sodium hydroxide solution was titrated against 0.10 mol dm^{-3} hydrochloric acid. An average of 20.00 cm^3 of the acid was needed to react completely. What is the concentration of the sodium hydroxide solution?

Step 1:

$$\text{number of moles of hydrochloric acid} = \text{concentration of hydrochloric acid (mol dm}^{-3}) \times \text{volume used (dm}^3)$$

$$\text{so, number of moles of hydrochloric acid} = 0.1 \times \frac{20.0}{1000} = 0.002 \text{ mol}$$

Step 2: Write the balanced equation for the reaction and use this to work out how many moles of sodium hydroxide reacted with this number of moles of acid:

sodium hydroxide + hydrochloric acid → sodium chloride + water

$$NaOH + HCl \rightarrow NaCl + H_2O$$

The equation shows that 1 mol of hydrochloric acid reacts with 1 mol of sodium hydroxide. So, 0.002 mol of hydrochloric acid reacts with 0.002 mol of sodium hydroxide.

Step 3:

$$\text{concentration of sodium hydroxide} = \frac{\text{moles of sodium hydroxide}}{\text{volume of sodium hydroxide solution (dm}^3)}$$

$$= \frac{0.002}{0.025} = 0.08 \text{ mol dm}^{-3}$$

Maths skills

A **ratio** is a mathematical comparison of one quantity to another quantity. So the 'mole ratio' compares the moles of substances in a balanced equation. E.g. In the reaction between hydrogen and oxygen to make water

$$2H_2 + O_2 \rightarrow 2H_2O$$

the mole ratio of hydrogen to oxygen is 2:1.

More calculations from equations

Mole calculations can be used to predict the volume of one solution that will react with a measured volume of another. You need to know the concentrations of both solutions and the balanced equation. The ratio in moles between two substances in a balanced equation is called the 'mole ratio'.

e.g.

What volume of $0.50\,mol\,dm^{-3}$ hydrochloric acid will neutralise $20.00\,cm^3$ of $1.00\,mol\,dm^{-3}$ sodium hydroxide solution?

Step 1:

$$\text{moles of sodium hydroxide} = 1.00 \times \frac{20.0}{1000} = 0.02\,mol$$

Step 2: Use the balanced equation to calculate the number of moles of hydrochloric acid needed.

From the equation given earlier, 1 mol of sodium hydroxide reacts with 1 mol of hydrochloric acid. So, 0.02 mol of sodium hydroxide needs 0.02 mol of hydrochloric acid.

Step 3:

$$\text{volume of hydrochloric acid needed (dm}^3) = \frac{\text{moles of hydrochloric acid}}{\text{concentration of hydrochloric acid (mol dm)}}$$

$$= \frac{0.02}{0.50} = 0.04\,dm^3 \text{ (or } 40\,cm^3)$$

?

3 What volume of $0.40\,mol\,dm^{-3}$ sodium hydroxide is needed to neutralise $50.00\,cm^3$ of $0.50\,mol\,dm^{-3}$ hydrochloric acid?

4 The label has come off a bottle of dilute sulfuric acid. Winston titrates $25.00\,cm^3$ portions of the acid with a sodium hydroxide solution of concentration $0.10\,mol\,dm^{-3}$. He does the titration three times and gets the results shown in the table.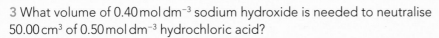

	Volume of sodium hydroxide solution needed (cm³)
Run 1	22.45
Run 2	22.40
Run 3	22.65

The equation for the reaction is:

$$H_2SO_4 + 2NaOH \rightarrow Na_2SO_4 + 2H_2O$$

Determine the concentration of the sulfuric acid solution, showing all the steps in your working.

?

1 In a titration, $20.00\,cm^3$ of a sodium hydroxide solution required $30.00\,cm^3$ of $0.20\,mol\,dm^{-3}$ hydrochloric acid to react completely.
a How many moles of hydrochloric acid were in the $30.00\,cm^3$?
b How many moles of sodium hydroxide reacted with the hydrochloric acid?
c What is the concentration of the sodium hydroxide solution?

2 Anna uses a pipette to put $20.00\,cm^3$ of sodium hydroxide in a flask and adds an indicator. In a titration, she finds that a mean value of $24.75\,cm^3$ of hydrochloric acid of concentration $0.25\,mol\,dm^{-3}$ is just sufficient to change the colour of the indicator. What is the concentration of the sodium hydroxide solution? Show your working.

Skills spotlight

Explain, using mathematical language, how to calculate the concentration of an acid given the volume of acid required to neutralise a measured volume of a soluble base of known concentration.

Learning Outcomes

H **2.15** Carry out simple calculations using the results of titrations to calculate an unknown concentration of solution or an unknown volume of solution required

HSW **11** Present information using scientific conventions and symbols

What happens to ions and electrons during electrolysis?

Your sweat contains salts and so your skin conducts electricity. The more you sweat, the more current your skin will conduct. Most people sweat more if they tell lies, and so lie detectors measure the amount of current that skin conducts.

A A lie detector

---

1 Look at Figure C.
a Explain why copper ions are attracted to the cathode.
b Explain why chromate ions are attracted to the anode.

2 a Are cations positive or negative?
b In the following ionic compounds, identify the anion and cation and state which would be attracted to the anode and which to the cathode if a solution of the compound was electrolysed:
i $K^+ F^-$
ii $Cu^{2+}(Cl^-)_2$

When an ionic solid is either melted or dissolved in water, the ionic bonds are broken allowing the ions to move freely. Ionic substances that conduct electricity when in aqueous solution or when molten are called **electrolytes**.

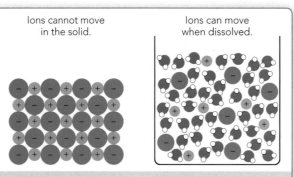

B (a) Lattice structure of solid sodium chloride; (b) sodium chloride dissolved in water

In **electrolysis**, two **electrodes** attached to a DC electricity supply are put into the electrolyte. The two types of ions carry opposite charges and so migrate (move) towards opposite electrodes:
- **cations** are positive ions attracted to the negative **cathode**
- **anions** are negative ions attracted to the positive **anode**.

Skills spotlight

Models are useful to help explain what happens in chemical changes. Imagine you have a large drawing of electrodes in an electrolyte, together with small card circles to represent positive and negative ions and electrons. Write a checklist to show how you could use this model to explain electrolysis.

The electrolysis of copper chromate solution shown in Figure C illustrates the migration of ions. Chromate ions form an orange-brown solution; copper ions form a blue solution.

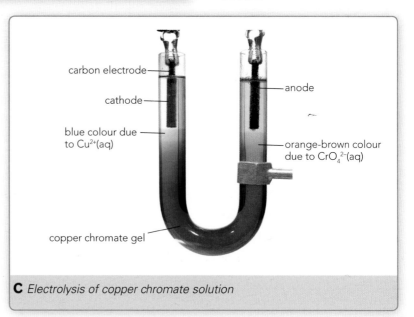

carbon electrode
cathode
blue colour due to $Cu^{2+}(aq)$
anode
orange-brown colour due to $CrO_4^{2-}(aq)$
copper chromate gel

C Electrolysis of copper chromate solution

Reactions at the electrodes

At the cathode, electrons are transferred from the electrode to the positive ions; at the anode, negative ions lose electrons. When positive ions gain electrons, we call it **reduction**. When electrons are lost by a negative ion, we call it **oxidation**.

This transfer of electrons changes charged ions into atoms or molecules, resulting in chemical changes at the electrodes. For example, in molten sodium chloride Na^+ ions are attracted to the cathode, where they gain electrons and become sodium atoms; similarly Cl^- ions are attracted to the anode, where they lose electrons and become chlorine molecules – sodium metal plus chlorine gas are produced. Both products have important uses.

Sodium is used:
- In street lamps – sodium vapour gives out a bright yellow light when an electric current is passed through it
- As a coolant in nuclear reactors – liquid sodium metal has a high thermal conductivity and transfers heat very efficiently from the core of the reactor to water, which then turns to steam and drives the generators.

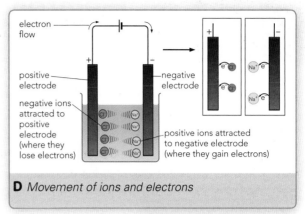

D *Movement of ions and electrons*

Half-equations

A **half-equation** shows the change at just one of the electrodes. In the electrolysis of molten sodium chloride, the reaction at the cathode is:

$$2Na^+ \quad + \quad 2e^- \quad \rightarrow \quad 2Na$$

The reaction at the anode is:

$$2Cl^- \quad \rightarrow \quad Cl_2 \quad + \quad 2e^-$$

Note that two Cl^- ions are needed to form one chlorine molecule, Cl_2.

H 5 Add electrons and then balance these half-equations: **a** $Br^- \rightarrow Br_2$ **b** $H^+ \rightarrow H_2$

6 Explain how you could use a beaker, wires, electrodes, a lamp and DC power supply to test unlabelled liquids to identify which are electrolytes. Describe first how you would assemble the apparatus. ✎

ResultsPlus
Watch Out!

Many students get mixed up about what happens at each electrode. One way to remember this is Cathode = reduCtion when the ions gain electrons and Anode = oxidAtion when the ions lose electrons.

3 The bromide ion is Br^-. Work out the charges on the other ions in the following compounds, and state the likely products at each electrode using molten electrolytes: **a** AgBr **b** $PbBr_2$.

4 In the electrolysis of molten sodium chloride:
a what is oxidised?
b what is reduced?

Learning Outcomes

3.1 Explain that electrolytes are ionic substances in the molten state or dissolved in water

3.2 Describe the movement of ions during electrolysis, such that: **a** positively charged cations migrate to the negatively charged cathode **b** negatively charged anions migrate to the positively charged anode

3.3 Demonstrate an understanding that oxidation can involve the loss of electrons and reduction can involve the gain of electrons

3.4 Demonstrate an understanding that reduction occurs at the cathode and that oxidation occurs at the anode in electrolysis reactions

H *3.5* Write half-equations for reactions occurring at the anode and cathode in examples of electrolysis reactions in this unit

3.6 Describe the manufacture of sodium by the electrolysis of molten sodium chloride (details of the electrolytic cell are not required)

3.7 Recall that sodium can be used in street lamps and as a coolant in some nuclear reactors

HSW 3 Describe how phenomena are explained using scientific models

C3.14 Electrolysis of sodium chloride solution

How can we produce hydrogen quickly from a solution?

The aeroplane in the picture uses hydrogen as its fuel. Hydrogen is a clean fuel because it does not produce any of the same pollutants that fossil fuels produce. It also does not produce carbon dioxide which is a greenhouse gas. Getting the hydrogen is the problem. There is plenty of hydrogen on Earth but most of it is attached to oxygen in water. Electrolysis can be used to split water and produce hydrogen at the cathode.

A This aeroplane does not use fossil fuels but uses hydrogen as its fuel instead.

There is a lot of water in the oceans but it contains dissolved sodium chloride. Sodium chloride solution contains sodium ions, chloride ions, water molecules, hydrogen ions and hydroxide ions. If we wanted to produce hydrogen on a large scale from sea water we would need to find out what effect these ions had.

To investigate the electrolysis of sodium chloride solution we need to pass an electric current through the solution. When the electric current is switched on all of the ions move through the solution. This includes the ions from the water and the ions from the salt. A power pack or battery pack delivering up to 12V can be used to supply the electricity. The electrodes should be made of an inert material, such as carbon. An inert material is something that will not react with the electrolyte or the products. The electrodes can be arranged in the electrolyte so that gases given off can be collected in small test tubes. Timing how long it takes for the tubes to fill can tell us about the rate of the reaction.

B Hoffman's voltameter collects gases given off during electrolysis of solutions and the volumes can be read from the vertical tubes.

Your task

You are going to plan an investigation that will allow you to find out what happens when different concentrations of sodium chloride solution undergo electrolysis.

Learning Outcomes

3.8 Electrolyse sodium chloride solution

ResultsPlus
Build Better Answers

When planning an investigation like this, one of the skills you will be assessed on is your ability to *evaluate the conclusion*. There are 4 marks available for this skill. Here are two extracts focusing on this skill. Other skills that you need for the practical assessment are dealt with in other lessons.

Student extract 1 — A basic response for this skill

The student gives a reason why they thought the conclusion was good.

> In my conclusion I said that how quickly hydrogen is produced depends on the concentration of the sodium chloride solution. This was a good conclusion because there was a clear pattern in my results which showed that more hydrogen was produced when the concentration of sodium chloride was higher.

No weaknesses are noted. Realizing where the weakness in the conclusion is can help when planning further work.

There is no suggestion of how the conclusion could have been supported by more evidence.

Student extract 2 — A good response for this skill

The student has used scientific knowledge as well.

> I think that my conclusion is a good one because I can see from my results that there is a clear link between the time it takes to fill a test tube with hydrogen and the concentration of the salt solution. There are no unexpected results and the results support my hypothesis. I know from my lessons on electrolysis that ions are needed to carry a charge in a solution so if there are more ions I would expect more ions to move and more hydrogen to be given off. This also matches the graph I found as secondary evidence. To gather more evidence for my conclusion I could use a different solution and measure the rate of the reaction at different concentrations. This would tell me if all solutions of salts react in the same way as the concentration increases.

The student has explained that the conclusion is a strong one and then explained why they think this is the case.

The student has used their own evidence and some secondary evidence.

The student has explained how the investigation could be extended.

ResultsPlus

To access 2 marks
- Evaluate the conclusion based on all collected evidence
- Suggest how all the collected evidence can be improved to provide stronger support for the conclusion

To access 4 marks
- Evaluate the conclusion based on all collected evidence and relevant scientific ideas
- Suggest how all collected evidence can be improved and extended to provide stronger support for the conclusion

C3.15 Electrolysis of salts

How can we predict the products of electrolysis?

Solution mining is used in Cheshire to obtain salt for the chemical industry. Pumped water dissolves the underground salt, but not the surrounding rocks. Removal of salt this way can cause subsidence and collapse of buildings.

A *This factory in Runcorn, Cheshire, manufactures chlorine and sodium hydroxide by the electrolysis of salt water.*

When a molten salt is electrolysed, ions are **discharged** as atoms or molecules at the electrodes. For example, when molten lead bromide is electrolysed, the anode product is bromine (seen as a brown vapour) and the cathode product is molten lead metal.

H

The reaction at the cathode is:

$$Pb^{2+}(l) + 2e^- \rightarrow Pb(l)$$

The lead ion has a 2+ charge so it needs to gain two electrons to become a lead atom. The reaction at the anode is:

$$2Br^-(l) \rightarrow Br_2(g) + 2e^-$$

Electrolysis of salt solutions

Water ionises to a very small extent, so in an aqueous solution of a salt there are hydrogen ions (H^+) and hydroxide ions (OH^-), as well as ions of the dissolved solid. Copper chloride solution contains four aqueous ions: $Cu^{2+}(aq)$ and $Cl^-(aq)$ from the salt; and $H^+(aq)$ and $OH^-(aq)$ from the water. Copper ions lose charge (gain electrons) more readily than hydrogen ions. Chloride ions lose charge (lose electrons) more readily than hydroxide ions. This means that when copper chloride solution is electrolysed, copper metal is discharged at the negative cathode and chlorine gas is discharged at the positive anode. The other ions are left in solution.

Copper sulfate solution contains four aqueous ions: $Cu^{2+}(aq)$ and $SO_4^{2-}(aq)$ from the salt; and $H^+(aq)$ and $OH^-(aq)$ from the water. When copper sulfate solution is electrolysed, the cathode product is copper as before. However, hydroxide ions lose charge more readily than sulfate ions, so hydroxide ions are discharged at the anode. When hydroxide ions, $OH^-(aq)$, are discharged, they lose electrons to form water and oxygen.

Sodium sulfate solution contains four aqueous ions: $Na^{2+}(aq)$ and $SO_4^{2-}(aq)$ from the salt and $H^+(aq)$ and $OH^-(aq)$ from the water. As with copper sulfate solution, the anode product is oxygen. Hydrogen gas is discharged at the cathode because hydrogen ions lose charge more readily than sodium ions.

1 What products would be made by the electrolysis of:
a molten potassium bromide
b molten lithium chloride?

H 2 The charge on a potassium ion is 1+. Write the half-equation for the cathode reaction in the electrolysis of molten potassium bromide.

H 3 Write the half-equation for the anode reaction when OH^- ions are discharged.

4 In the electrolysis of copper chloride solution, is copper oxidised or reduced?

5 In the electrolysis of copper sulfate solution, explain why oxygen is formed at the anode.

H 6 Write the half-equation for the cathode reaction in the electrolysis of aqueous copper chloride.

Some of the products of electrolysis are very **corrosive**. The electrodes must be **inert** – they must not react with any substances produced at the electrodes. Carbon (graphite) electrodes are good conductors and are inert.

Electrolysis of salt water

Salt water contains four aqueous ions: $Na^+(aq)$ and $Cl^-(aq)$ from the salt; and $H^+(aq)$ and $OH^-(aq)$ from the water. At the cathode, it is easier to discharge hydrogen ions, $H^+(aq)$, than sodium ions, $Na^+(aq)$. At the anode, chloride ions, $Cl^-(aq)$, are discharged first to give chlorine gas.

The overall equation for the reaction is:

$$2NaCl(aq) + 2H_2O \rightarrow 2NaOH(aq) + Cl_2(g) + H_2(g)$$

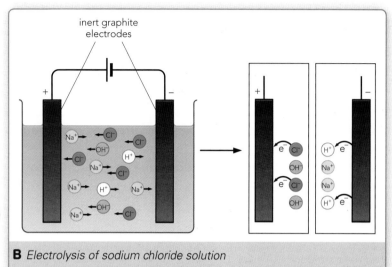

B *Electrolysis of sodium chloride solution*

H

The half equations for the reactions are:

At the cathode:

$$2H^+(aq) + 2e^- \rightarrow H_2(g)$$

At the anode:

$$2Cl^-(aq) \rightarrow Cl_2(g) + 2e^-$$

$Na^+(aq)$ and $OH^-(aq)$ ions are left behind in solution, forming a solution of sodium hydroxide, $NaOH(aq)$.

The electrolysis of salt water gives three products – hydrogen, chlorine and sodium hydroxide solution. All three products are important in industry.

C *Many scientists think that hydrogen-fuelled vehicles are the way forward. Hydrogen cars in Japan can be filled using hydrogen produced by the electrolysis of brine.*

Skills spotlight

Imagine that a large deposit of pure salt has been discovered underground near a major town. A company wants to build a factory here to manufacture sodium hydroxide by the electrolysis of salt water (brine). Describe some of the social, economic and environmental factors in the decision to build the factory.

7 Explain why electrodes for electrolysis are made of graphite, and not a metal such as aluminium.

8 Draw a labelled diagram of the apparatus for the electrolysis of an aqueous solution of potassium chloride. Explain what happens at each electrode.

ResultsPlus
Watch Out!

Students often forget that the first step in the electrolysis of a salt needs to get the salt to dissociate into ions by heating it or dissolving it.

Learning Outcomes

3.9 Explain the formation of the products in the electrolysis of sodium chloride solution

3.10 Describe how the electrolysis of aqueous solutions can give products from ions in water, rather than from ions of the dissolved solid

3.11 Explain the formation of the products in the electrolysis, using inert electrodes, of some electrolytes, including:
   a copper chloride solution *b* copper sulfate solution *c* sodium sulfate solution *d* molten lead bromide

H 3.5 Write half-equations for reactions occurring at the anode and cathode in examples of electrolysis reactions in this unit

HSW 13 Explain how and why decisions about uses of science and technology are made

What happens if you use electrodes made of the same metal as the electrolyte?

C3.16 Investigating the electrolysis of copper sulfate solution

What effect does the use of copper electrodes have on the electrolysis of copper sulfate solution?

The electrolysis of solutions could be an important way of producing hydrogen for use as a fuel in future. The electrolysis processes uses platinum electrodes because they are inert and are good conductors. Unfortunately platinum is very expensive. If we are going to produce a lot of hydrogen by electrolysis then cheaper electrodes must be used. Scientists are investigating the effect of using various electrodes in the electrolysis of solutions.

A Hydrogen is a clean, carbon neutral fuel if produced by electrolysis using renewable energy sources, but finding cheap and efficient electrodes is a problem that has to be solved.

Platinum is an inert material. It does not react with ions present in solutions, such as the Na^+ and Cl^- ions in sodium chloride solution. Copper is a fairly unreactive metal but it is not inert. This means that it does react with other elements so you might expect it to have some effect on the products of electrolysis.

When using inert electrodes in the electrolysis of copper sulfate solution you would expect copper to be deposited on the cathode. This is because copper is low in reactivity. Also you would expect oxygen from the water to be discharged as a gas at the anode. But what would happen if the electrodes were made of copper?

As well as the type of electrode used there are several other factors which can have an effect on an electrolysis reaction. For example, the concentration of the solution can have an effect, as can the distance between the electrodes and the current. The current flowing through an electrolysis cell is a measure of the number of electrons available at the electrodes for oxidation and reduction. You might expect increasing the current to have an effect on the amount of products formed through electrolysis.

Your task

You are going to plan an investigation that will allow you to find out how changing the current affects the mass of copper electrodes when the copper sulfate solution is electrolysed.

Learning Outcomes

3.12 Investigate the mass changes at the electrodes during the electrolysis of copper sulfate solution using copper electrodes

ResultsPlus
Build Better Answers

When planning an investigation like this, one of the skills you will be assessed on is your ability to *process evidence*. There are 4 marks available for this skill. Here are two extracts focusing on that skill. Other skills that you need for the practical assessment are dealt with in other lessons.

Student extract 1 **A basic response for this skill**

This is a good start because it is a clear table with headings and units but if you have more results you can present them as graph or bar chart.

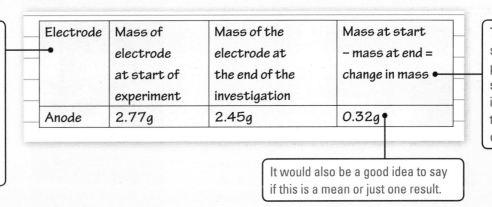

Electrode	Mass of electrode at start of experiment	Mass of the electrode at the end of the investigation	Mass at start – mass at end = change in mass
Anode	2.77g	2.45g	0.32g

The marks in this section are for processing results so it is a good idea to show how this number was calculated.

It would also be a good idea to say if this is a mean or just one result.

Student extract 2 **A good response for this skill**

It is a good idea to show how you do one of your calculations.

To calculate mass gained by cathode subtract the initial mass of the electrode from the final mass.

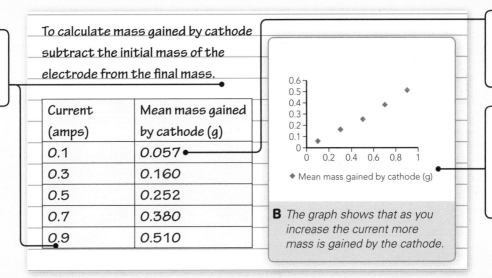

Current (amps)	Mean mass gained by cathode (g)
0.1	0.057
0.3	0.160
0.5	0.252
0.7	0.380
0.9	0.510

♦ Mean mass gained by cathode (g)

B *The graph shows that as you increase the current more mass is gained by the cathode.*

3 significant figures can only be used if the original results were to 4.

The graph is a good way to present the results but axes of the graph should be labeled.

ResultsPlus

To access 2 marks

- Attempt to process all collected evidence, using appropriate mathematical skills
- Attempt to present the processed evidence in a way appropriate for the topic

To access 4 marks

- Process all collected evidence in a way that is appropriate to the task, using appropriate mathematical skills
- Present processed evidence in a way that allows conclusions to be drawn

How is pure copper made using electrolysis?

Copper ore may contain only 0.5% copper, but the copper used for electrical wires must be 99.95% pure copper. Below that, impurities increase the resistance of the wire and can cause wires to get hot when a current flows. This can be dangerous.

B *Impure copper is purified by electrolysis.*

Copper is extracted from its ore by heating the ore with carbon ('smelting') – similar to extracting iron by heating its ore with carbon. This produces an **impure** product – a mixture of copper with other elements and compounds. This mixture is purified, or **refined**, on an industrial scale using electrolysis. The impure copper obtained from smelting is used as an anode, and the cathode is a thin sheet of pure copper. The electrolyte is copper sulfate solution.

A *Copper used in the manufacture of wire must be very pure.*

C *Purifying copper by electrolysis*

- electrons
- impure copper anode (+)
- pure copper cathode (–)
- impurities from the copper anode collect here
- solution containing $Cu^{2+}(aq)$ ions (for example, copper sulfate)

During electrolysis, the copper atoms in the anode lose two electrons each and become copper ions. These dissolve in the solution and migrate to the cathode, where they are deposited as pure copper. For every copper atom that leaves the anode, one is deposited on the cathode. So, the impure copper anode loses mass and the pure copper cathode increases in mass. Impurities from the anode are insoluble and collect below the anode as 'sludge'. The anode sludge is collected because it may contain valuable metallic elements such as gold, silver and platinum.

1 Is the change at the anode oxidation or reduction? Explain your answer in terms of electrons.

2 In Figure C, why does the concentration of copper ions in solution remain constant?

The half-equation for the anode reaction is:

$$Cu(s) \rightarrow Cu^{2+}(aq) + 2e^-$$

The half-equation for the cathode reaction is:

$$Cu^{2+}(aq) + 2e^- \rightarrow Cu(s)$$

H

Electroplating metals

Electroplating deposits a thin layer of one metal on the surface of another. The cathode is the object to be plated, and the anode is the pure metal. The electrodes are placed in an electrolyte containing ions of the plating metal. At the cathode, positive metal ions are reduced, depositing an even layer of metal atoms. A thicker layer is achieved by increasing the current or by carrying out the electrolysis for longer.

Silver or gold plating gives an attractive appearance and is cheaper than making the object out of pure metal. Electroplating is also used to improve resistance to **corrosion**. Electroplating protects the plated metal by preventing contact with air (and, for rusting, with water) so preventing corrosion.

'Galvanised' steel is steel coated with zinc. The protection against rusting (corrosion of iron) works even when the coating gets scratched because zinc is more reactive.

D Amy Williams' 2010 Winter Olympic medal for the skeleton bob wasn't pure gold – it was silver that had been plated with gold.

Metal added by electroplating	Applications
silver	cutlery, sports trophies
gold	jewellery
chromium	wheel rims, jewellery
tin	steel food cans
zinc	iron nails, steel railings

E Uses of electroplating

4 Describe how you would electroplate a nickel medal with silver and suggest how to vary the thickness of the coating.

H 3 The symbol for a tin ion is Sn^{2+}. Write a half-equation to show what happens at the cathode when a steel object is electroplated with tin.

Skills spotlight

Decisions on how to use science are made for many different reasons. Suggest some reasons why food 'tins' are made out of steel electroplated with tin – rather than just using steel, or plating with a more reactive metal like zinc.

ResultsPlus
Watch Out!

Be careful not to confuse electrolysis and electroplating. In electrolysis, substances are decomposed (broken down) giving products at both the anode and the cathode. In electroplating, the anode goes into solution and a layer of metal is plated on to the cathode.

Learning Outcomes

3.13 Describe the purification of copper by electrolysis using a pure copper cathode and an impure copper anode

3.14 Explain how electroplating can be used to improve the appearance and/or the resistance to corrosion of metal objects

HSW *12* Describe the benefits, drawbacks and risks of using new scientific and technological developments

>>>>>>>>>>>>>>>>>>>>>>>>>>>> Why can gas leaks be so dangerous?

How can we work out the volumes of gases in a reaction?

Toxic ammonia gas leaked into the air for 4 days during November 2008 in Florida, USA, after someone drilled into a chemical pipeline. The ammonia quickly spread across a town. About 300 people were evacuated while the pipe was repaired.

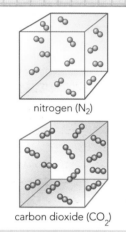

B *The same volume of different gases contains the same number of molecules.*

The particles in gases can move freely – so gases spread easily and can be hard to contain. This makes measuring their volumes difficult, but being able to calculate volumes of gases in reactions is very useful. The Italian scientist Amadeo Avogadro (1776–1856) stated that one **mole** of any substance contains 6.02×10^{23} particles. We can use this to work out how many moles are in a certain mass of any substance by using the equation:

A *People involved in cleaning up gas leaks have to wear gas-masks to avoid inhaling the gas.*

$$\text{number of moles} = \frac{\text{mass (grams)}}{\text{relative atomic (or formula) mass}}$$

Avogadro also stated in Avogadro's law that 1 mole of *any* gas at room temperature (25 °C) and normal atmospheric pressure (1 **atmosphere**) has a volume of 24 dm³. This is true for most gases and is known as the **molar volume** of a gas.

Gases can be collected using the apparatus in Figure C. Using the balanced equation for a reaction, you can calculate the volume of gas that should be released, in order to check the result.

Use the following relative atomic masses: Cl = 35.5, C = 12, H = 1, O = 16, He = 4. At room temperature and normal pressure:

1 What is the volume of 2 moles of carbon dioxide?

2 How many moles are in 48 dm³ of helium?

3 Calculate the volume of:
a 213 g of chlorine gas (Cl₂)
b 56 g of methane (CH₄)

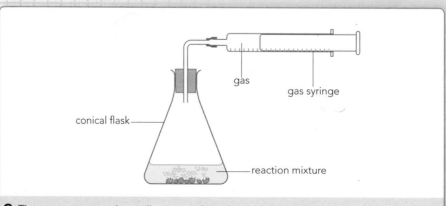

C *The apparatus used to collect a gas in order to calculate the molar volume.*

Using the idea of 'molar volume' means that we can calculate volumes of gases.

For example, how much hydrogen is needed to obtain 2.54 g of copper by reducing copper oxide?

Step 1: Write out the balanced symbol equation for the reaction:

$$H_2 + CuO \rightarrow Cu + H_2O$$

Step 2: Work out the number of moles in 2.54 g of copper:

$$\text{moles} = \frac{\text{mass}}{\text{relative atomic mass}} = \frac{2.54}{63.5} = 0.04 \text{ moles}$$

Step 3: Use the balanced symbol equation to work out the number of moles of hydrogen needed:
To make 1 mole of Cu needs 1 mole of H_2 so 0.04 moles of H_2 are needed.

Step 4: Calculate the volume of hydrogen:
1 mole of hydrogen has volume 24 dm^3 so

$$0.04 \text{ moles} = 24 \times 0.04 = 0.96 \text{ dm}^3$$

0.96 dm^3 of hydrogen will be needed to produce 2.54 g of copper.

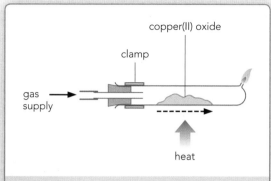

e.g.

D Apparatus for reducing copper oxide to copper

(diagram labels: copper(II) oxide, clamp, gas supply, heat)

ResultsPlus
Watch Out!

Students sometimes forget to check that the equation is balanced before doing a mole calculation.

Maths skills

The numbers in the example gave results to two decimal places. For more complicated calculations you may need to round the result to a certain number of decimal places. E.g. **Rounding** to 2 decimal places: if the digit in the third decimal place is greater than or equal to 5, round the second decimal place up. If not, leave off this digit and any that follow.
So 0.676 rounds to 0.68, but 0.674 rounds to 0.67.

4 What volume of oxygen (O_2) is required for the complete combustion of 40 g of methane (CH_4)? The word equation for the reaction is:
methane + oxygen → carbon dioxide + water

5 Explain how you would work out the volume of a gas produced in a reaction such as the thermal decomposition of calcium carbonate:
$$CaCO_3 \rightarrow CaO + CO_2$$
Use your method to calculate the volume of carbon dioxide that can be produced from 200 kg of calcium carbonate
(RAM of Ca = 40, C = 12, O = 16).

Learning Outcomes

H 4.1 Demonstrate an understanding that one mole of any gas occupies 24 dm^3 at room temperature and atmospheric pressure and that this is known as the molar volume of the gas

H 4.2 Use molar volume and balanced equations in calculations involving the masses of solids and volumes of gases

H 4.3 Use Avogadro's law to calculate volumes of gases involved in gaseous reactions, given the relevant equations

HSW 8 Evaluate methods of data collection and consider their validity and reliability as evidence

What problems do fertilisers cause?

African penguins used to burrow into a soft layer of penguin guano (penguin 'poo') to build their nests. The burrows protected the chicks from predators and the sun. During the 19th century, the guano was scraped off the rocks to be sold as fertiliser and the numbers of penguins dropped by 90%. Our dependence on guano has reduced since the discovery of artificial fertilisers.

A Without the guano layer, penguins have to nest on open rock.

Fertilisers contain soluble nitrogen compounds, which plants need to make proteins. They are added to soil to promote fast and strong growth in plants. They can be natural – such as manure or guano – or they can be artificial. Ammonia is a nitrogen-containing compound used as a raw material to make **nitrogenous fertilisers**. Ammonia was first made artificially in the 1900s by a scientist called Fritz Haber (1868–1934). The **Haber process** to make ammonia is named after him. The reaction involved in the Haber process is shown in Figure B.

1 Why do farmers use fertilisers?

2 Why did people use only natural fertilisers before the 20th century?

3 Suggest one advantage of artificial fertilisers over natural ones.

ResultsPlus
Watch Out!

In a reversible reaction, what we refer to as the 'forward reaction' is the reaction going from left to right as the equation has been written. The 'backward reaction' goes from right to left.

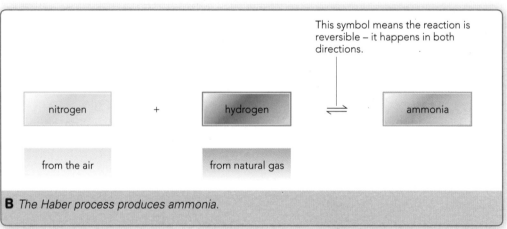

This symbol means the reaction is reversible – it happens in both directions.

nitrogen + hydrogen ⇌ ammonia

from the air   from natural gas

B The Haber process produces ammonia.

Some chemical reactions are **reversible**. This means that the reaction can happen in both directions – the forward and backward reactions. The Haber process uses a reversible reaction between nitrogen and hydrogen to form ammonia. The nitrogen is extracted from the air and the hydrogen is produced from methane, the main gas in natural gas. Both the forwards and backwards reactions are happening at the same time, so ammonia is broken down into hydrogen and nitrogen at the same time as it is made.

The Haber process happens in giant vessels called reactors (see Figure C). The conditions in the reactor allow the forward reaction to happen faster than the backward reaction.

Advantages and disadvantages

The use of artificial fertilisers has meant that more crops can be grown and more people fed – but they also have disadvantages. Because artificial fertilisers contain highly soluble chemicals they can easily be washed out of the soil when it rains and get into rivers and lakes. This can greatly increase the levels of nutrients in the water – in a process called **eutrophication**. This causes algae and plants in the water to grow quickly and soon the water becomes overgrown. When the plants die, they are **decomposed** by bacteria and fungi, which use up the oxygen in the water. This decreases the amount of oxygen available for other organisms, which then cannot survive.

C A Haber reactor

4 During the Haber process, unreacted nitrogen and hydrogen coming out of the reactor are pumped back into the reactor. Explain why.

5 In a reactor, ammonia is cooled and turned into a liquid as soon as it is formed. It is then quickly pumped away. Explain why.

Skills spotlight

Scientists need to design experiments to test their ideas. Duckweed is a small water plant that grows on the surface of ponds. How would you carry out an investigation to find out if adding fertiliser to the water increases the growth of duckweed?

6 Artificial fertilisers are very soluble. Explain why this means:
a they are useful for plants
b they cause environmental problems.

7 A farmer uses chemical fertilisers on a wheat field. Suggest why there are no longer any fish in the pond next to the field.

Learning Outcomes

4.4 Recall that nitrogenous fertilisers are manufactured from ammonia and that they promote plant growth

4.5 Demonstrate an understanding of the environmental consequences of the over-use of fertilisers, including excessive plant growth in rivers and lakes

4.6 Recall that chemical reactions are reversible and that the Haber process uses a reversible reaction between nitrogen (extracted from the air) and hydrogen (obtained from natural gas) to form ammonia

HSW **5** Planning to test a scientific idea, answer a scientific question, or solve a scientific problem

>>>>>>>>>>>>>>>>>> What is the connection between the First World War and the Haber process?

Why is using the correct conditions in the Haber process so important?

Ammonia is used to make explosives. The invention of the Haber process just before the First World War enabled ammonia and explosives to be made cheaply, quickly and in huge quantities.

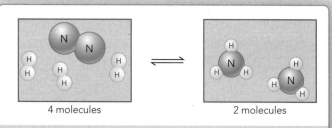

A *The Haber process enabled the German army to use weapons such as these in World War One.*

The reaction between hydrogen and nitrogen to form ammonia is reversible:

nitrogen + hydrogen ⇌ ammonia

This means that it can be considered as two reactions:

Forward: nitrogen + hydrogen → ammonia

Backward: ammonia → nitrogen + hydrogen

When ammonia is formed, heat is released. This means the forward reaction is **exothermic** (releases heat). The backward reaction is always the opposite, so it is **endothermic** (takes in heat). Eventually the forward and backward reactions will happen at the same rate. This is called **dynamic equilibrium**.

If a system in equilibrium is subject to a change in conditions, then it will adjust in such a way as to nullify (cancel out) the change.

Decreasing the temperature for the ammonia reaction will result in an increase in the rate of the forward reaction. This counteracts the decrease in temperature because this reaction is exothermic. We say that the equilibrium has shifted 'to the right'.

Choosing the conditions for the Haber process

Knowing how to shift the equilibrium position is important when choosing the conditions for industrial processes such as the Haber process. Manufacturers want to produce a high **yield** quickly in order to make maximum profits. The symbol equation for the reaction is:

$$N_2(g) + 3H_2(g) \rightleftharpoons 2NH_3(g)$$

Because the reaction involves gases, altering the pressure will also affect the position of the equilibrium.

4 molecules ⇌ 2 molecules

B *The forward reaction produces fewer gas molecules. Shifting the equilibrium to the right will decrease the pressure.*

ResultsPlus
Watch Out!

When asked to explain what happens when a reversible reaction reaches dynamic equilibrium do not say that the reaction stops, describe the forward and back reactions as happening at the same rate.

1 Write a definition for each of the words in bold in the description of the Haber process reaction on the right.

2 For each of these examples, state which way the equilibrium will shift:

a A + B ⇌ C+D; forward reaction is exothermic. The temperature is increased.

b A ⇌ B + C; forward reaction is exothermic. The concentration of B is increased.

c 2A + B ⇌ 2D; forward reaction is endothermic. D is removed from the system as soon as it is made.

Increasing the pressure causes the equilibrium to shift to the right, as the system tries to nullify the increase. This will increase the yield of ammonia. The usual pressure chosen for the reaction is high (200 atmospheres) – it could be made even higher (and produce even more ammonia) but the equipment to do this is expensive to produce and maintain.

3 Explain why a high pressure shifts the equilibrium to the right in the Haber process.

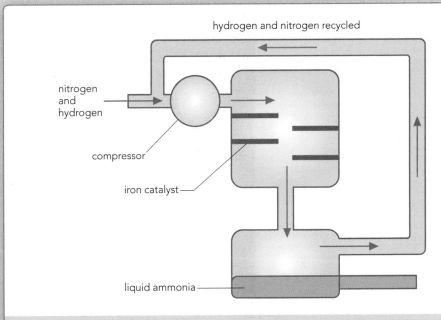

C *The walls of the reactor vessel are very thick so they can withstand high pressure.*

4 Explain why a high temperature shifts the equilibrium to the left in the Haber process

5 What does a catalyst do?

6 Why is it useful to increase the rate of the reaction in the industrial preparation of ammonia?

A high temperature will shift the equilibrium to the left, in order to favour the endothermic reaction – this will decrease the yield of ammonia. A low temperature would produce a higher yield of ammonia, but very slowly. So a high temperature is used because it increases the rate of the reaction and means that it will reach dynamic equilibrium quickly. This is also the reason why an iron **catalyst** is used. The conditions for the Haber process are normally:

- a high temperature – about 450 °C
- a high pressure – about 200 times normal atmospheric pressure
- the presence of an iron catalyst.

7 The ammonia produced in the reactor is liquefied and removed as soon as it is made. Explain why, using ideas about dynamic equilibrium.

8 Explain the choices for the conditions in the Haber process.

Skills spotlight

A chemical company needs to think about the economic effects of the reaction conditions inside a Haber reactor. Outline the factors that a company will need to take into account when determining the conditions to be used for making ammonia.

Learning Outcomes

(H) **4.7** Demonstrate an understanding of the concept of dynamic equilibrium

(H) **4.8** Explain how the position of a dynamic equilibrium is affected by changes in: *a* temperature *b* pressure

(H) **4.9** Demonstrate an understanding of the consequential effects of these changes on the rate of attainment of equilibrium and of the need to use a catalyst

(H) **4.10** Describe how, in industrial reactions such as the Haber process, the temperature, pressure and catalyst used produce an acceptable yield at an acceptable rate

HSW **13** Describe the social, economic and environmental effects of decisions about the uses of science and technology

C3.21 Fermentation

How do we produce alcohol from carbohydrates?

Beer making has been known for thousands of years. Ancient civilisations in Sumeria (now Iraq) recorded their recipes on stone tablets. One of these is the 'Hymn to Ninkasi', which is both a prayer to their goddess and a way of remembering the method of brewing.

A This old stone tablet shows the allocation of beer, which was the most popular drink and was issued as rations to workers.

Beer and wine are produced from **carbohydrates**, such as sugars and starch. Many fruits, such as grapes, contain natural sugars. Other crops, such as wheat, barley and rice, contain starch that can be broken down into sugars (e.g. glucose). Yeast is a single-celled fungus that can use sugars for a type of respiration that produces **ethanol**. This process is called **fermentation** and is controlled by enzymes, which the yeast cells release. The equations are:

Fermentation lock

mixture of yeast, water and grape juice

B Wine making at home

$$\text{sugar} \xrightarrow{\text{yeast}} \text{ethanol} + \text{carbon dioxide}$$

$$C_6H_{12}O_6(aq) \rightarrow 2C_2H_5OH(l) + 2CO_2(g)$$

Fermentation must happen in **anaerobic** conditions and must be kept warm. This is because the yeast works best in warm conditions. If the temperature is too low the reaction is very slow, but at high temperatures the yeast is killed. If oxygen is present aerobic respiration will take place, producing carbon dioxide and water, but no ethanol.

Photo B shows a small-scale home wine making kit. The 'fermentation lock' in the neck of the jar allows the bubbles of carbon dioxide gas to escape, but stops any air getting in.

Your task

You are going to plan an investigation that will allow you to find out what effect using different concentrations of sugar solution has on a fermentation reaction.

Learning Outcomes

5.1 Describe how ethanol is produced during the fermentation of carbohydrates, including:
   a that the fermentation mixture is kept warm and under anaerobic conditions   *b* that yeast provides an enzyme in this reaction
5.2 Prepare a solution of ethanol by fermentation

Build Better Answers

When planning an investigation like this, one of the skills you will be assessed on is your ability to *choose equipment*. There are 2 marks available for this skill. Here are two extracts focusing on that skill. Other skills that you need for the practical assessment are dealt with in other lessons.

Student extract 1 | A basic response for this skill

There are pieces of equipment missing. We don't know how the volume of carbon dioxide is to be measured.

> I am going to put the mixture of yeast, water and sugar in a conical flask. I will put a bung in the top with a delivery tube in one hole in the bung and a thermometer in the other hole. I will then use the equipment to measure how much carbon dioxide is made in five minutes.

The student has not given the concentrations of the solutions.

It would be a good idea to say why each piece of equipment is needed.

Student extract 2 | A good response for this skill

This student has used a table which is a good way to make everything clear – but a list is fine too.

To access the higher marks the student should explain why each piece of equipment is needed.

I am going to need the following equipment for my experiment:

Piece of equipment	Reason
100 cm³ conical flask	To hold the reaction mixture
7% yeast suspension	We are testing the factors which effect how quickly yeast ferments
thermometer and delivery tube in a bung	To monitor temperature and deliver carbon dioxide gas to a measuring cylinder so that we can measure the rate of carbon dioxide production.
sugar solutions (different ones)	To provide food for the yeast
water bath for the conical flask (e.g. a 400 cm³ beaker)	To keep the yeast at a warm temperature so that it ferments the sugar as fast as it can
one 100 cm³ and one 25 cm³ measuring cylinder	Small one to measure the solutions, large one to fill with water and use to collect carbon dioxide gas
clamp and stand,	To hold equipment safely
glass stirring rod	To stir the solutions around and make sure that the yeast is mixed with the sugar solution.

To access 2 marks

a) Choose the most relevant pieces of equipment
b) Explain the reasons for your choices and make sure that the choices are fully relevant to the method

How does the alcoholic content of drinks vary?

Many societies have tried to control the use of alcohol. The Prohibition law in the USA in the 1920s made it illegal to make, sell or drink alcohol. Gangsters like Al Capone set up drinking dens and many people carried on drinking illegally.

> **1** Look at Figure B. Put the wine, beer and vodka in order of alcoholic strength – weakest first.
>
> **2** True or false? The vodka is twice the strength of the wine. Explain your answer.

What are the effects of alcohol?

Different drinks contain different percentages of alcohol – for example, wine has more alcohol per litre than beer.

The ethanol in alcoholic drinks acts as a drug that can affect both the brain and the body. In small amounts, ethanol makes some people less self-conscious and more talkative. In larger amounts, the negative effects of ethanol take over. These include:

- slower reaction times
- violent or aggressive behaviour
- loss of balance and coordination
- vomiting and fainting
- dehydration (lack of fluid in the body) leading to a hangover.

A Customs officials break open illegally brewed barrels of beer in 1920s America.

Skills spotlight

Some questions cannot be answered by science. Politicians and religious leaders may debate whether or not banning alcohol is a good idea. Why is this not a scientific question?

B The different percentages of alcohol in different drinks

Drinks are rated in terms of the number of units of alcohol that they contain. One unit is $10\,cm^3$ of pure ethanol. Recent government guidelines recommend:

- no alcohol for young people under 15
- alcohol only once a week for young people aged 15 to 17
- a maximum of 4 units per day for adults.

If you drink more than this on a regular basis, your health is at risk. Excessive drinking over a long period increases the risk of heart disease and strokes, as well as some types of cancer. It also causes **liver cirrhosis**, which can be fatal. Britain spends about £2 billion per year on alcohol-related medical conditions. This includes conditions caused by both the long-term and the short-term effects of alcohol. Binge drinking is an increasing problem. It has caused deaths and can also lead to public order problems in city centres.

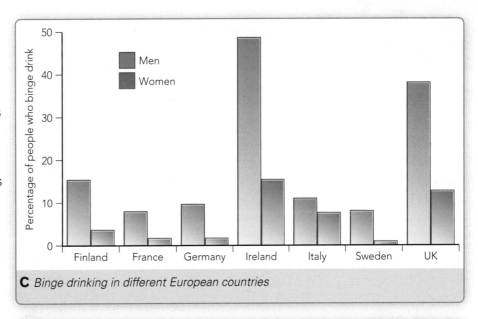

C Binge drinking in different European countries

How are spirits made?

Ethanol is toxic and it affects living organisms. At levels of about 15%, ethanol kills the yeast cells that made it, stopping fermentation. If you want to make a stronger drink, you must heat the fermentation mixture. Ethanol boils at a lower temperature than water, so the **fraction** of the liquid that boils first will contain a higher percentage of ethanol. This vapour is collected and condensed to produce stronger drinks (e.g. vodka and rum) known as spirits. This process is called **fractional distillation**.

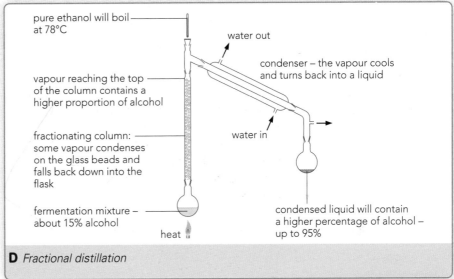

pure ethanol will boil at 78°C

water out

condenser – the vapour cools and turns back into a liquid

vapour reaching the top of the column contains a higher proportion of alcohol

fractionating column: some vapour condenses on the glass beads and falls back down into the flask

water in

fermentation mixture – about 15% alcohol

heat

condensed liquid will contain a higher percentage of alcohol – up to 95%

D Fractional distillation

3 Using Figure C, list the three European countries that have the biggest percentages of binge drinkers.

4 Describe in detail how the binge drinking statistics for women compare with those for men.

5 Explain how you can use fractional distillation to make a solution of alcohol more concentrated. Use some or all of the following words or phrases in your answer: *boil, evaporate, vapour, condense, boiling point, dilute, concentrated.*

ResultsPlus
Watch Out!

Describe *in detail* means that you are expected to make several points. Look at how many marks are available for each question. Don't just make one point and lose the rest of the marks.

Learning Outcomes

5.3 Recall that different percentages of ethanol are present in various drinks

5.4 Demonstrate an understanding of the social issues and possible harmful effects of ethanol in alcoholic drinks

5.5 Explain how to obtain a concentrated solution of ethanol by fractional distillation of the fermentation mixture

HSW 4 There are some questions that science cannot currently answer and some that science cannot address

How could we make alcoholic drinks from crude oil?

Why do we make ethanol in different ways?

The Model-T Ford, built between 1908 and 1927, was the world's first car to be built on an assembly line. Henry Ford, the company's founder, wanted it to run on ethanol. In fact, it could run on petrol or ethanol but the decreasing cost of petrol and prohibition meant that petrol became the main fuel.

A A Model-T Ford

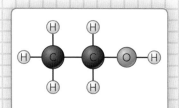

B Ethanol is a compound of carbon, hydrogen and oxygen.

Making ethanol by fermentation

Ethanol is used in drinks, as a solvent, as a fuel and as a reagent to make other chemicals.

During fermentation, sugars such as glucose are converted into ethanol and carbon dioxide through anaerobic respiration:

$$\text{glucose sugar} \xrightarrow{\text{yeast}} \text{ethanol} + \text{carbon dioxide}$$
$$C_6H_{12}O_6(aq) \rightarrow 2C_2H_5OH(l) + 2CO_2(g)$$

1 Name the three elements in glucose.

2 Glucose is a carbohydrate
a What does 'hydrated' mean?
b Use the formula to explain why glucose is a carbohydrate.

C Sugar cane being harvested

In Britain, sugar is extracted from sugar beet. In hotter climates, sugarcane provides a good source of sugar. Other carbohydrates from plants such as wheat can also be broken down into sugars.

Making ethanol from crude oil

Ethanol can also be made by reacting ethene with steam in the presence of a catalyst. This is called **hydration** because you are adding water to the ethene:

$$\text{ethene} + \text{steam} \xrightarrow{\text{catalyst}} \text{ethanol}$$
$$C_2H_4(g) + H_2O(g) \rightarrow C_2H_5OH(l)$$

Ethene is produced from crude oil. A small amount of ethene occurs naturally in the petroleum gases that are found with the oil. Large amounts of ethene are made by **cracking** larger molecules in the higher-boiling fractions of crude oil.

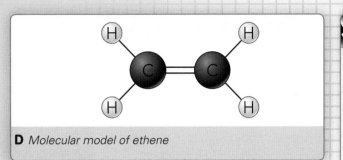

D *Molecular model of ethene*

Which method?

Each method has advantages and disadvantages. The hydration of ethene will give a product that is nearly 100% pure, with little or no waste. But crude oil is a **non-renewable** resource.

Fuels made from plant crops are called **biofuels** and these are **renewable** because we can always grow more crops. But fermentation produces ethanol at only 15% concentration. Fractional distillation can be used to make ethanol that is 95% pure, which is good enough for most uses. Countries without oil supplies, but with climates that are good for growing crops, will prefer to use the fermentation method.

Making ethene

Heating ethanol to a high temperature in the presence of a suitable catalyst produces ethene and steam. This is an example of a **dehydration** reaction.

$$\text{ethanol} \xrightarrow{\text{catalyst}} \text{ethene} + \text{steam}$$

$$C_2H_5OH(g) \rightarrow C_2H_4(g) + H_2O(g)$$

3 Which of the two methods for making ethanol:
a is sustainable **b** gives the purest product **c** has no by-product?

4 Which of the reactions in this spread is a dehydration reaction? Use the equation to explain why.

5 State one advantage and one disadvantage of using fermentation as a method of producing ethanol.

6 Brazil is the world's largest producer of ethanol from sugar cane. In Britain, we produce more ethanol from oil. Explain why this is, and why this might change in the future.

Skills spotlight

Biofuels could be a sustainable source of renewable fuel for cars, but should we use food crops to make fuel when many people in the world still go hungry? Who makes the decision about whether to grow and use biofuels in the UK? What do you think?

ResultsPlus
Watch Out!

When writing about the effects of something on the environment, students often use the phrase 'environmentally friendly', this is too vague. Be specific about the environmental benefits that you mean.

Learning Outcomes

H 5.6 Recall how ethanol can also be manufactured by reacting ethene (from cracking of crude oil fractions) with steam

H 5.7 Evaluate the factors which are relevant to the choice of method used in the manufacture of ethanol, including: **a** the relative availability of sugar cane or sugar beet and crude oil **b** the quality of the final product and whether it needs further processing

H 5.8 Recall that dehydration of ethanol results in the formation of ethene

HSW 13 How and why decisions about science and technology are made, including those that raise ethical issues, and about the social, economic and environmental effects of such decisions

How can drinking alcohol make someone go blind?

What is a homologous series?

Ethanol in alcoholic drinks is taxed very heavily. Ethanol for use as a solvent is not taxed, so it's much cheaper. However, the ethanol in solvents is not drinkable because about 5% of methanol, a toxic alcohol, is added, usually with a blue or purple dye. This mixture is called 'methylated spirits'.

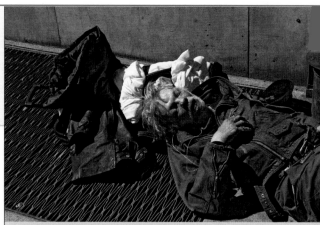

A People who drink 'methylated spirits' are at serious risk of damaging their health, including their eyesight and brain function.

> **ResultsPlus**
> **Watch Out!**
>
> When drawing the structure of an alkene, students often forget to put in the one double bond between two of the carbon atoms in the molecule. Remember all the other atoms are joined with single bonds.

Alkenes

Ethene is a **hydrocarbon** that contains a double bond between two carbon atoms. Propene is also a hydrocarbon with a double bond – they are both members of the **alkene** series. A family of compounds that all have the same feature but have different numbers of carbon atoms is called a **homologous series**. Alkenes all contain a double bond and have names that end in 'ene'. The number of hydrogen atoms in an alkene is always twice the number of carbon atoms. The **general formula** C_nH_{2n} can be used to work out the formula of any alkene.

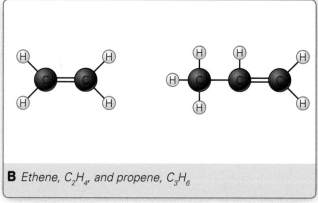

B Ethene, C_2H_4, and propene, C_3H_6

1 Which two chemical elements are present in alkenes?

2 How are ethene and propene:
a similar
b different?

3 What is the formula of the alkene with six carbon atoms?

4 State one similarity and one difference between the structures of the alkanes and the alkenes.

Alkanes

Another homologous series is the **alkanes**. These are hydrocarbons that contain only single bonds. The names of the alkanes all end in 'ane'.

Alkanes and alkenes have similar chemical properties. They are both flammable and can be used as fuels.

Table D shows some physical properties of the first four members of the alkane series. The alkanes also have a general formula. To work out the number of hydrogen atoms in an alkane, you double the number of carbon atoms and add two – the general formula is C_nH_{2n+2}.

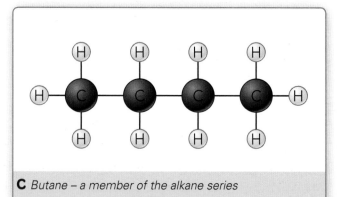

C Butane – a member of the alkane series

Name	Formula	Structure	Formula mass	Boiling point (°C)
methane	CH_4		16	−164
ethane	C_2H_6		30	−88
propane	C_3H_8		44	−42
butane	C_4H_{10}		58	0

D *Some properties of the alkanes*

5 a Plot a line graph to show how the boiling point of different alkanes varies with the number of carbon atoms.
b Use your graph to predict the boiling point of the next member of the alkane series, pentane.

Alcohols

Methanol, ethanol and propanol all belong to the homologous series of **alcohols**. All alcohols have a name ending in 'ol' and contain the **hydroxyl** group (OH). Their general formula is $C_nH_{2n+1}OH$. Like alkanes, alcohols are also good fuels – they burn with a cleaner blue flame than hydrocarbons.

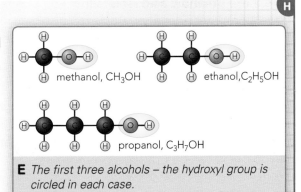

E *The first three alcohols – the hydroxyl group is circled in each case.*

methanol, CH_3OH ethanol, C_2H_5OH propanol, C_3H_7OH

Maths skills

General chemical formulae relate the number of atoms in a compound using a simple expression. We know that alkanes consist of carbon and hydrogen atoms in the ratio $n : 2n+2$.
So for an alkane compound with 4 carbon atoms:

$n = 4$

and the number of hydrogen atoms

$= 2n + 2 = (2 \times 4) + 2 = 10$

giving the chemical formula for butane or C_4H_{10}

H 6 a What element is present in alcohols but not in hydrocarbons?
b Use this fact to explain why alcohols burn with a clean flame.

H 7 True or false? The difference in the formula between one member of a homologous series and the next is the same for the alkanes, alkenes and alcohols. Give your reasons.

8 Butane is in the same homologous series as ethane, but propene is not. Explain why, using molecular model diagrams to help you.

Learning Outcomes

5.9 Define homologous series as a series of compounds which: **a** have the same general formula **b** show a gradual variation in physical properties as exemplified by their boiling points **c** have similar chemical properties

5.10 Recall the names, formulae and structures of members of the following homologous series: **a** alkanes, up to 4 carbons per molecule **b** alkenes, up to 3 carbons per molecule **H c** alcohols, up to 3 carbons in length

HSW **1** The analysis of scientific data

C3.25 Ethanoic acid

What is vinegar and why is it useful?

Vinegar is made from ethanol that has been produced by fermentation. The 'chip shop style' product looks and tastes exactly like vinegar because it contains the same chemicals. But if the ethanol has been produced from crude oil, you can't call it vinegar. It has to be sold as 'non-brewed condiment'.

A *The same … or different?*

> **1** How is ethanol converted into ethanoic acid?
>
> **2** What is an 'aerobic process'?

Making and using vinegar

If you leave a bottle of wine open to the air, it will 'go off'. The ethanol in the wine reacts with oxygen in the air to make **ethanoic acid**. This is the active ingredient in vinegar. Adding oxygen in this way is an example of an **oxidation** reaction. The word 'vinegar' comes from the French *vin aigre*, meaning 'sour wine'. The reaction occurs due to bacteria. Unlike ethanol production, in this reaction you need oxygen – it is an **aerobic** process. Left naturally, the process takes several months, but modern manufacturing techniques mean that vinegar containing up to 15% of ethanoic acid can be produced in 24 hours.

The ethanoic acid gives food its tangy, sharp taste. The acid also acts as a **preservative**. Some foods are stored in vinegar – the foods last longer because bacteria can't survive in the acidic environment. This is called pickling.

Ethanoic acid is a member of a homologous series called the **carboxylic acids**.

> **3** Name three foods that can be preserved by pickling.
>
> **4** If you put a piece of magnesium into a tube containing ethanoic acid:
> **a** state one observation you would make
> **b** write a word equation for the reaction.
>
> **H 5** State one way in which an ethanoic acid molecule is similar to an ethanol molecule and one way in which it is different.

B *All these products contain vinegar (ethanoic acid).*

Pure ethanoic acid is corrosive, but the vinegar that you put on your food is safe to taste because it is very dilute. Ethanoic acid shows the normal properties of acids. For example, it will:

- turn litmus paper and universal indicator red
- react with some metals (e.g. calcium) making hydrogen
- react with **bases** or carbonates to form salts called 'ethanoates'.

Carboxylic acids

Like the alkanes, alkenes and alcohols, **carboxylic acids** are a **homologous series**. These acids are carbon compounds containing a **carboxyl group** (–COOH). Members of the series have different numbers of carbon atoms in their molecules. The first member of the series, with only one carbon atom per molecule, is called methanoic acid. Propanoic acid is C_2H_5COOH. The general molecular formula for carboxylic acids is $C_nH_{2n}O_2$.

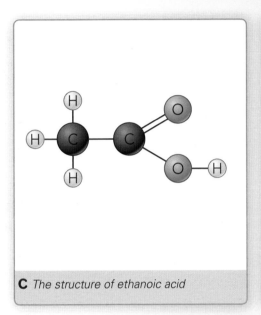

C The structure of ethanoic acid

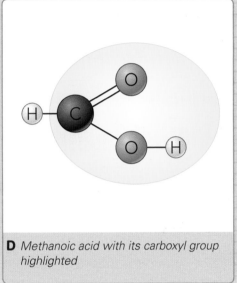

D Methanoic acid with its carboxyl group highlighted

Skills spotlight

It is useful to use standard scientific conventions and know what they mean. The molecular formula of ethanoic acid is $C_2H_4O_2$. Scientists usually write the formula as CH_3COOH. Why is this formula more helpful?

H 6 Copy the molecule of ethanoic acid in Figure C. Label the carboxyl group on your diagram.

H 7 a What group do all the carboxylic acids have in common?
b How is each compound in the carboxylic acid homologous series different from the previous one?

H 8 a How many atoms of carbon, hydrogen and oxygen are there in propanoic acid?
b Draw the structure of the molecule.

9 Explain why some foods are pickled – and why this is not suitable for all foods.

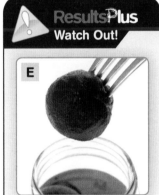

ResultsPlus
Watch Out!

E

It's easy to forget names. Use a mnemonic such as Mark Eats Pickled Beetroot to help you remember the initial letters of the first four prefixes meth-, eth-, prop- and but-.

Learning Outcomes

5.10 Recall the names, formulae and structures of members of the following homologous series: **H d** carboxylic acids, up to 3 carbon atoms per molecule

5.11 Demonstrate an understanding that ethanol can be oxidised to form ethanoic acid and that this reaction occurs in open bottles of wine and in the production of ethanoic acid in vinegar

5.12 Describe the use of vinegar as a flavouring and as a preservative

5.13 Demonstrate an understanding that ethanoic acid is a typical acid, including: **a** its reaction with metals **b** its reaction with bases and carbonates to form salts (ethanoates) **c** its typical effect on indicators

HSW 11 Presenting information, using scientific, technical language, conventions and symbols

>>>>>>>>>>>>>>>>>>>>>>>> What is the link between perfumes, plastic bottles and shirts?

C3.26 Esters

What are esters and how do we use them?

Since ancient times, people have used perfumes. Traditional perfumes contain extracts from plants like jasmine, roses and tangerine. More modern perfumes contain synthetic chemicals designed to delight our senses ... including the smell of meat!

A Flame body spray contains a hint of 'flame-boiled meat'.

The chemicals that are responsible for the attractive smells in perfumes are called **esters**. Esters occur naturally in fruits, and we can also use esters as **flavourings** in sweets such as pear drops. You can smell esters because their molecules escape easily.

B Many everyday items contain esters.

Esters are made when carboxylic acids (like ethanoic acid) react with alcohols (like ethanol):

ethanoic acid + ethanol → ethyl ethanoate + water
(acid)   (alcohol)   (ester)

?

1 State two uses of esters.

2 Esters are hydrocarbons – true or false? Give a reason.

H 3 What is the molecular formula of:
a ethanol
b ethyl ethanoate?

H 4 Draw out the equation for the formation of ethyl ethanoate using structural formulae.

H

$$CH_3-C \overset{O}{\underset{O-H}{}} + HO-CH_2-CH_3 \longrightarrow CH_3-C \overset{O}{\underset{O-CH_2-CH_3}{}} + H_2O$$

ethanoic acid   ethanol   ethyl ethanoate   water

C The production of ethyl ethanoate shown using structural formulae

A **structural formula** shows the arrangement of the atoms in a molecule. A **molecular formula** shows the total number of atoms in a molecule – but not how they are arranged. For ethanoic acid the molecular formula is $C_2H_4O_2$.

You can use the reaction of alcohols and carboxylic acids to make long-chain esters, which contain thousands of individual ester molecules joined together. This is a **polyester** – 'poly' means many. The long-chain molecules can be made into fibres, which can be woven into fabrics.

Unlike some plastics, plastic bottles made from polyesters can be recycled. The bottles are collected, washed, shredded and melted. The recycled polyester is then used to make a number of products including a fleece material that is used to make clothing, or fibres in a carpet. Because there are uses for the recycled bottles, it is economic to collect and process them.

D From this … to this

Figure E represents a section of a polyester molecule – the ester group is circled. The yellow box and the green hexagon represent hydrocarbon chains. An actual polyester molecule would contain a long chain of several thousand atoms, with this section repeated thousands of times.

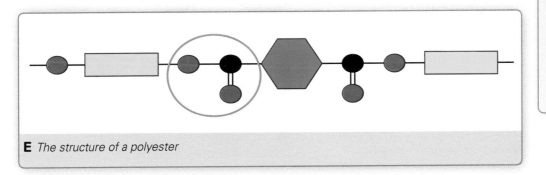

E The structure of a polyester

Skills spotlight

Modern technology brings benefits and drawbacks. If we replace wool with polyester, there might be less need to raise sheep. Would this be a good or a bad thing?

5 State two uses of polyesters.

H 6 Look back at Figure E. What is the meaning of:
a the black sphere
b the red sphere?

H 7 Write a balanced symbol equation for the reaction of ethanol and ethanoic acid.

8 Explain why almost all local councils collect plastic bottles for recycling but do not always collect other plastics such as food trays and yoghurt pots.

ResultsPlus
Watch Out!

When writing about recycling plastics try to be as precise as you can about what plastic you are talking about, because some cannot be recycled.

Learning Outcomes

5.14 Describe the reaction of ethanol with ethanoic acid to produce an ester, ethyl ethanoate and water **H** including writing an equation for this reaction using molecular and structural formulae

5.15 Describe uses of: *a* esters as flavourings and perfumes, as they are pleasant-smelling *b* polyesters as fibres to make fabric and as plastics for making bottles (no consideration of the formation of polyester is required)

5.16 Demonstrate an understanding that polyesters can be recycled to form fleece that is used to make clothing

HSW 12 The use of contemporary science and technological developments and their benefits, drawbacks and risks

Why do alkalis feel soapy if you spill them on your skin?

···· How can we make soap from oils and fats?

In the 1930s, the first drama serials on the radio in the USA were sponsored by soap companies and became known as 'soap operas'. The name stuck, and TV programmes today like Eastenders and Coronation Street are still called 'soaps'.

A *This radio theatre was sponsored by Lux soap.*

Fats and oils

Fats and oils are big **esters**. They are made from alcohols and carboxylic acids that contain a long chain of carbon and hydrogen atoms. Fats and oils are very similar – the only difference is the melting point. Fats are solids at room temperature and oils are liquids.

Making soap

Glyceryl tristearate is an ester – when it is boiled with an alkali, such as sodium hydroxide, the fat is broken down into glycerol and sodium stearate (Figure B):

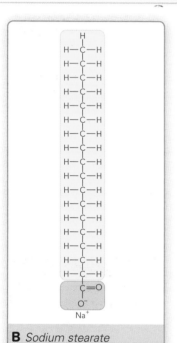

B *Sodium stearate*

sodium hydroxide + glyceryl tristearate → sodium stearate + glycerol

The general equation is:

concentrated alkali + oil/fat → soap + glycerol

Sodium stearate is an example of a soap. Soaps can also be made by using potassium hydroxide as the alkali. Both sodium stearate and potassium stearate are **salts** of long chain carboxylic acids.

1 What type of compound are fats and oils?

2 What is the difference between fats and oils?

3 Olive oil stays liquid when you put it in the fridge, but turns solid when you put it in a freezer. Suggest a value for the melting point of olive oil.

4 What are the two types of ingredient needed to make soap?

How does soap work?

A soap can be shown as a tadpole shaped structure – see Figure C (a). The 'head' is **hydrophilic** (water-loving). Look at Figure B. Notice that one of the oxygen atoms has a negative charge – this means that it is an **anion**. The 'tail' is a long chain of carbon atoms– it is **hydrophobic** (water-hating).

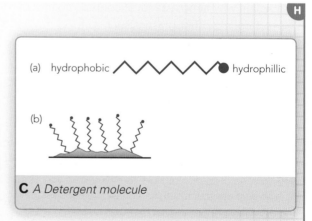

C *A Detergent molecule*

Figure C (b) shows how the hydrophobic end of the soap sticks into the grease. In Figure D (a), some of the soap gets underneath the grease and starts to lift it off the fabric. In (b) the blob of grease is now surrounded by soap with the 'heads' (anionic ends) pointing outwards into the water. This means that the grease mixes with the water.

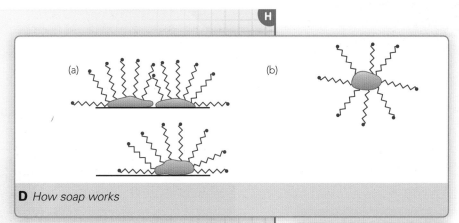

D *How soap works*

Turning oils into fats

Vegetable oils are **unsaturated** compounds – they contain double bonds. Animal fats such as butter and lard are **saturated.** To turn a liquid oil into a solid fat you can add hydrogen to the double bonds. These **hydrogenated** oils are the main ingredient in margarine. Margarine is made by bubbling hydrogen through vegetable oils in the presence of a metal catalyst – usually nickel. The overall reaction is described as **catalytic hydrogenation**.

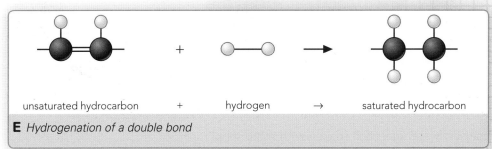

unsaturated hydrocarbon   +   hydrogen   →   saturated hydrocarbon

E *Hydrogenation of a double bond*

5 Which compound has the chemical formula $C_{18}H_{25}O_2Na$?

H 6 Draw the groups of atoms in sodium stearate that are:
a hydrophilic b hydrophobic.

H 7 Explain how hydrogenating an unsaturated compound can make it saturated.

8 Describe how soaps are made. Include the following words in your answer: *fat*, *oil*, *ester*, *alkali* and *salt*.

Skills spotlight

When scientific and technological decisions are made, we need to think about economic factors and the environment. Soaps and detergents can be made from animal fats, vegetable oils or petroleum oil. Which would be best for the environment, and why?

ResultsPlus
Watch Out!

Students often confuse 'unsaturated' and 'saturated' and forget to refer to the presence or absence of double bonds between the carbon atoms. Remember that a saturated hydrocarbon has as many hydrogen atoms as possible because it has no double bonds between the carbon atoms.

Learning Outcomes

5.17 Recall that oils and fats are esters

5.18 Describe the breaking down of oils and fats, by boiling with concentrated alkali solution, to produce soaps, which are sodium or potassium salts of long carbon chain carboxylic acids

H 5.19 Demonstrate an understanding of how a soap removes dirt or grease, including: a that part of the soap anion is hydrophobic and dissolves in dirt or grease b that the other part is hydrophilic and dissolves in water

H 5.20 Demonstrate an understanding that liquid oils can be converted to solid fats by catalytic hydrogenation which removes the C=C unsaturation and that this process is used to manufacture margarine

HSW *13* How and why decisions about science and technology are made, including those that raise ethical issues, and about the social, economic and environmental effects of such decisions

Water

1. Tap water in different parts of the country is either hard water or soft water.
   The picture shows a pipe from a hard water area.

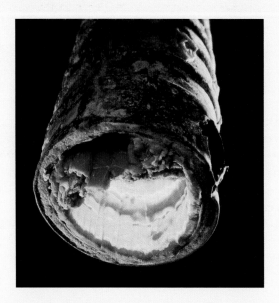

(a) Use the picture to explain a problem caused by hard water. (2)

(b) Some hard water and some soft water are each shaken with some soap.
   What do you see in each sample?

	In hard water	In soft water
A	scum	lather
B	nothing	scum
C	lather	nothing
D	lather	lather

(2)

(c) Give the name or formula of an ion that causes water to be hard. (1)

(d) How can hardness be removed from temporary hard water? (1)

*(e) Many different salts dissolve in water. Emma has been given 1,000 cm³ of
   a solution of sodium chloride. Describe how she could find the mass of
   sodium chloride that had been dissolved, and also show that the solution
   contained chloride ions. (6)

Ammonia and the Haber process

2. In industry, nitrogen and hydrogen are reacted together to form ammonia, NH_3.

The diagram shows an outline of the Haber process, starting with nitrogen and hydrogen.

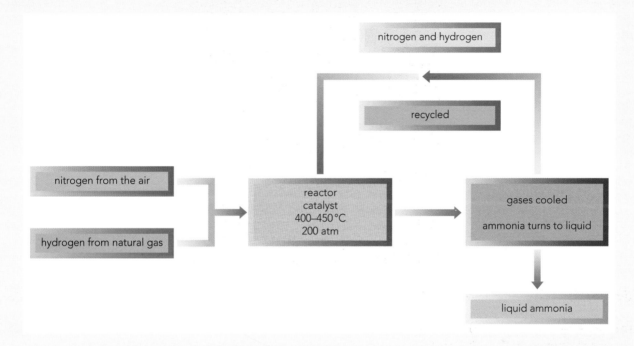

(a) (i) Balance the equation for the reaction that takes place in the Haber process.

$$N_2 + H_2 \rightleftharpoons NH_3$$

(1)

(ii) What does the symbol $\rightleftharpoons$ mean in the equation for the Haber process? (1)

(iii) The speed of the reaction is increased by using a catalyst in the reactor.
Name the catalyst used in the Haber process. (1)

(b) Most of the ammonia that comes out of the Haber process is used to make artificial fertilisers.
What are the consequences of using too much fertiliser for growing crops? (3)

(c) In the Haber process, in addition to the catalyst, a temperature of about 450 °C and a pressure of about 200 atm are used. The reaction is exothermic. Explain how these conditions of temperature and pressure produce an acceptable yield in an acceptable time. (3)

Ethanoic acid

3. When a bottle of wine is left open and exposed to the air, the wine turns sour and ethanoic acid, $C_2H_4O_2$, is formed.

(a) Explain why ethanoic acid is formed in this reaction. (2)

(b) Which of the following represents the structural formula of ethanoic acid?

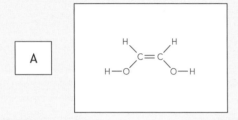

(1)

(c) Describe two chemical reactions of ethanoic acid that are typical of an acid. (2)

(d) Ethanoic acid reacts with ethanol, C_2H_6O, to form ethyl ethanoate and water. Write the balanced equation for this reaction using molecular formulae. (2)

(e) In industry, ethanoic acid can be manufactured from methanol. The final stage in the manufacture of methanol is shown by this equilibrium reaction.

$$CO(g) + 2H_2(g) \rightleftharpoons CH_3OH(g)$$

(i) What is the maximum volume of methanol vapour that can be obtained from $500\,dm^3$ of hydrogen under the conditions of the reaction? (All gases are measured at the same conditions of temperature and pressure.) (1)

(ii) The reaction is exothermic. One company uses a copper based catalyst at a temperature of 280 °C and 100 atmospheres pressure. Explain whether the equilibrium yield would increase, decrease or stay the same if a different catalyst were used in this reaction. (2)

Useful products from vegetable oils

4. Many plants are grown commercially for the oils that can be extracted from their seeds. Some examples include olive oil and sunflower seed oil.

   Some uses of these oils include making soaps and margarine.

   (a) Vegetable oils can be converted into soaps.

   (i) Which substance is reacted with the vegetable oil to make soap? (1)

   (ii) How is this mixture then treated to make the soap? (1)

   (iii) Which type of compound is present in the vegetable oil?

   A alcohol
   B alkali
   C alkane
   D ester (1)

   (iv) Water is said to be hard when it contains dissolved calcium or magnesium ions. Soft water does not contain these ions. Emily carried out an experiment to test the hardness on three samples of water, **A**, **B** and **C**.

   In each case, she added some soap solution to the sample of water. She then shook the mixture vigorously and then measured the height of the lather formed. Emily's results showed that water sample **A** produced 2 cm of lather, whereas samples **B** and **C** produced no lather.

   What do these results tell about the hardness of waters **A**, **B** and **C**? (2)

   (v) Explain how soap molecules remove dirt and grease from an article of clothing. (3)

   (b) Explain how vegetable oils are converted into solid fats in the process used to manufacture margarine. (2)

Titration

5. James was asked to find out the solubility of calcium hydroxide in water. He shook excess calcium hydroxide with water in a large, stoppered flask and then left it overnight to settle. He then filtered the mixture to remove the undissolved solid.

James then analysed the solution by titration. He titrated $10.00\,cm^3$ samples with $0.0500\,mol\,dm^{-3}$ hydrochloric acid, HCl, to determine how much calcium hydroxide had been dissolved. He used methyl orange as the indicator.

His results were:

Volume of calcium hydroxide solution used for each titration		$=10.00\,cm^3$
Volume of hydrochloric acid used	trial titration	$= 9.30\,cm^3$
	1st titration	$= 8.90\,cm^3$
	2nd titration	$= 9.80\,cm^3$
	3rd titration	$= 8.80\,cm^3$

(a) What colour change would be seen using methyl orange as an indicator? (2)

(b) James then used the results to calculate the concentration of the calcium hydroxide solution.

   (i) Which of the following is the volume of hydrochloric acid that should be used in the calculation?

   A $8.80\,cm^3$
   B $8.85\,cm^3$
   C $8.90\,cm^3$
   D $9.00\,cm^3$ (1)

   (ii) The equation for the reaction in the titration is

   $$Ca(OH)_2(aq) + 2HCl(aq) \rightarrow CaCl_2(aq) + 2H_2O(l)$$

   Write the ionic equation for the titration reaction. (2)

   (iii) James calculated the concentration of the calcium hydroxide solution to be $0.022\,mol\,dm^{-3}$. Convert this concentration into $g\,dm^{-3}$.
   [Mass of 1 mole of calcium hydroxide, $Ca(OH)_2 = 74.0\,g$] (1)

(c) Describe how James should carry out the titration, giving as much experimental detail as possible to ensure a reliable result. (6)

Homologous series

6. The graph shows the boiling points of the first ten members of the homologous series called the alkanes.

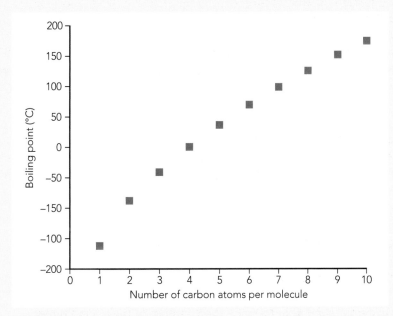

(a) (i) What is meant by the phrase **homologous series**? (2)

(ii) Use the graph to predict the boiling point of the alkane with 11 carbon atoms per molecule. (1)

(b) (i) The diagram shows the structural formula of an alkane.

Give the name of this alkane. (1)

(ii) The general formula of the alkanes is

A C_3H_8
B C_nH_n
C C_nH_{2n+2}
D C_nH_2 (1)

(c) (i) A further homologous series is the esters. Write a balanced equation to show how the ester ethyl ethanoate, $CH_3COOC_2H_5$, can be made from ethanol and ethanoic acid. (3)

(ii) You are given a sample of two different gases. They are both colourless. One is an alkane and one is an alkene. How could you distinguish between the two gases? (3)

Making copper chloride crystals

7. Carlos and Diana were asked to make copper chloride crystals from copper carbonate and dilute hydrochloric acid. The equation for the reaction is

$$CuCO_3(s) \ + \ 2HCl(aq) \ \rightarrow \ CuCl_2(aq) \ + \ H_2O(l) \ + \ CO_2(g)$$

(a) They collected a beaker of acid, but were unsure if it was hydrochloric acid or sulfuric acid. Since both substances are acids, the students decided to test for the anions present.

   (i) Carlos tested for the presence of chloride ions, Cl^-.
      What test could Carlos do to show the presence of chloride ions? (3)

   (ii) Diana tested for sulfate ions, SO_4^{2-}, using barium chloride solution which contains barium ions, Ba^{2+}. A white precipitate of barium sulfate would form if sulfate ions were present. Write the ionic equation for the reaction. (2)

(b) Carlos and Diana were aiming to produce 0.05 moles of copper chloride.
   What mass of copper chloride is this?
   [Formula mass of copper chloride, $CuCl_2$ = 134.5] (1)

(c) Carlos and Diana wrote out their plan to make their sample of pure, dry copper chloride crystals:
   1 Pour some hydrochloric acid into a beaker.
   2 Weigh out 0.05 moles of copper carbonate.
   3 Add this to the acid.
   4 Stir until all the solid reacted.
   5 Add more acid if necessary.
   6 Pour the mixture into an evaporating basin and heat on a tripod and gauze using a roaring Bunsen burner flame.
   7 Take the copper chloride out of the evaporating basin and weigh it.

   The plan contains some errors. Describe how these errors would affect the final result. (6)

Electrolysis of ionic compounds

8. This apparatus is used to electrolyse lead bromide.

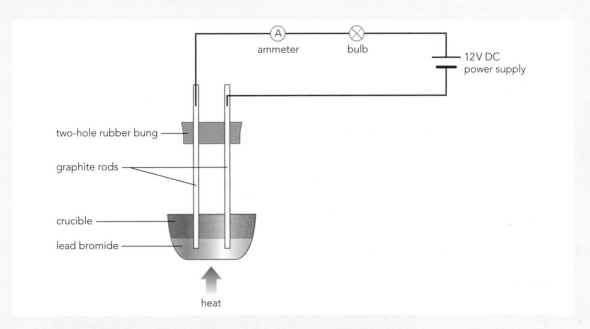

(a) The graphite rods are

    A cathodes
    B electrodes
    C electrolytes
    D electrons   (1)

(b) The bulb lights up only after the Bunsen burner has been lit. Explain why.   (2)

(c) What is produced at the cathode and at the anode in the electrolysis of lead bromide?

	Cathode	Anode
A	bromine	lead
B	bromine	oxygen
C	hydrogen	lead
D	lead	bromine

(1)

(d) When molten sodium chloride is electrolysed, sodium is produced at the cathode.

$$Na^+ + e^- \rightarrow Na$$

    (i) Why is this process called reduction?   (1)

    (ii) Give a use for sodium.   (1)

    (iii)In the same process, chlorine is produced from chloride ions, Cl^-.
         Write the half equation for this reaction.   (2)

Copper

9. The first modern Olympic Games was in Athens in 1896. Athletes who came first were awarded a silver medal, and those who came second got a copper medal.

(a) Copper can be extracted from copper compounds. One copper compound is copper sulfate, $CuSO_4$.

Copper sulfate is made of copper ions and sulfate ions.
What is the formula of a copper ion? (1)

(b) (i) In a test for copper ions, Julia adds sodium hydroxide solution to a solution containing copper ions. What can be *seen* when this reaction occurs? (2)

(ii) This test for copper ions is a qualitative test.
State why the test Julia did is a *qualitative test*. (1)

(iii) Complete the ionic equation for this reaction.

_____ + _____ OH^- → _____ (2)

*(c) In electrical circuits very pure copper is needed to make wires. Explain how impure copper can be purified using electrolysis. You may use equations for the reactions at the electrodes. (6)

Ethanol

10. This apparatus can be used to separate ethanol from a fermentation mixture.

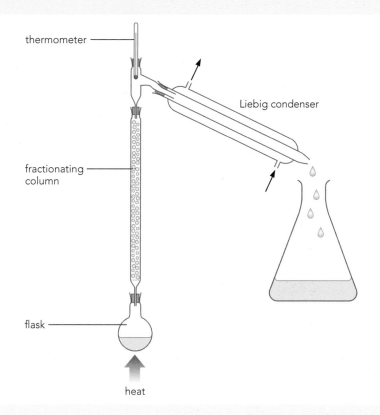

(a) Explain how ethanol is made from a carbohydrate in the process of fermentation. (3)

(b) Give the name of the process used to separate ethanol after fermentation, using the apparatus above. (1)

(c) Explain a safety precaution that should be used when carrying out the separation of ethanol from the fermentation mixture. (2)

*(d) Ethanol can be manufactured by the fermentation of carbohydrates or by the reaction of ethene with steam. Evaluate these two methods of manufacturing ethanol, giving advantages and disadvantages. (6)

Here are three student answers to the following question. Read the answers together with the examiner comments around and after them.

| Question | Passing electricity through sodium chloride | Grade | D–A* |

When electricity is passed through sodium chloride, the results depend on whether it is solid, liquid or in solution. Explain, in each case, the products formed, if any, and how they are formed. Illustrate your answer with suitable equations. (6)

Student answer 1 — Extract typical of a level ① answer

The products formed are given for the solid and liquid sodium chloride, but the question also asks what happens in solution.

Examiners will be looking for good English in your answer.

> When electricity is passed through solid sodium chloride, nothing happens because it dosent conduct. When electricity is passed through liquid sodium chloride, sodium is formed at the cathode and chloride is formed at the anode. This is 'cos metals form at the cathode and non-metals form at the anode.

Be careful – chloride ions do collect at the anode, but they lose electrons to form chlorine gas, which is given off.

Explain why these are the products with liquid sodium chloride.

Examiner summary
This answer includes basic statements about what happens during the electrolysis of molten sodium chloride. However, there is nothing about what happens if you pass electricity through sodium chloride solution, and there are no equations for the reactions involved. It also states that solid sodium chloride would not form any products. To improve the answer, you would need to explain why not.

Student answer 2 — Extract typical of a level ② answer

A good description of how the ions form the products at the electrodes.

One of the ions is wrongly named and oxygen is not formed. Explain why different products form in electrolysis of the solution compared to electrolysis of molten NaCl.

> When electricity is passed through solid NaCl, nothing happens. When electricity is passed through NaCl liquid, sodium forms at the cathode because it's a metal and chlorine forms at the anode. At the cathode, the sodium ions pick up electrons to form sodium atoms and at the anode chloride ions lose electrons to form chlorine. In the electrolysis of sodium chloride solution, hydrogen forms at the cathode and chlorine forms at the anode. The water contains hydrogen and oxide ions, which form hydrogen and oxygen.

It would be useful to say why nothing happened.

This is good: it correctly identifies the products formed during electrolysis of molten sodium chloride.

Examiner summary
This answer explains clearly what happens for both molten sodium chloride and for the solution. It also gives the correct products, However, be careful to avoid the common mistake of thinking that oxide ions are found in water and that they form oxygen. In fact water separates into hydrogen ions and hydroxide (OH^-) ions and the hydrogen formed at the cathode is from the discharge of the hydrogen ions. To improve the answer further, electrode reactions could be included.

Solid sodium chloride does not conduct electricity as its ions are not free to move, so nothing happens. When electrolysis of liquid sodium chloride happens, sodium collects at the cathode and chlorine forms at the anode. The sodium is a grey metal and the chlorine is a green gas.

Sodium ions are attracted to the cathode:

$$Na^+ + e^- \rightarrow Na$$

Sodium ions pick up electrons to form sodium atoms. At the anode, chloride ions form chlorine atoms

$$2\,Cl^- \rightarrow Cl_2 + 2\,e^-$$

When sodium chloride solution is electrolysed, hydrogen gas forms at the cathode and chlorine at the anode. The hydrogen comes from the water in the solution.

$$H_2O \rightarrow H^+ + OH^-$$

$$2\,H^+ + 2\,e^- \rightarrow H_2$$

The sodium ions and hydrogen ions stay in solution.

> **Good** – this is the correct explanation for solid sodium chloride.

> This is a good account of the electrolysis of molten sodium chloride, with the correct equations.

> This is very good, but misses out *why* hydrogen is discharged at the cathode.

Examiner summary

This answer explains the effect of electricity on the sodium chloride in the different situations very well. It includes equations for the electrode reactions. Although the explanation is not perfect for the electrolysis of sodium chloride solution, the overall answer is one that would achieve a high level. Knowing the correct equations for the electrode reactions will always help to produce a good answer of this type.

ResultsPlus

Move from level ① to level ②

To progress to Level 2, make sure you have answered all parts of the question. Give information about the electrolysis of sodium chloride in solution as well as electrolysis of the molten salt.

Move from level ② to level ③

To progress to Level 3, include equations to explain what happens at the anode and cathode. It would also be useful to give an explanation of why solid sodium chloride does not conduct electricity.

ResultsPlus
Build Better Answers

Here are three student answers to the following question. Read the answers together with the examiner comments around and after them.

Question	The Haber process	Grade	D–A*

In industry, ammonia is formed by the Haber process.

$$N_2(g) + 3\,H_2(g) \rightleftharpoons 2\,NH_3(g)$$

The reaction is exothermic. In industry, optimum conditions of temperature, pressure and use of a catalyst allow the amount of ammonia in the equilibrium mixture to achieve an acceptable yield. Explain how at least two of these conditions allow an acceptable yield to be achieved. (6)

Student answer 1 — Extract typical of a level ① answer

Careful – the rate of ammonia formation increases with temperature, but the yield decreases.

Good – yield does increase as pressure increases.

> More ammonia gets formed when it is hot. Tempretuare used is 450 degrees which is very hot. When the pressure is high then more ammonia gets formed. The pressure used is 200.

Examiners will expect to see words like temperature spelled correctly.

Put in units when you give reaction conditions.

Examiner summary

This answer gives a brief outline of two of the three reaction conditions, as the question asks. The temperature and pressure values given are valid, although no unit is given for the pressure. However, the effect of temperature on the Haber process is not explained correctly. Because the forward reaction is exothermic, the back reaction is favoured as temperature is increased. This causes the yield to decrease at higher temperatures.

Student answer 2 — Extract typical of a level ② answer

Good explanation for why increasing the pressure give a better yield.

True, but this does not answer the question about achieving optimum yield. Catalysts affect the rate, but not the yield, of a reaction.

> The optimum conditions for the Haber process are temperature = 400 °C, pressure = 150 atmospheres, catalyst = iron lumps. There are 4 molecules on the reactant side and only 2 on the product side. This means that if a high pressure is used (150 atmospheres pressure), the reaction is forced to go from the left to the right which means that the amount of ammonia formed is high. The catalyst used is iron. The iron speeds up the reaction and so the amount produced is higher. The iron is in small lumps so it has a bigger surface area and the reaction is faster.

Conditions given are mostly correct, although the pressure used is normally 200 – 250 atmospheres.

The catalyst will speed up the rate, but it has no effect on the amount of product (yield).

Examiner summary

This answer gives approximately correct optimum conditions for the Haber process, and there is a good explanation of why increased pressure increases yield. However it does not mention the disadvantages of using high pressure (i.e. high cost). The role of the catalyst is explained well, but the answer is incorrect in saying that the catalyst increases the yield.

Student answer 3 | **Extract typical of a level ③ answer**

> A good explanation of why the particular temperature is used in terms of yield and rate.

> A good explanation of why the high pressures are used.

The temperature used for the Haber process is 450 °C and the pressure used is 200–250 atmospheres. These conditions are chosen because :-
At a high temperature, the reverse reaction would happen because the reaction is exothermic. But the reaction has to be fast enough for the yield to be acceptable. A lower temperature would mean a bigger yield but the reaction happens very slowly.
The pressure used is about 150–200 atmospheres because a high pressure would give a higher yield this is because there are more molecules on the left than on the right of the equation. But if the pressure is too high, it gets very expensive to build a container that won't burst open. This is why only 150–200 atmospheres is used.

> Two correct conditions have been given.

> Good – an explanation of why higher pressures are not used.

Examiner summary

This answer includes a good explanation of both pressure and temperature and their effects on both the rate and yield of the reaction. Although nothing is said about a catalyst, remember that the question only asked for two from three factors, so this is enough for a level 3 answer.

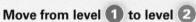 ResultsPlus

Move from level ① to level ②

To progress to level 2, include an explanation of why more ammonia is formed at higher pressures. You also need to be clear that an increase in temperature *decreases* yield. However, a fairly high temperature is needed for the reaction to happen quickly enough.

Giving a full explanation of one of the conditions helps to produce a better answer as well as relating the amount produced (the yield) to the optimum conditions being used. For pressure, increasing pressure increases the yield but using too high a pressure is expensive and potentially dangerous. Remember to use good English with correct spellings.

Move from level ② to level ③

To progress to level 3, include an explanation of why the pressure used is a compromise between increased yield and increased cost. Make clear that the catalyst speeds up the *rate* of the reaction but does not affect the yield.

Give a full explanation of why two optimum conditions are used. Remember that with increasing temperature, yield of product decreases for exothermic reactions as the reaction that absorbs the heat energy is the back reaction. To help speed up the rate of forming the product a catalyst (iron) is used, but this has no effect on the yield.
Remember to make accurate and good use of technical terms that will aid your answer.

ResultsPlus
Build Better Answers

Here are three student answers to the following question. Read the answers together with the examiner comments around and after them.

Question	Ions present in a salt	Grade	D–A*

Your teacher gives you three salts and asks you to carry out tests to show the ions present in *one* of the salts.
The three salts you are given are: copper bromide, iron(II) iodide and iron(III) chloride.
Explain, using relevant tests and equations where necessary, how you would confirm the ions present in *one* of these salts. (6)

Student answer 1 — Extract typical of a level ① answer

Most copper salt solutions are blue – but a blue *precipitate* forms

The correct chemical has been added, but the result is wrong.

> Salt chosen: copper bromine
>
> Description: Add sodium hydroxide and it goes blue. Add silver nitrate and it goes white.

It is very important to spell the names of chemicals correctly, especially if they are given in the question.

Examiner summary
Remember that you must dissolve solid salts before these tests are carried out. The answer has given two tests (one for the cation and one for the anion), and it is a pity that it has not been said which is for copper ions and which for bromide ions. The results should be given in detail – when sodium hydroxide solution is added, a blue precipitate is formed. When silver nitrate solution is used, nitric acid should be added first. The result in this case is a cream precipitate. Try to give equations – word equations can be used.

Student answer 2 — Extract typical of a level ② answer

A well-described test, but the precipitate colour for Fe(III), not Fe(II), has been given

> Salt chosen: iron(II) iodide
>
> Description: To test for the iron add sodium hydroxide and you get a brown precipitate. $Fe^{2+} + OH \rightarrow Fe(OH)$. To test for the iodide, add silver nitrate and you get a yellow precipitate.

Don't forget to add nitric acid before using silver nitrate

A good try at an equation, but the hydroxide ion needs a charge and the formula for iron(II) hydroxide is incorrect

Examiner summary
The salt should be made into a solution before the tests. The answer has some good detail, but has errors in each test. The test for iron(II) has been described but the precipitate colour for iron(III) has been given, and the equation is not fully correct. Apart from missing the nitric acid, the test for bromide ions is correct, although no equation has been given for this.

Salt chosen: iron(III) chloride.

Description: Make a solution of the iron(III) chloride. To the first part of the solution, add sodium hydroxide solution. A brown precipitate of iron(III) hydroxide is formed. $Fe^{3+} + OH^- \rightarrow Fe(OH)_3$. To the second part of the solution add acid and silver nitrate solution. A white precipitate forms. $Ag^+ + Cl^- \rightarrow AgCl$

This test is well described.

Nitric acid must be used in this test.

Don't forget to balance your equations.

This is a correct ionic equation for the reaction.

Examiner summary

This is a very good attempt at an answer. For the first test, it gives a detailed description (including saying what the precipitate is) and an equation. It would be better if the equation was balanced. Full or ionic equations could have been used. In the test for halide ions, the acid must be specified as nitric acid; hydrochloric acid contains chloride ions and would cause a white precipitate. Apart from this, it describes the test well. The answer has correct spelling, punctuation and grammar and is clearly expressed.

 ResultsPlus

Move from level ① to level ②

In ion tests, remember to dissolve your solid first. Give a test for the cation and a test for the anion; explain which test is which. Observations should be described properly. If you say 'blue', do you mean a blue precipitate, a blue liquid or a blue solution? It might help to think:

- how you prepare the sample
- what you add
- what you observe
- try to give equations.

Move from level ② to level ③

An ionic compound has a cation and an anion. Describe carefully each test, and give the result clearly. Examiners are very pleased when precipitates are identified. It's important that you learn these tests, particularly the ones with similar results e.g. the tests for halide ions. Give equations for each test. Full or ionic equations can be given, but make sure that these are balanced.

Here are three student answers to the following question. Read the answers together with the examiner comments around and after them.

| Question | Titration | Grade | D–A* |

Describe, in detail, how a titration between dilute hydrochloric acid and sodium hydroxide solution should be carried out.

In your answer you should refer to the equipment and the experimental technique involved. (6)

Student answer 1 — Extract typical of a level ① answer

This is wrong – universal indicator is not suitable for titrations.

> Put the acid in a beaker. Add sodium hydroxide to the burette. Add it untill the universal indicator goes green. Repeat the titration to get an average.

Good – correct identification of apparatus.

It is correct that the titration should be repeated, but this is to get concordant results, not to get an average.

Examiner summary

The basic idea of adding alkali to the acid until neutralisation is correct. However, many points of technique have been left out, e.g. how to measure out the acid. An indicator with a colour change is mentioned, but universal indicator should never be used in a titration as it gives a range of colours, not a sharp change.

Student answer 2 — Extract typical of a level ② answer

It would be good to name the indicator and give the correct colour here.

> Measure out the acid using a pipette. Fill the burette with alkali. Add indicator. Add the alkali slowly and swirl. Stop when the indicator changes colour. Do the experiment until the results are the same.

Both the main pieces of apparatus are correctly identified.

Be careful here – the results do not have to be identical, just concordant

Examiner summary

This answer gives more detail and names the pipette and burette (both spelt correctly). Unfortunately, the indicator hasn't been named. An easy one to remember the colour change is phenolphthalein – but not so easy to spell! The alkali only needs to be added slowly near the end. Remember to describe how many titrations need to be carried out – enough to get concordant results (results that are close enough to each other).

Student answer 3 | **Extract typical of a level ③ answer**

It is correct that you should go slowly at the end of a titration.

Pipette 25 cm³ acid into a flask and put on a white tile. Add a few drops of phenolthalein. Fill the burette with alkali. Add the alkali and swirl. Add slowly towards the end, and stop when the mixture goes pink. Repeat the titration until several similar results are obtained.

A good amount of detail has been included.

The correct colour change is given for the indicator named (although the indicator is spelt incorrectly).

This explains why the experiment should be repeated – the correct term is 'concordant results'.

Examiner summary

This is a good answer with lots of detail, including the measuring out of the acid. Names of the equipment are given and a correct indicator is named with the colour it turns at the end. The answer is expressed clearly and spelt correctly, except for the indicator's name.

ResultsPlus

Move from level ① to level ②

A titration has lots of steps, so try to think through each one. Could someone carry out the experiment using your description? You might find it helpful to list them using bullet points. Remember to name the apparatus used for each step. Learn an indicator so that you can name it with the colour change.

Move from level ② to level ③

To move to level 3, each step in the titration needs to be described in detail with the correct apparatus and technique. Don't forget the use of a pipette to measure out acid and a white tile to help you see the colour change. Learn the colour change for either methyl orange or phenolphthalein. Many answers confuse the reason for repeating the titration, so explain why, using the word 'concordant'.

ResultsPlus

About 80% of ammonia manufactured is used to make artificial fertilisers. Give an advantage and a disadvantage of using artificial fertilisers to grow food crops. (2)

▲ **Correct answer:** Any advantage, such as replacing nutrients or improving crop yield (1), and any suitable disadvantage, such as causing water pollution. (1)

■ Student's lost marks for answers such as:
- Giving 'cheaper' as an advantage (food grown using fertilisers is often cheaper than organic food, but the fertilisers themselves are not cheaper than organic fertilisers).
- Saying it was not organic as a disadvantage (this doesn't really explain anything).
- Saying that the fertiliser would poison the crop, or put chemicals into the food (*all* food is made of chemicals!)
- Saying that they damage the environment (this answer is too vague; you would need to say *how* they damage the environment).

ResultsPlus

Sodium chloride conducts electricity when it is molten. Explain why. (1)

 Correct answer: The ions can move when it is a liquid.

■ Only a few students got this mark. Wrong answers included students writing about electrons moving, about atoms being free to move, about sodium being a metal, or just saying that is must be a liquid to work.

ResultsPlus

A small sample of a brown substance was reacted with an acid to form a solution. This solution contains iron(III) ions, Fe^{3+}. Excess sodium hydroxide solution was added to the solution. Describe what would be seen when the sodium hydroxide solution was added. (2)

▲ **Correct answer:** A brown precipitate (1 mark for the colour, 1 mark for stating that a precipitate forms).

● Most students scored both marks. However, several gave the wrong colour and some gave the name of the compound formed. For these questions, keep the descriptions of colours simple and try not to make it complicated.

ResultsPlus

A nylon airbag in a car has a volume of $60 \, dm^3$ Calculate the number of moles of nitrogen, N_2, in $60 \, dm^3$ of the gas at room temperature and atmospheric pressure. (1) [1 mol of any gas occupies $24 \, dm^3$ at room temperature and atmospheric pressure]

▲ **Correct answer:** $60/24 = 2.5$ moles

■ Less than half of the students carried out this calculation correctly. Many made the mistake of using the atomic mass of nitrogen instead. Remember the molar volume of a gas was given for a reason – information like this will always be given and will need to be used in a calculation. Some students just gave a simple numerical answer with no working shown. Remember to always show your working.

Exam question report

The diagrams show glasses containing four different alcoholic drinks. Which glass actually contains the most ethanol? (1)

	A	B	C	D
alcoholic drink	wine	whisky	beer	port
volume of drink (cm³)	125	25	250	50
ethanol in drink (%)	10	40	4	20

Answer: The correct answer is A.

How students answered

0 marks

1 mark

Most students who got this wrong answered B (as whisky has the highest percentage of alcohol). They forgot to take into account the volume of drink in each glass.

Glass A had the most alcohol (10% of 125 cm³ is 12.5 cm³ alcohol). Each of the other drinks has 10 cm³ of alcohol.

ResultsPlus

In the Haber process, nitrogen reacts with hydrogen to make ammonia. The equation for the reaction is shown below.

$N_2(g) + 3H_2(g) \rightleftharpoons 2NH_3(g)$

a) Nitrogen and hydrogen are mixed and left under suitable conditions, until no further change in the amount of each substance occurs. What substances will be present in the final mixture? Explain your answer. (2)

 As there are two marks, you need to make two good points. A good answer would be: Hydrogen, nitrogen and ammonia (1) because the reaction is going both ways at the same time (1).

Many students included compounds such as water, carbon dioxide, nitrates, etc. This may show that they had not read the question, or that they had not revised reversible reactions!

b) The Haber process is carried out at 400 °C and 200 atm. How would the equilibrium amount of ammonia change if the pressure were increased? Explain your answer. (2)

Again, two points are needed. A good answer would be: More ammonia would be produced (1) because higher pressure favours the fewer molecules on the right hand side of the equation (1).

Many students gained one mark for saying 'more ammonia', but could not explain their answer. Others seemed to assume that 200 atmospheres was the ideal pressure for the reaction, and so any change would reduce the yield.

ResultsPlus

In the electrolysis of brine, chloride ions are converted to chlorine. Write the balanced half equation for the conversion of chloride ions, Cl⁻, into chlorine. (2)

 Correct answer: $2Cl^- \rightarrow Cl_2 + 2e^-$

Many students score badly on this type of question. Half equations will always involve electrons on one side or the other. In this case, chloride ions, Cl⁻, need to lose electrons to form chlorine molecules, Cl₂.

Physics 3
Applications of physics

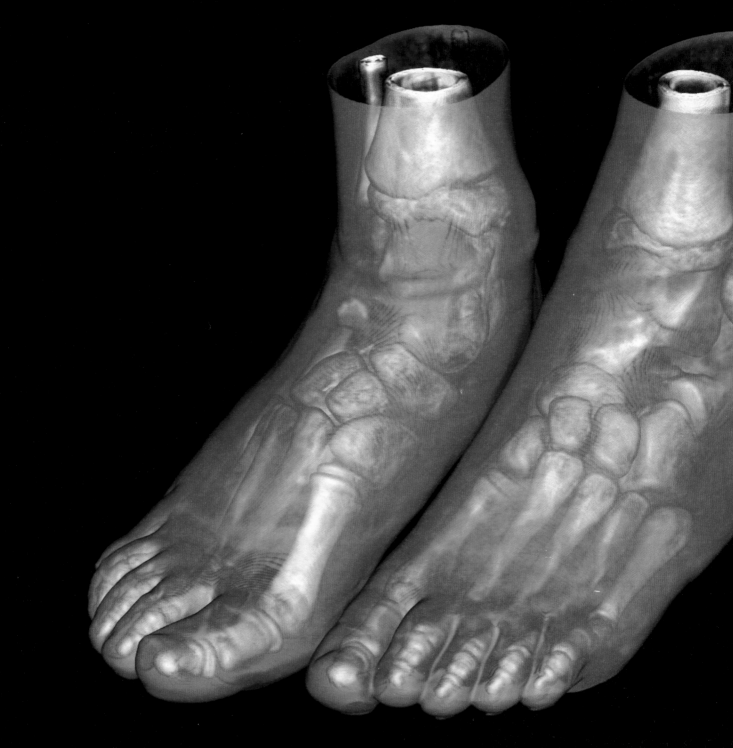

These feet are from a 'CT scan', which shows the skin, bones and ligaments (cords of tissue that connect bones to one another). A computer builds the 3D image using many scans produced using a source of X-rays. Developments in scanning have allowed scientists to understand more about how our bodies work, to quickly and accurately diagnose patients who are ill and to develop better treatments.

In this unit you will learn more about the use of different types of radiation in the treatment and detection of problems within our bodies. You will also find out about how radioactive isotopes, for use in some treatments for cancer, are produced in particle accelerators and how these machines are also being used to help scientists find out more about atoms.

Learning Outcomes

Throughout the unit you will be asked to:

    0.1 Use equations given in this unit, or in a given alternate form

  H *0.2* Use and rearrange equations given in this unit

    0.3 Demonstrate an understanding of which units are required in equations

How is radiation used in medicine?

The 'Interstellar Light Collector' in Arizona, USA, uses mirrors to gather moonlight into one spot. People who are hoping to be cured of various conditions from cancer to eczema stand in that spot to absorb the light. One user said: 'As I was standing there, I could feel myself becoming happier'. There is no scientific proof that it works.

A *The 'Interstellar Light Collector'*

Visible light is an example of **radiation** – energy carried by waves or particles from a source. Light and other types of radiation are used to identify and treat medical problems.

Radiation for diagnosis

In order to reach a **diagnosis**, doctors may use radiation to produce images that show features inside the body. Some methods are shown in Figure B.

> **1** Which of the techniques in Figure B seems to be the odd one out? Explain your answer.

Radiation detected	How it forms an image	Where it is used
Visible light	Light reflects off features to form an image	**Endoscopes**
X-rays	X-rays are absorbed by some materials inside the body but not others. A negative image is produced	X-ray photography and **CAT scanners**
Gamma rays	The movement of substances producing gamma rays is detected and the positions shown on a screen	PET scanners
Ultrasound	High-frequency sound waves reflect off features inside the body to form an image	Ultrasound scanners

B *Some types of radiation used in medical diagnosis.*

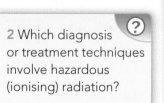

Skills spotlight

New technology has benefits as well as risks. Suggest a benefit and a risk of using ionising radiation to create images of the inside of the body.

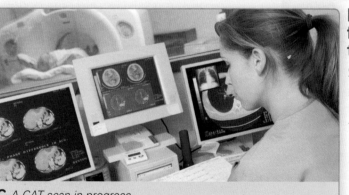

C *A CAT scan in progress*

> **2** Which diagnosis or treatment techniques involve hazardous (ionising) radiation?

Radiation for medical treatments

Some types of radiation are **ionising** – they create reactive ions in the body, which can cause damage. Gamma rays and X-rays are ionising and can be used to damage and destroy cancer cells.

Various types of **non-ionising radiation** (e.g. light, ultrasound) are also used in treatments. Lasers are used in eye surgery to correct vision defects and absorption of ultrasound is used to treat swollen tissues.

The **intensity** of the radiation decreases further away from the source. Different cancer tumours are treated with different intensities of gamma radiation and so doctors place the source at different distances from the tumour. Intensity is also affected by the **medium** the radiation is travelling through. The denser the medium, the weaker the radiation gets.

D The lasers used in eye surgery are light waves.

3 Lucy is pregnant and goes into hospital for an ultrasound scan. Why is the scan not done using X-rays?

4 Draw a table to show how the different types of radiation you have read about are used to treat medical conditions.

H

Intensity is the power of the incoming beam of radiation (called the **incident** radiation) divided by the area over which it is spread:

$$\text{Intensity} = \frac{\text{power of incident radiation}}{\text{area}}$$

$$I = \frac{P}{A}$$

Power is measured in watts (W) and the standard unit of area is metres squared (m^2), so intensity will be in watts per square metre (W/m^2).

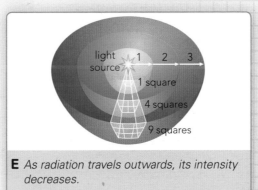

E As radiation travels outwards, its intensity decreases.

Maths skills

Intensity is another example of a **compound measure** and therefore its units are determined by the units used in the calculation. The standard unit of intensity is watts per square metre (W/m^2) so you have to make sure you use the units watts and metres in your calculation.

H 5 Calculate the intensity of a 100 W beam of radiation spread over an area of 5 cm^2.

H 6 Calculate the intensity of a laser pointer with a power output of 1.0×10^{-3} W (1 mW) on a board if the dot is a square measuring 1 mm by 1 mm.

H 7 If the intensity of a torch's beam is 6 W/m^2 over an area of 4 m^2, what was the power output of the bulb?

8 Compare the techniques of using ultrasound and X-rays to form an image of a broken bone in the body.

Learning Outcomes

1.1 Demonstrate an understanding of the methods that medical physicists can employ to help doctors solve medical problems, including: a CAT scans b ultrasounds c endoscopes d ionising and non-ionising radiation

1.2 Use the word 'radiation' to describe any form of energy originating from a source, including both waves and particles

1.3 Demonstrate an understanding that the intensity of radiation will decrease with distance from a source and according to the nature of the medium through which it is travelling

H 1.4 Use the equation: $\text{intensity} = \dfrac{\text{power of incident radiation}}{\text{area}}$ $I = \dfrac{P}{A}$

HSW 12 Describe the benefits, drawbacks and risks of using new scientific and technological developments

There are tiny muscles inside the eye – what are they there for?

How do our eyes work?

Lasers can be used to create spectacular outdoor shows that can be seen by huge numbers of people across a large area. This is because the laser beams have a very high intensity and so can travel long distances.

You can see laser light shows because the light enters your eyes through the **pupils**. The light rays pass through the **cornea** and the **lens** before reaching the **retina** at the back of the eye. The image formed is converted into electrical impulses by cells in the retina and neurones carry the impulses to the brain, which interprets them. The amount of light reaching the retina is controlled by the **iris**, which makes the pupil larger or smaller.

1 Find the iris and the pupil on Figure B. Draw a picture of what they look like if you are looking at the eye from the front.

A *Laser light can be used to produce amazing and rapidly changing effects.*

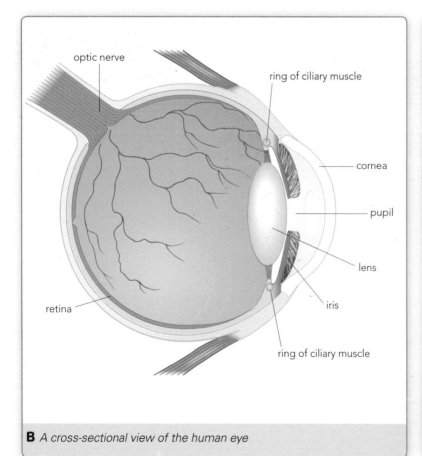

B *A cross-sectional view of the human eye*

optic nerve
ring of ciliary muscle
cornea
pupil
lens
iris
ring of ciliary muscle
retina

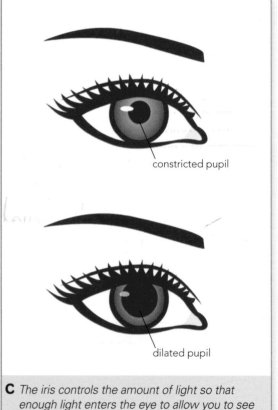

constricted pupil

dilated pupil

C *The iris controls the amount of light so that enough light enters the eye to allow you to see but not so much that the light damages the retina.*

To form a sharp image on the retina, light rays must **converge** on the retina. This means the path of the rays has to be changed by the eye. This bending, or **refracting**, is done partly by the cornea and partly by the lens. If the object being viewed is nearer or further away, the shape of the lens is changed by the **ciliary muscles** in order to keep the image in focus on the retina.

There is no limit to how far away you can focus on distant objects. Your **far point** is at infinity. The closest you can see an un-blurred image is your **near point**. On average this is about 25cm in adults.

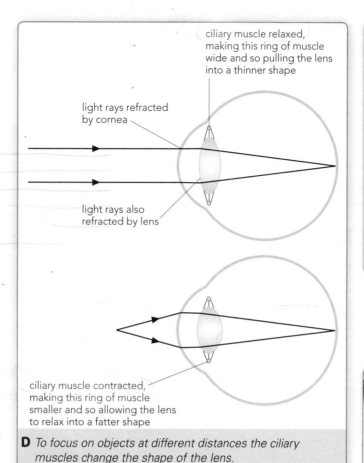

ciliary muscle relaxed, making this ring of muscle wide and so pulling the lens into a thinner shape

light rays refracted by cornea

light rays also refracted by lens

ciliary muscle contracted, making this ring of muscle smaller and so allowing the lens to relax into a fatter shape

D To focus on objects at different distances the ciliary muscles change the shape of the lens.

2 How could you measure the position of your near point?

3 Explain why muscles in the eye have to work hard when you're looking at something near to you.

4 Why might your eyes feel tired after you've been examining small print for a while?

Skills spotlight

What models or ideas about how light behaves help to explain how the eye works?

5 Explain the role of the ciliary muscles in enabling someone to focus on objects nearer to and further away from them.

6 Look at the cat's eyes in Figure E. Compare the iris with that of a human, referring to shape and function.

7 Write a paragraph explaining what happens to light when it enters the eye. Make sure you are explaining as well as describing what happens.

E The iris in a cat's eye is a different shape to that in a human eye but it does the same job.

ResultsPlus
Watch Out!

Students have difficulty when writing about the iris and the pupil. They often forget that it is the iris that causes the size of the pupil to change. When the iris becomes smaller the pupil widens and lets in more light.

Learning Outcomes

1.10 Identify the following features in a diagram of the eye – cornea, iris, pupil, lens, retina, ciliary muscles

1.11 Demonstrate an understanding that light is focused on the retina by the action of the lens and cornea

1.12 Recall that the average adult human eye has a near point at about 25cm and a far point at infinity

HSW **3** Describe how phenomena are explained using scientific models

>>>>>>>>>>>>>>>>>>>> How can a laser beam be used to correct someone's vision?

How can sight be short or long?

This is the cat with *purrfect* vision. Almost blind moggie Ernest had his life transformed when his thoughtful owner got him a set of contact lenses.

A *Ernest having a contact lens fitted.*

(?)

1 Why is it important that the rays meet on the retina?

2 Why must the lens in the eye be flexible?

The lens in a human eye changes shape in order to help focus on objects that are at different distances. The ciliary muscles contract to make the lens shorter and fatter (for near objects) or relax to give a thinner lens (for far objects) so that rays meet on the retina.

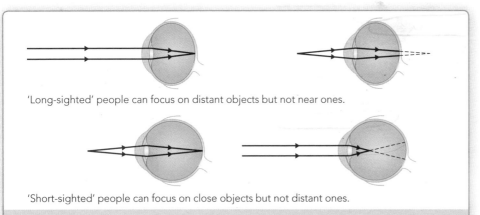

'Long-sighted' people can focus on distant objects but not near ones.

'Short-sighted' people can focus on close objects but not distant ones.

B *The difference between long-sightedness and short-sightedness*

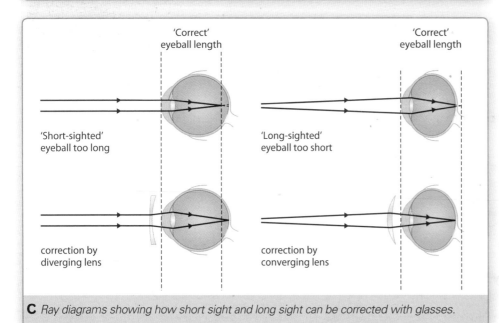

'Correct' eyeball length

'Correct' eyeball length

'Short-sighted' eyeball too long

'Long-sighted' eyeball too short

correction by diverging lens

correction by converging lens

C *Ray diagrams showing how short sight and long sight can be corrected with glasses.*

If someone has **short sight** then objects a *short* distance away are clear but far-away objects are blurred. This is caused either by the eyeball being too long or by the cornea being curved too sharply. Rays of light from a distant object are focused in front of the retina.

In **long sight,** *distant* objects are clear but near objects are not. This might be caused by the eyeball being too short or the lens not being thick enough or not curved enough. The ciliary muscles are taut but the lens can't bend the light enough.

Correcting vision

Short sight can be corrected by wearing glasses with **diverging lenses**. This type of lens bends the incoming rays apart so that the cornea and lens can focus the rays correctly onto the retina. Long sight can be corrected by wearing glasses with **converging lenses**. A converging lens refracts the rays more, so that they meet on the retina.

An alternative is contact lenses, placed on the front of the cornea. Some are softer than others, but all allow oxygen to permeate to the eye. To prevent infections it is important that the lenses are cleaned regularly, although some are now disposable.

D *These swimming goggles also correct vision.*

Laser correction uses a finely controlled laser beam to reshape the front of the cornea.

A laser can make precise incisions in tissue without damaging the surrounding area. By permanently altering the shape of the cornea, the point at which light rays meet inside the eye can be changed.

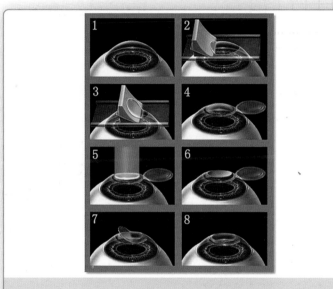

H

E *In this form of laser eye surgery a flap of tissue from the front of the cornea is removed before the cornea is reshaped and the flap replaced.*

3 Why might someone suspect that they were short-sighted?

Skills spotlight

Explanations can be developed using scientific models such as ray diagrams. What are the key features of the ray diagram models on these pages?

H 4 Explain with the use of diagrams how laser eye treatment could correct short-sightedness.

H 5 a A typical laser used in sight correction will transfer 1 mJ of energy $(1 \times 10^{-3}\,\text{J})$ in a 10 ns $(10 \times 10^{-9}\,\text{s})$ pulse. What is the power output of the laser in watts $(1\,\text{W} = 1\,\text{J/s})$?

H b If this laser beam was directed into an area 100 μm × 100 μm $(100 \times 10^{-6}\,\text{m} \times 100 \times 10^{-6}\,\text{m})$, what would the intensity of the light be?

6 Explain why some people might prefer to use contact lenses rather than glasses.

ResultsPlus
Watch Out!

Don't get confused between short and long sight. Short sight means you *can* see things clearly that are a short distance away.

Learning Outcomes

1.5 Describe the refraction of light by converging and diverging lenses

1.13 Explain the symptoms and causes of short sight and long sight (you will not be expected to draw scaled ray diagrams, but you may be asked to interpret them)

1.14 Compare and contrast treatments for short sight and long sight, including the use of:
a simple lenses b contact lenses **H** c laser correction (combined lens equation is not required, you will not be expected to draw scaled ray diagrams, but you may be asked to interpret them)

HSW *3* Describe how phenomena are explained using scientific models

P3.4 Investigating effect of object distance on image characteristics

How can lenses bend light rays to make images?

It is thought that eye glasses were first made in Pisa, in Italy around 1286. This 15th century painting is from the German School and accompanies text concerning the use of glasses.

A *An early recorded use of spectacles*

Eye glasses are made of a pair of lenses. The ones shown in the painting consisted of two converging lenses, allowing the wearer to see nearby objects clearly. **Converging** lenses **focus** light to make an **image.** As the lens has a curved surface, rays arriving at different points on the surface from an object are refracted by different amounts and will meet at the same place.

If the rays have arrived from a distant source they will be parallel and they will meet at the **focal point** of a converging lens. The distance from the lens to the focal point is called the **focal length**.

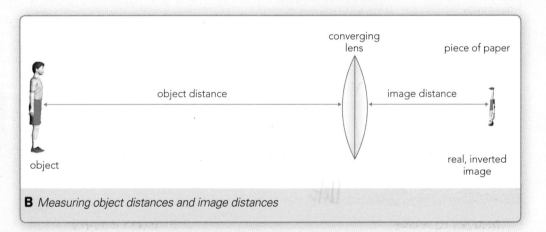

B *Measuring object distances and image distances*

Your task

You are going find out how a converging lens will change an image if the object is at different distances from the lens.

Learning Outcomes

1.8 Investigate variations of image characteristics with objects at different distances from a converging lens

ResultsPlus
Build Better Answers

When planning an investigation like this, one of the skills you will be assessed on is your ability to judge the *quality of evidence.* There are 4 marks available for this skill. Here are two extracts focusing on that skill. Other skills that you need for the practical assessment are dealt with in other lessons.

Student extract 1 — A basic response for this skill

This is a good start because the student has looked at their results to see if there is a general pattern.

> When I looked at my results I saw that one of them didn't fit in the pattern. Instead of getting smaller like the others did it was larger.

This answer is not complete because the student hasn't referred to the secondary data.

As well as saying what the anomaly is you can also suggest how to deal with it – for example you might not include it in any calculations.

Student extract 2 — A good response for this skill

The anomaly has been identified and dealt with.

> When I put the results in order according to the increasing distance from object to lens I could see the distance to the image became less. All of my results fitted this pattern and so did the results from the secondary data I was given, apart from one distance which was 52 cm. I think this should have been 5.2 cm so I ignored this when carrying out my calculations. I did this because if I had included the anomaly in my results it could have changed the calculation and made it harder to see the true result.

This section is looking at anomalies so you don't need to include a conclusion here.

The student has also explained why it is important not to include anomalies.

ResultsPlus

To access 2 marks

- Comment on the quality of the primary evidence, dealing with anomalies appropriately (if there are no anomalies in the evidence then you need to say that this is the case).
- Comment on the quality of the secondary evidence, dealing with anomalies appropriately (if there are no anomalies in the evidence then you need to say that this is the case).

To access 4 marks

- Explain any adjustments to the evidence which are needed, or explain why you have decided not to exclude evidence
- Take account of anomalies in primary and secondary evidence when processing the evidence (using all evidence if no anomalies)

How do different lenses have different powers?

Powerful lenses of conventional design are thick in the middle, and so large ones are heavy. A Fresnel lens is lighter than a conventional lens. The image isn't as sharp but this isn't a problem in lighthouses and car lamps.

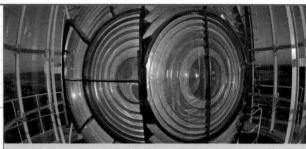

A Fresnel lenses are composed of many small lenses that work together.

> 1 What units might we use to measure focal length in?
>
> 2 What is meant by 'parallel rays'?
>
> 3 Which has the longer focal length – a gently curving lens or a more sharply curved lens? Explain why.

For a converging lens, parallel rays of light are refracted and meet at the focal point. The distance from the lens to the focal point is the focal length.

For a diverging lens, the focal point is the point from which the rays seem to be coming after passing through the lens. The focal length is the distance from the lens to this point. A more powerful diverging lens will have more sharply curved faces and cause rays to diverge more, so the focal length is shorter.

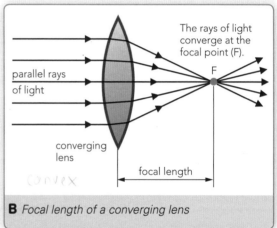

B Focal length of a converging lens

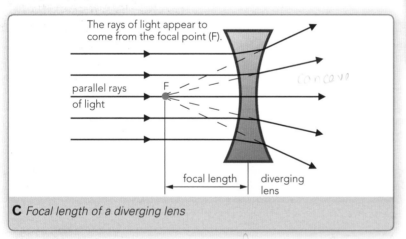

C Focal length of a diverging lens

The **power of a lens** is measured in **dioptres** and calculated from its focal length:

$$\text{Power of a lens (dioptre, D)} = \frac{1}{\text{focal length (metre, m)}}$$

A lens with a focal length of one metre has a power of one dioptre.

> 4 What is the power of a lens with a focal length of:
> a 0.1 m b 20 cm c 5 cm?
>
> H 5 The combination of lens and cornea in the human eye has a power of about 60 D. What is the focal length?

The lens equation

An image will only form at the same distance as the focal length if the incident rays are parallel. When rays from an object are not parallel the **lens equation** links the object distance u, the image distance v and the focal length f:

$$\frac{1}{f} = \frac{1}{u} + \frac{1}{v}$$

All distances are measured from the lens. The metre is often too large a unit for focal length. It is important, however, to use the same units for all variables.

A focused image from a converging lens can be shown on a screen so this is a **real image**. Real images therefore have positive image distances. Using a diverging lens, you cannot focus the image onto a screen. We can only see the image when our eyes focus the diverging rays leaving the lens. The image on the retina is a real image but the point where the rays appear to come from is described as a **virtual image**.

There is also a virtual image formed in front of the converging lens in Figure E. Virtual images cannot be focused to a point on a screen and have negative image distances.

e.g.

An object is 10 cm from a lens with a focal length of +5 cm. Where will the image be?

So $\dfrac{1}{v} = \dfrac{1}{5} - \dfrac{1}{10} = \dfrac{1}{10}$

Therefore $v = 10$ cm
Since v is positive, the image is real.

An object is 5 cm away from a converging lens with a focal length of +10 cm. Where will the image be?

So $\dfrac{1}{v} = \dfrac{1}{10} - \dfrac{1}{5} = \dfrac{-1}{10}$

$v = -10$ cm and the image is virtual.

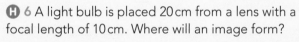

D *Images to the right of the lens are real and the distance between the image and the lens (v) is positive; those to the left of the lens are virtual and v is negative.*

Skills spotlight

H Explain how the **real is positive sign convention** enables us to predict the type of image formed by a lens.

H 6 A light bulb is placed 20 cm from a lens with a focal length of 10 cm. Where will an image form?

H 7 A pupil sits 100 cm from a converging lens with a focal length of 5 cm. Where will her image be formed?

H 8 A magnifying glass with a focal length of 5 cm is used to examine a postage stamp 3 cm away.
a Where will the image be formed?
b What indicates the image is virtual?

9 A converging lens can be used on a sunny day to focus the Sun's rays onto paper. Explain how this is possible.

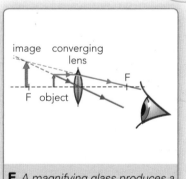

E *A magnifying glass produces a virtual image, seen in the lens.*

ResultsPlus
Watch Out!

Students often overlook the importance of the positive and negative signs in the focal lengths in questions. Be careful with positive and negative signs marked on lenses. A converging lens has a positive sign on the focal length and a diverging lens has a negative sign.

Learning Outcomes

1.5 Describe the refraction of light by converging and diverging lenses

1.6 Relate the power of a lens to its shape

1.7 Use the equation: power of lens (dioptre, D) $= \dfrac{1}{\text{focal length (metre, m)}}$

H **1.9** Use the lens equation: $\dfrac{1}{f} = \dfrac{1}{u} + \dfrac{1}{v}$

(f = focal length (m), u = object distance (m), v = image distance (m))
The use of the real is positive sign convention is preferred and will be used in the exam

HSW **11** Present information, develop an argument and draw a conclusion, using scientific, technical and mathematical language

What makes light waves change direction?

Refraction causes the bottom of the straw in Figure A to appear to be shifted. Scientists are working on materials that could reverse the appearance of the lower part of the straw. Such a material could be used to make an invisibility cloak.

A

Reflection

We can predict the path of a particular **reflected** ray from the **law of reflection**, which states that:

$$\text{angle of incidence} = \text{angle of reflection}$$

Both angles are measured between the ray and a line at right angles to the surface called the **normal**.

1 What happens to the angle of reflection if the angle of incidence increases?

2 What happens to light that hits a mirror along the normal?

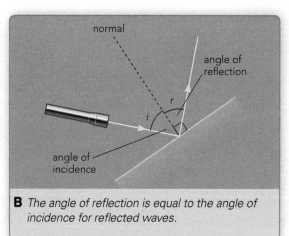

B The angle of reflection is equal to the angle of incidence for reflected waves.

Refraction

When waves enter a medium in which they travel more slowly, the wave's direction of travel changes. This is called refraction.

Rays are **refracted** *towards* the normal when they enter a medium in which they travel more slowly. Rays are refracted *away* from the normal when they enter a medium in which they travel faster.

3 In Figure C how does the angle of refraction compare with the angle of incidence?

4 Redraw Figure C to show how the diagram would be different if the boundary was between air and water. (Light travels more slowly in glass than in water.)

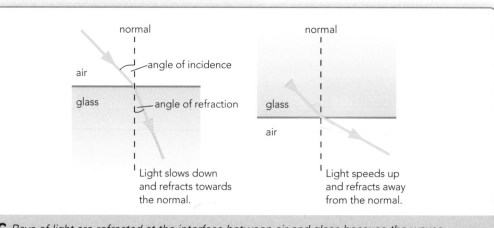

C Rays of light are refracted at the interface between air and glass because the waves change speed.

When waves enter a medium where the speed decreases, the part still moving at the higher speed catches up with the part that is slowing down. This alters the wave's direction of travel (see Figure D).

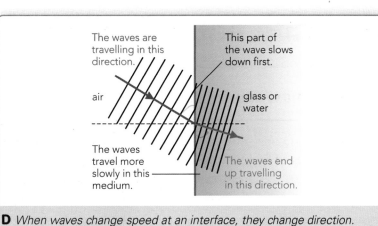

The waves are travelling in this direction.

air

glass or water

The waves travel more slowly in this medium.

This part of the wave slows down first.

The waves end up travelling in this direction.

D *When waves change speed at an interface, they change direction.*

H

Snell's law

For waves passing from one medium into another, **Snell's law** links the angle of incidence, i, and angle of refraction, r:

$$\frac{\sin i}{\sin r} = \text{constant}$$

The constant in Snell's law is related to the **refractive index**, n, of each material:

$$\frac{\sin i}{\sin r} = \frac{n_r}{n_i}$$

where n_i is the refractive index of the medium the ray is travelling from, and n_r is the refractive index of the medium the ray is travelling into.

e.g.

A light ray approaches a glass block at 30° to the normal. The refractive indices of air and glass are 1 and 1.5 respectively. At what angle will the light be refracted?

$$\frac{\sin 30}{\sin r} = \frac{1.5}{1}$$

$$\frac{0.5}{1.5} = \sin r = 0.33$$

$$\sin^{-1} 0.33 = 19.3°$$

7 A swimming pool is fitted with underwater lighting. Consider the path that light takes through the water and air into the eyes of someone standing on the side of the pool. Explain how the light is refracted, referring to its changing speed.

5 a What happens to light that approaches the boundary along the normal in Figure C?
b Would it still be true to say that the ray had been refracted?

H 6 A light ray travelling from water to air approaches the surface at 20° to the normal. If the refractive index of air is 1 and that of water is 1.33, what will the angle of refraction be?

incident medium

refractive index = n_i

refractive medium

refractive index = n_r

i

r

E *The angle of refraction depends on how different the refractive indices of the two materials are.*

Skills spotlight

In ray diagrams the arrows represent the direction energy travels away from a source. Draw two diagrams, one showing light travelling out from a source as waves and the other showing light as rays. Compare your diagrams to explain why at distances far from the source, light rays are almost parallel.

Learning Outcomes

1.15 Explain, with the aid of ray diagrams, reflection and refraction, including the law of reflection

H 1.16 Calculate critical angle using Snell's Law

1.17 Explain refraction in terms of change of speed of radiation

HSW 3 Describe how phenomena are explained using scientific models

P3.7 Total Internal Reflection in Perspex

How can light be reflected by glass and not pass through at all?

A hall of mirrors is a fairground attraction consisting of a maze of mirrors and sometimes panels of Perspex as well. Finding the way through is difficult because some of what you see is reflections of the path you're on and other parts are the path you can't yet reach.

A *A hall of mirrors or is it windows? How can you tell?*

When a ray, such as light, approaches the boundary between one medium and another it can change direction. What happens depends on the angle of the light and the speed that the light can travel at through each of the media. Imagine that the ray is travelling from a medium where it travels slower to a medium where it travels faster. If the ray is travelling at less than the **critical angle** some of it will pass into the second medium but if it is at a larger angle it will all be reflected. This is called **total internal reflection**.

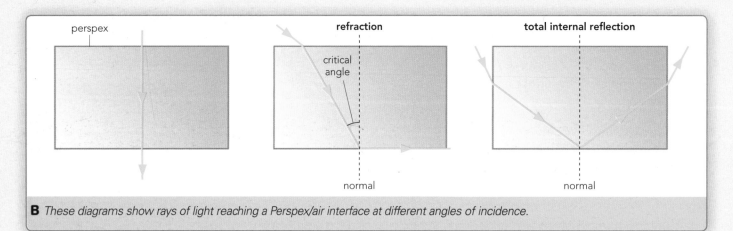

B *These diagrams show rays of light reaching a Perspex/air interface at different angles of incidence.*

Your task

You are going to plan an investigation that will allow you to find out the critical angle for Perspex.

Learning Outcomes

1.19 Investigate TIR between different media

Build Better Answers

In an investigation like this, one of the skills you will be assessed on is your ability to *write a conclusion* based on the available evidence. There are 6 marks available for this skill. Here are two extracts focusing on this skill. Other skills that you need for the practical assessment are dealt with in other lessons.

Student extract 1 | A basic response for this skill

The student hasn't linked their conclusion with the hypothesis.

> When I looked at my results I could see that when the angle of incidence got larger all of the light was reflected and none of it escaped from the block.

The conclusion is based on the evidence.

Student extract 2 | A good response for this skill

The conclusion draws on all the evidence, including the amount and angle of reflection.

> The results showed that as the angle of incidence was increased from 0° the light was refracted, passing out of the glass. As the angle of incidence increased more light was reflected until the angle of incidence was reached at 46°. At this angle the light travelled along the boundary. Beyond this, no light passed out of the glass. This supported my hypothesis that once the incident angle became greater than the critical angle there would be total internal reflection. This is because when waves reach a medium in which they can travel faster and this happens at more than the critical angle they will be completely reflected. I can see no mathematical relationship between the medium and the critical angle.

The student has referred back to their hypothesis and explained if the hypothesis is supported by the evidence or not.

The student has used their scientific knowledge and explained that light travels as waves.

 ResultsPlus

To access 2 marks

- Provide a conclusion based on all collected evidence, but do not link it to the hypothesis
- Attempt to explain the conclusion using all the collected evidence, including appropriate mathematical relationships

To access 6 marks

- Provide a conclusion which refers to the hypothesis and is based on all collected evidence and relevant scientific ideas
- Explain the conclusions using relevant scientific ideas and all the collected evidence, including appropriate mathematical relationships

P3.8 Investigating the critical angle

Is total internal reflection the same in any transparent medium?

When diamonds are found in the ground they can look like pieces of glass. Only when they have been cut and shaped do they show all their beauty. Diamonds are cut to increase the amount of total internal reflection in the gemstone. The critical angle of a diamond is very low and this means that once light enters the stone it tends to get trapped and bounce around. This makes the diamond sparkle. Diamonds are cut so that their surfaces are at the best angle to increase total internal reflection – and so make the diamond sparkle as much as possible.

Think about rays travelling through a medium and approaching the boundary with another medium in which they will travel faster. If they approach at more than a certain angle, the rays will be completely reflected; none will pass through. This is called total internal reflection. If the incident ray is greater than this critical angle all of the rays are reflected. If the incident ray is less than the critical angle some of the rays will be reflected but some will still pass through the medium. The size of the critical angle depends upon how fast the rays can travel through the two media.

A *A sparkling diamond*

Your task

You are going to plan an investigation that will allow you to measure the critical angle for a particular medium

Learning Outcomes

1.19 *Investigate the critical angle for perspex/air or glass/air or water/air boundaries*

When planning an investigation like this, one of the skills you will be assessed on is your ability to *judge the quality of evidence*. There are 4 marks available for this skill. Here are two extracts focusing on this skill. Other skills that you need for the practical assessment are dealt with in other lessons.

Student extract 1 — A basic response for this skill

The result that doesn't fit the pattern is clearly spotted.

When I looked at the other set of results I was given I saw that after the critical angle was passed and the incident angle got bigger the reflected angle grew as well apart from one result which was smaller and obviously wrong. I decided to not use this result when calculating a mean.

The student only refers to the secondary evidence and hasn't talked about their own results.

The student has explained how they have dealt with the anomaly.

Student extract 2 — A good response for this skill

The student hasn't referred to the secondary evidence and how that compares to the primary evidence.

When I looked at my results for measuring the critical angle I saw that three of the values were very close to each other with only 1° between them whereas the other result was 5° off. Therefore we ignored that figure when carrying out our calculations and took an average of the other three. This meant that the anomalous result would not shift the answer away from the true result.

This is a good answer because the student has recognised that one of the results is probably wrong and has excluded it from their calculations.

The student has explained why they have eliminated one of the figures.

ResultsPlus

To access 2 marks

- Comment on the quality of the primary evidence, dealing with anomalies appropriately (if there are no anomalies in the evidence you need to state this)
- Comments on the quality of the secondary evidence, dealing with anomalies appropriately (if there are no anomalies in the evidence you need to state this)

To access 4 marks

- Explain any adjustments to the evidence needed, or the decision not to exclude evidence
- Take account of anomalies in primary and secondary evidence when processing evidence (using all the evidence if there are no anomalies)

Why does light mostly travel through transparent objects but is sometimes totally reflected?

If you place a coin on the table and put an empty glass on top of it, you can see the coin by looking down through the side of the glass. As you gradually fill the glass with water, the coin vanishes.

A *Who took the money?*

1 The critical angle for light going from water to air is 49°. Explain why refraction is not possible at every angle of incidence.

When a wave enters a medium where the wave's speed is greater, as the angle of refraction decreases so does the angle of incidence. However, at an angle greater than the **critical angle**, there is no refraction and all the wave is reflected. This is called **total internal reflection**.

2 A light ray travelling through glass hits a glass-air boundary, and refracts. The angle of incidence is then changed, and the light ray is totally internally reflected.
a Has the angle of incidence been increased or decreased?
b Explain why a light ray travelling through water into air at the same angle of incidence as the light ray at the glass-air boundary may leave the water, and not be totally internally reflected

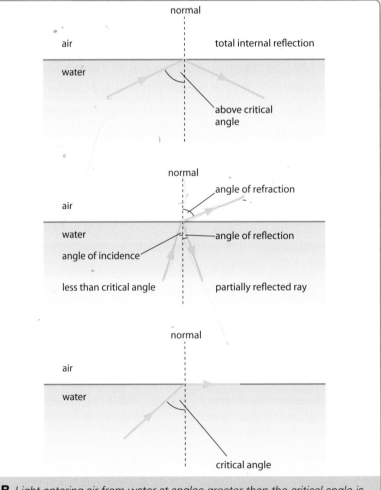

B *Light entering air from water at angles greater than the critical angle is totally internally reflected.*

At angles less than the critical angle, part of the wave's energy is refracted and some is reflected. There is partial reflection and refraction. As the angle of incidence decreases the more refraction there is and less reflection.

When light rays pass into a medium in which they travel faster, something unexpected can occur at the critical angle; the ray of light will travel along the boundary.

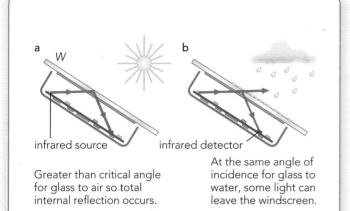

a W

infrared source   infrared detector

Greater than critical angle for glass to air so total internal reflection occurs.

b

At the same angle of incidence for glass to water, some light can leave the windscreen.

C *Less infrared reaches the detector in a car rain sensor when it rains*

Many cars now have automatic rain sensors, which turn on the windscreen wipers when it starts to rain. Many of these devices rely on total internal reflection to work. An infrared source inside the car directs a beam into the windscreen. The beam travels through the windscreen and reaches the boundary between the glass and the outside air at an angle that is greater than the critical angle.

Skills spotlight

Things that happen to radiation can be explained by using scientific models such as ray diagrams. Figure B shows how a ray of light may be reflected at the edge of a glass block. What would this diagram look like if we were to draw the light as a sequence of waves?

So the beam is totally internally reflected back into the windscreen. However, when it rains, the water on the glass allows some of the infrared to refract into the water so less of it reaches the detector. This signals the windscreen wipes to start.

H 3 Calculate the critical angle for perspex of refractive index 1.48 when in air.

H 4 a Calculate the critical angle at the interface between glass (refractive index = 1.5) and water (refractive index = 1.33).
b Explain why it is greater than the critical angle for glass in air.

Calculation of critical angle

We can apply Snell's law to light approaching the edge of a medium at the critical angle c. Remember that at the critical angle light travels along the boundary, so the angle of refraction is 90°.

$$\frac{\sin c}{\sin r} = \frac{n_r}{n_i}$$

In this case r is 90° and sin 90° = 1. For light entering air from glass or water, n_r is the refractive index of air, which is 1.
Therefore:

$$\sin c = \frac{1}{n_i}$$

This shows that the greater the refractive index, the smaller the critical angle. If the angle of incidence is greater than c then sin r would have to be greater than 1 to obey Snell's Law. No angle has a sine value of more than 1.

ResultsPlus
Watch Out!

Students have difficulties explaining the term critical angle. The critical angle only occurs when a ray is approaching a medium in which the wave can travel faster.

5 If you are diving underwater on a bright sunny day and you look up, you will see clearly what is directly above you. However, the surface of the water a few metres in either direction looks dark. Explain why, using a ray diagram to help your explanation.

Learning Outcomes

1.15 Explain, with the aid of ray diagrams, total internal reflection (TIR), including the law of reflection and critical angle

H 1.16 Calculate critical angle using Snell's Law

HSW 3 Describe how phenomena are explained using scientific models

How can ideas about waves help us to diagnose and treat medical conditions?

Ancient Egyptians preserved the bodies of their rulers by coating them in chemicals. Over time these formed 'mummies'. Mummies can be formed naturally when buried in certain soils. The mummy in Figure A was found in South Korea. Scientists are using an endoscope to look inside it in an attempt to work out what the person died from.

A

> **1 What is total internal reflection?**

Total internal reflection occurs in a medium when a ray approaches the interface at an angle greater than the critical angle. For example, if a light ray travelling through clear plastic reaches the boundary with air at an angle greater than the critical angle, the light will be reflected back into the plastic. The edge is acting like a mirror and the angles obey the law of reflection: the angle of incidence is equal to the angle of reflection.

high transparency glass

ray of light

light leaves the fibre

light enters fibre

light reflects off transparent wall

B *Because of total internal reflection (TIR) the light ray is guided to the end.*

Figure B shows how an **optical fibre** works. No matter how the fibre twists and turns the light ray is repeatedly reflected back into the fibre. Optical fibres transmit infrared or visible light signals by total internal reflection for telephone, TV and other data communications.

One use of optical fibres is in an endoscope, to enable a surgeon to examine inside a patient. The endoscope consists of optical fibres in a flexible rod that is inserted into the body. Some of the optical fibres carry light inside them. Light reflected off the inside of the body is then gathered and focused by an eyepiece lens to form a clear image of the inside of the body.

> **2 Why does an endoscope have two sets of optical fibres?**
>
> **3 Explain how total internal reflection makes an instrument such as an endoscope possible.**

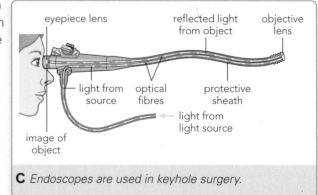

eyepiece lens

reflected light from object

objective lens

light from source

optical fibres

protective sheath

light from light source

image of object

C *Endoscopes are used in keyhole surgery.*

Ultrasound

Ultrasound waves are at frequencies higher than humans can hear. They travel through solid objects but are partly reflected when they enter a different medium. In medical scanning, the same device both transmits and receives the ultrasound waves. The waves travel through the body and are reflected at the interface between different tissues. The reflected waves are detected and converted to an image on a screen.

Ultrasound is useful for both diagnosis and treatment. For example, an ultrasound scan can help to locate kidney stones (hard deposits) and then high intensity ultrasound can be used to break them up when the stones absorb the ultrasound energy. Absorption of ultrasound energy can also be used by physiotherapists to treat injured muscles. The ultrasound can be focused and its intensity controlled so the energy can be directed effectively.

> **4** What causes ultrasound waves to be partially reflected?

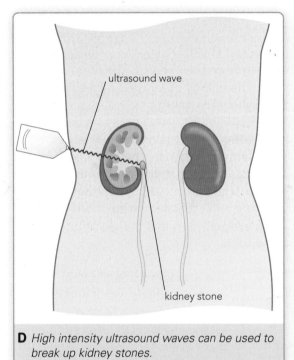

D High intensity ultrasound waves can be used to break up kidney stones.

E A kidney stone.

5 Kidney stones used to have to be removed by surgery. Suggest two reasons why more kidney stones are broken up by ultrasound today.

6 Explain how ultrasound waves can be used to break up a kidney stone.

7 What are the similarities and differences between endoscopy and ultrasound as imaging techniques?

Skills spotlight

Decisions about the risks and benefits of science and technology have to be made by both medical staff and patients. Ultrasound is commonly used to produce foetal scans, but there is some evidence of a relationship between the number of ultrasound examinations during pregnancy and a decrease in birth weight.

Suggest why this might happen and why foetal scanning is nevertheless widespread.

Learning Outcomes

1.20 Explain how TIR is used in optical fibres

1.21 Explain uses of optical fibres in endoscopes

1.22 Explain uses of ultrasound in diagnosis and treatment

HSW **13** Explain how and why decisions about uses of science and technology are made

How can X-rays be produced?

In the 1950s X-ray specs started to be sold as a novelty item. They supposedly allowed you to see bones – but this was an optical illusion.

A X-ray specs

B *These surgeons are using X-rays to show them where they need to operate.*

Ionising radiation turns atoms into ions by removing some of their outer electrons. Some types of electromagnetic radiation, **X-rays** for example, are ionising.

The ability of X-rays to ionise materials depends on their energy. The more energy the X-rays have, the more ionising they are. The energy of X-rays is related to their frequency – the higher the frequency, the higher their energy.

1 Why is the anode positively charged?

2 What is an electron gun?

An X-ray machine consists of an **evacuated tube** that contains two electrodes. The negative electrode (**cathode**) is a wire **filament**. When it is heated it becomes an **electron gun**, as it emits electrons in a process called **thermionic emission**. The other electrode is an **anode** (positively charged electrode). When there is a large **potential difference** between the anode and cathode, the electrons are accelerated towards the anode. The tube is evacuated so that the electrons do not collide with other particles as they cross the tube.

The anode is made of metal. The electrons collide with it and slow down very quickly. Most of the kinetic energy is transferred to thermal energy. However, some of the kinetic energy is transformed into X-rays.

A higher potential difference will produce X-rays with greater energy.

Comparing currents

Charged particles, or electrons, flow from the cathode to the anode and complete the circuit. This movement of charged particles is equivalent to an electric current between the cathode and anode.

If the temperature of the cathode is increased, the number of electrons emitted increases and this increases the number of X-rays produced.

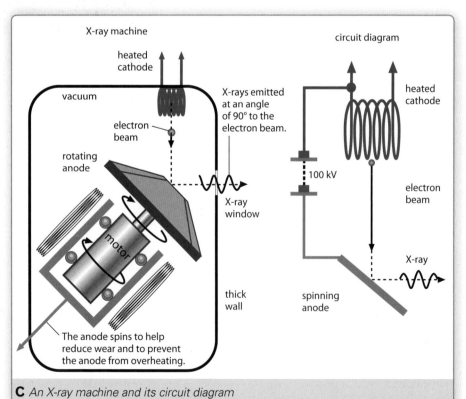

C *An X-ray machine and its circuit diagram*

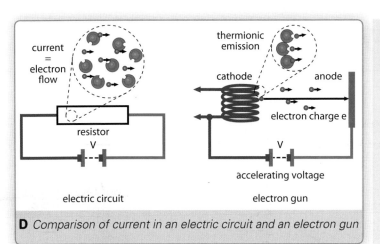

current = electron flow

resistor

V

electric circuit

thermionic emission

cathode   anode

electron charge e

V

accelerating voltage

electron gun

D *Comparison of current in an electric circuit and an electron gun*

H

The current in the X-ray machine is the rate of flow of electrons:

$$I = N \times q$$

where I = current in **amperes**, N = number of particles flowing each second, and q = charge on each particle in **coulombs**.

?

3 Why does the anode need to have a high melting point?

4 How is the energy of the X-rays increased?

H 5 The charge on an electron is 1.6×10^{-19} C. Calculate the current when the number of electrons flowing is:
a 2×10^{14} per second
b 9.4×10^{15} per second

Kinetic energy

H

The kinetic energy of an electron is given by the equation:

kinetic energy $= \frac{1}{2}\,mv^2$

where m is the mass of an electron in kg, and v is the velocity of the electron in m/s.

It can also be expressed as:

kinetic energy $= eV$

where e is the charge on an electron (1.6×10^{-19} C) and V is the potential difference in volts.

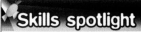

Skills spotlight

Scientists use both qualitative and quantitative approaches. Use a word explanation and the equation for the current in an X-ray machine to show how the number of electrons changes the current.

? H 6 a What is the kinetic energy of an electron when the potential difference is 100 kV?
H b The mass of an electron is 9.11×10^{-31} kg. What is the velocity of the electron in part **a**?

7 Explain how X-rays are produced.

ResultsPlus
Watch Out!

Students often forget that the cathode is negative and the anode is positive. It might help to think of the anode as the ADDode.

Learning Outcomes

2.1 Relate the ionisation by X-rays to their frequency and energy qualitatively ($E = hf$ is not required)

2.2 Explain the key features of passing a current through an evacuated tube, including:
 a thermionic emission of electrons from a heated filament
 b potential difference between the cathode (filament) and the anode (metal target)
 c why the vacuum is necessary
 d possible production of X-rays by collision with a metal target

2.3 Explain that a beam of charged particles is equivalent to an electric current

H 2.4 Use the equation: $I = Nq$
 current (ampere, A) = number of particles per second (1/second, 1/s) × charge on each particle (coulomb, C)

H 2.5 Use the equation: KE $= \frac{1}{2}\,mv^2 = e \times V$
 kinetic energy (joule, J) = electronic charge (coulomb, C) × accelerating potential difference (volt, V)

HSW **10** Use qualitative and quantitive approaches when presenting scientific ideas and arguments

>>>>>>>>>>>>>>>>>>>>>>>>>>> Why don't families have portraits taken using X-rays any more?

How do we use X-rays?

Soon after X-rays were discovered in 1895, it became a popular idea to have family photos taken using X-rays.

> **1 a** Explain why teeth show up as white on an X-ray.
> **b** Why don't gums show up on mouth X-rays?

When electromagnetic radiation is emitted by a source, it spreads out and its strength decreases the further you are from the source. When you double the distance from the source, the strength decreases to a quarter. The strength decreases according to the **inverse square law**.

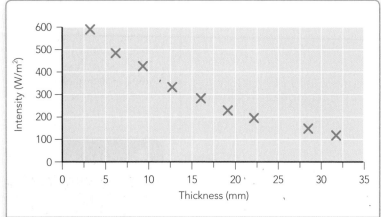

B The inverse square law. The radiation that passes through one square at one unit of distance passes through four squares at two units of distance.

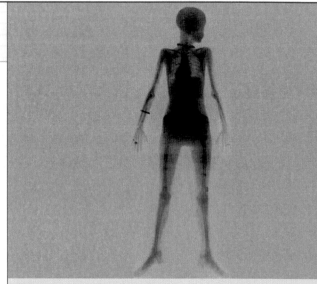

A This is the first whole body X-ray photo of a living person, taken in 1907. It took 30 minutes to take the photo!

Absorption of X-rays

Different materials absorb different amounts of X-rays. The thicker (denser) the material, the more X-rays it absorbs. Bone is denser than the tissues in organs like the lungs and heart, so it absorbs more X-rays. On an X-ray photo, dark areas are where lots of X-rays have been detected – not many have been absorbed. Light areas are where few X-rays have been detected – more of them have been absorbed.

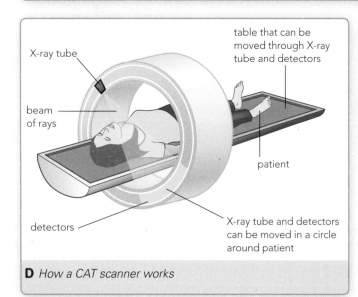

D How a CAT scanner works

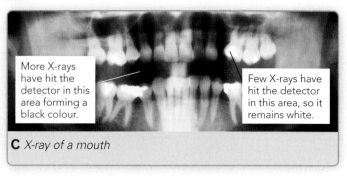

C X-ray of a mouth

More X-rays have hit the detector in this area forming a black colour.

Few X-rays have hit the detector in this area, so it remains white.

CAT scans and fluoroscopes

In a **CAT scan**, an X-ray source is moved around the patient in a circle. X-ray detectors are positioned opposite the X-ray source. The X-rays detected are used to build up many cross-sectional views of the body. Sometimes a computer is used to build up a 3D image.

CAT scan pictures are used in the diagnosis of many types of cancer. Unusual areas of brightness or darkness can indicate **tumours** or small areas of tissue that have died because their blood supply has been obstructed.

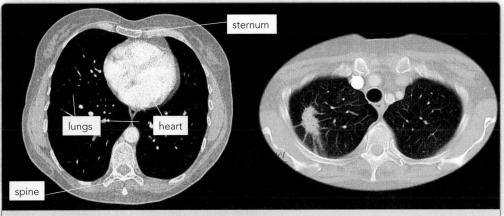

E *A CAT scan of a healthy patient's chest and an abnormal CAT scan*

2 What is a CAT scan?

3 What is a fluoroscope?

4 How is a CAT scan used to detect a tumour?

Fluoroscopes are used to show a patient's organs working. For example, they can be used to detect blocked blood vessels. They consist of an X-ray source and an X-ray detector attached to a digital video camera. The patient is placed between the X-ray source and the detector.

Risks and benefits

Both CAT scans and fluoroscopes are painless for the patient and non-invasive (nothing is put into the patient). They can eliminate the need for a biopsy (exploratory surgery) to help decide what a patient's treatment should be.

Fluoroscopes and CAT scans can give a patient a dose of radiation that is equivalent to up to 10 years of the dose from background radiation. The increased dose of radiation increases the risk of them developing cancer. For this reason, neither procedure is recommended for pregnant women or children. When X-rays are used to treat cancer, the dose is much higher. The risk of damaging other tissues is reduced by firing the X-rays at the patient from several directions so that only the tumour receives a high dose.

5 Why aren't CAT scans recommended for pregnant women and children?

6 In Figure E, which organ has a tumour? Explain why you think it is a tumour.

7 Explain how X-ray images are formed and how they can be used to detect an area that has no blood supply.

Skills spotlight

There are risks as well as benefits of using X-rays to diagnose medical problems. Discuss whether the risks of developing cancer from using X-rays outweigh the benefits.

Results Plus
Watch Out!

Many students confuse the light and dark areas on X-ray photos. Remember that the dark areas on an X-ray photo show where lots of X-rays have been detected.

Learning Outcomes

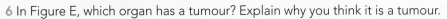

2.6 Demonstrate an understanding of the inverse square law for electromagnetic radiation

2.7 Relate the absorption of X-rays to the thickness of the material through which they are travelling, quantitatively

2.8 Describe how X-rays are used in CAT scans and fluoroscopes

2.9 Demonstrate an understanding of the comparison of the risks and benefits of using X-rays for treatment and diagnosis

HSW **12** Describe the use of contemporary science and technological developments and their benefits, drawbacks and risks

>>>>>>>>>>>>> Why might a heart patient in 1905 have put their limbs into buckets of salty water?

What is an ECG?

Your heart produces small potential differences. The first machines able to detect these were very cumbersome and involved the patient having to put an arm and a leg in buckets of salty water.

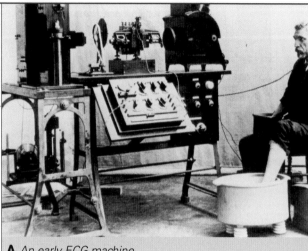

A An early ECG machine

When a heart beats, each muscle cell must contract at exactly the right moment in order to push the blood out of the heart. An **action potential** (electrical signal) is sent to each muscle cell to tell it when to contract. This electrical signal starts in the atria causing the muscles in the atria to contract.

1 What is an ECG?

2 What is an action potential?

3 Why can potential differences be detected on the skin?

The human body contains a high proportion of water with salt dissolved in it, which means that it will conduct electricity. The action potentials are conducted through the body to the skin, where they can be detected and used to produce an **electrocardiogram** or **ECG**. An ECG is a picture of the heart electrical signals.

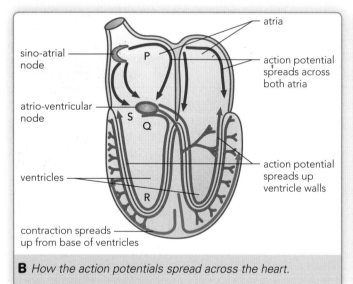

B How the action potentials spread across the heart.

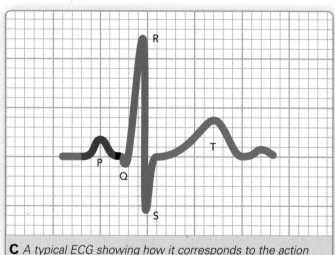

C A typical ECG showing how it corresponds to the action potentials shown in Figure B.

 **Maths skills**

Frequency is **inversely proportional** to the time period. The frequency increases at the same rate as the time period decreases.

When a heart is beating normally, there is a regular pattern. You can work out how fast the heart is beating and which part of the heart might not be working properly from an ECG. ECGs are printed on graph paper with a standard scale. The horizontal scale is usually 0.2 seconds for each larger square. To work out the frequency of the heartbeat in beats per second, you work out how long the average **time period** for a heartbeat is on the ECG and then use the equation:

$$\text{frequency, } f \text{(hertz)} = \frac{1}{\text{time period, } T \text{(second)}}$$

The **frequency** of a heartbeat is usually given as the number of beats per minute. So multiply the frequency by 60 to find the number of beats per minute.

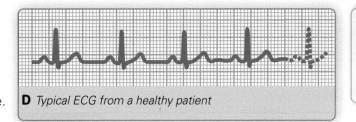

D *Typical ECG from a healthy patient*

4 Calculate the frequency of the heartbeat from the ECG Figure D.

Pulse oximetry

You can measure the pulse rate of a person using **pulse oximetry**. A **pulse oximeter** consists of two LEDs – one emitting red light and the other infrared radiation – and a detector. Each beat of the heart causes a surge of oxygenated blood in the arteries. Oxygenated blood absorbs more infrared than deoxygenated blood. By looking at the peaks of infrared absorbance, the machine will work out the pulse. By comparing the absorbance between the two LEDs it can also work out how much oxgen the blood is carrying (expressed as a percentage of its maximum).

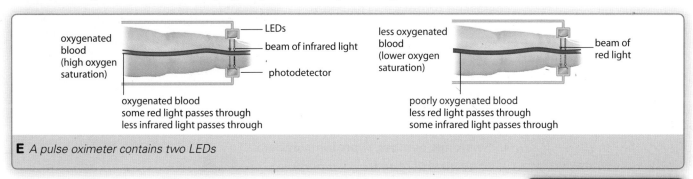

E *A pulse oximeter contains two LEDs*

Pacemakers

Some people's hearts do not beat properly. The action potentials do not spread across the heart properly. A **pacemaker** can be attached to the heart. The pacemaker detects the action potentials, amplifies them and transmits them to other parts of the heart, so that the chambers of the heart contract correctly.

5 How does a pulse oximeter detect a pulse?

6 Why are two different LEDs needed in a pulse oximeter?

7 Suggest why pulse oximeters are usually attached to fingers.

8 Explain how an ECG relates to the action of the heart and how you can use it to tell whether a heart is beating properly or not.

Skills spotlight

Technological developments can have many benefits. Pulses were traditionally taken by putting a finger over an artery and counting. What benefits does pulse oximetry have?

ResultsPlus
Watch Out!

Always check that you have read values from graphs correctly and don't forget the units.

Learning Outcomes

2.10 Explain how action potentials can be measured with an electrocardiogram (ECG) to monitor heart action

2.11 Relate the characteristic shape of a normal ECG to heart action

2.12 Use the equation:

$$\frac{\text{frequency}}{\text{(hertz, Hz)}} = \frac{1}{\text{time period (second, s)}} \qquad f = \frac{1}{T}$$

2.13 Describe the use of a pacemaker to regulate the heart action

2.14 Describe the principles and use of pulse oximetry

HSW 12 Describe the use of contemporary science and technological developments and their benefits, drawbacks and risks

>>>>>>>>>>>> How can radioactivity help to ensure that your printer paper is just the right thickness?

What is beta decay?

Lights that need no external energy supply can be made using tritium, a radioactive form of hydrogen. The tritium is placed in a sealed glass tube coated on the inside with a material (a phosphor) that glows when hit by the particles released during radioactivity.

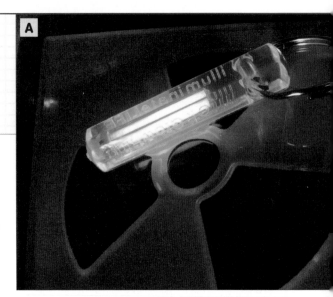

A

?
1 Identify the numbers of protons, neutrons and electrons in each of these neutral atoms.
a $^{27}_{13}$Al b $^{32}_{16}$S c $^{16}_{8}$O

2 What is the charge on:
a a neutron b a proton
c an electron?

3 What is the charge on a positron?

An atom consists of a small nucleus containing **protons** and **neutrons**, with **electrons** around it. The numbers of protons and electrons are equal. As protons and electrons have equal and opposite charges, the atom is electrically neutral. Protons and neutrons are referred to collectively as **nucleons**.

- The **atomic number** or **proton number** is the number of protons in the atom.
- The **mass number** or **nucleon number** is the number of protons and neutrons.

Some radioactive materials, when decaying, emit **beta (β) particles**: electrons or **positrons** (similar to electrons but with a positive charge). This is called **beta (β) decay**.

B

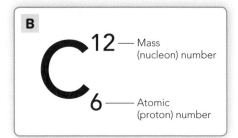

C$^{12}_{6}$ — Mass (nucleon) number
— Atomic (proton) number

C

Particle	Proton	Neutron	Electron	Positron
Mass (compared to a proton)	1	1	$\frac{1}{2000}$	$\frac{1}{2000}$
Charge	+1	0	−1	+1

Beta minus (β−) decay

In **β− decay** a neutron becomes a proton plus an electron. β− radiation consists of a stream of high energy electrons that can penetrate paper but not thin sheets of metal. The particles are ionising: they are capable of turning atoms into ions (charged particles). If the atom that is ionised loses an electron it will become a positive ion; if it gains an electron it becomes a negative ion.

β− decay increases the atomic number by one but leaves the mass number unaffected.

electron (beta particle)

D A neutron (shown in blue) has changed into a proton (shown in red), emitting an electron (beta particle).

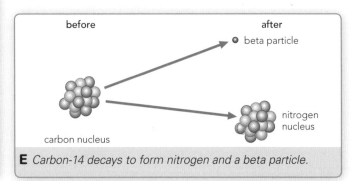

before   after
                          beta particle
carbon nucleus   nitrogen nucleus

E Carbon-14 decays to form nitrogen and a beta particle.

Beta plus (β+) decay

In positron or **β+ decay**, a proton becomes a neutron plus a positron. Positron decay decreases the atomic number by one but leaves the mass number unaffected.

H 4 In β+ decay, what happens to the balance of charges overall?

H 5 Why does β+ decay:
a reduce the atomic number by one
b leave the mass number unchanged?

6 Why does β− decay:
a increase the atomic number by one
b leave the mass number unchanged?

7 β− radiation is used to check the thickness when manufacturing paper. Paper is made by rolling pulp into a thin sheet. The harder the rollers squeeze, the thinner the paper comes out. Beta particles can penetrate paper but the number decreases if the paper is thicker. The detector indicates whether the roller pressure is correct (Figure F).
a What happens to the radioactive count if the paper is too thick?
b What then needs to happen to the rollers?
c What is it about the penetration of beta particles that makes this type of radiation suitable for this application?

8 Plastic bottles are filled on a production line. A system using beta radiation checks the bottles have all been filled. Explain how the system detects the empty bottles (Figure G).

Skills spotlight

We can explain events using scientific models. For example, we show sub-atomic particles such as protons and electrons as little balls. Why is this acceptable even though they don't actually look like this?

ResultsPlus
Watch Out!

Protons have a positive charge but neutrons don't have a negative charge. They are neutral.

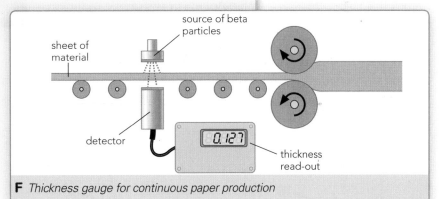

F *Thickness gauge for continuous paper production*

G

Learning Outcomes

3.2 Describe the properties of beta and positron radiation

3.3 Recall the relative masses and relative electric charges of protons, neutrons, electrons and positrons

3.4 Recall that in an atom the number of protons equals the number of electrons

3.5 Describe the process of β− decay (a neutron becomes a proton plus an electron)

H 3.6 Describe the process of β+ decay (a proton becomes a neutron plus a positron)

3.7 Explain the effects on the atomic (proton) number and mass (nucleon) number of radioactive decay (β decay)

HSW 3 Describe how phenomena are explained using scientific models

What are alpha and gamma decay?

The Cassini space probe, which is exploring Saturn and its moons, cannot use solar energy as a power source due to its large distance from the Sun. Instead it uses heat from the natural decay of plutonium-238 (an alpha source) to generate electricity.

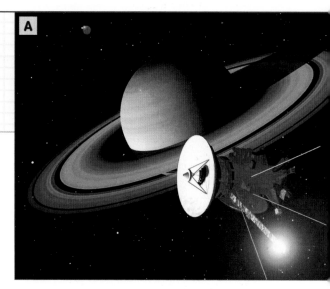

A

1 Look at the table shown on page 206.
a What charge does an alpha particle have?
b What is its mass compared to:
i a proton ii a beta particle?

2 In what way is an alpha particle the same as a helium nucleus?

There are three types of radioactive emission, named after the first three letters in the Greek alphabet: alpha (α), beta (β) and gamma (γ). Alpha and beta emissions consist of particles but gamma emissions are a type of electromagnetic radiation, similar to X-rays.

Alpha radiation

Each **alpha (α) particle** is made up of two protons and two neutrons. They are not very penetrating but they are very ionising. They are massive compared with beta particles so are easily capable of dislodging electrons from any atoms they collide with. However, this means that they soon lose energy and so have a limited range.

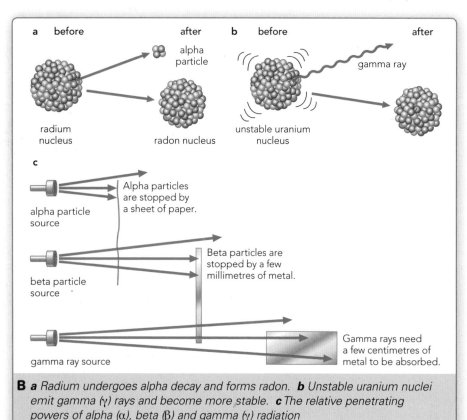

B *a Radium undergoes alpha decay and forms radon. b Unstable uranium nuclei emit gamma (γ) rays and become more stable. c The relative penetrating powers of alpha (α), beta (β) and gamma (γ) radiation*

Alpha (α) decay results in the atomic number decreasing by two and the mass number decreasing by four.

Gamma radiation

When some radioactive materials decay, they release gamma (γ) rays instead of particles. Gamma rays are very penetrating but not as ionising as alpha or beta radiation.

Gamma radiation has no mass and therefore causes no change to either the atomic number or the mass number. When gamma rays are released, the nucleus loses energy and so becomes more stable.

3 Explain why alpha particles are not very penetrating but are very ionising.

Neutron radiation

Radioactive decay sometimes results in a neutron being ejected. Neutrons have no charge and so are not directly ionising but they are as penetrating as gamma rays.

4 When a neutron is ejected:
a Why does the mass number drop?
b Why does the atomic number stay the same?

Nuclear reactions

H

The reactants and products in a nuclear reaction are shown using a nuclear equation. A **nuclear equation** has to be balanced. The total atomic number and the total mass number must be the same on either side.

In nuclear reaction equations:

- an alpha (α) particle (helium nucleus) is shown as $_2^4\text{He}$
- an electron is shown as $_{-1}^{0}e$
- a positron is shown as $_{+1}^{0}e$
- a gamma ray has zero mass and zero charge, so is shown as $_0^0\gamma$.

Skills spotlight

Explanations can be developed using scientific models. What are the key features of the model used for alpha and beta radiation?

e.g.

Radium-226 emits an alpha particle. What is the other product?

$$_{88}^{226}\text{Ra} \rightarrow\ _2^4\text{He}\ +\ ?$$

The atomic numbers need to balance: 88 – 2 = 86. The element with an atomic number of 86 is radon (Rn).

The mass numbers need to balance as well: 226 – 4 = 222. Therefore:

$$_{88}^{226}\text{Ra} \rightarrow\ _2^4\text{He}\ +\ _{86}^{222}\text{Rn}$$

ResultsPlus
Watch Out!

Students often confuse penetrating capability with ionising capability. Alpha particles are not very penetrating but if they do reach other materials they are very ionising.

H 5 What is the new element formed when:
a plutonium-239 undergoes α decay
b technetium-99 undergoes β– decay
c potassium-37 undergoes β+ decay?

6 A smoke detector uses an americium source, which ionises air, turning it into charged particles. Any smoke in the detector will absorb the ionised particles. Explain why smoke entering the detector will cause the alarm to sound.

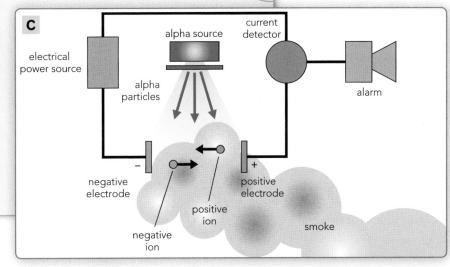

C

electrical power source

alpha source

current detector

alarm

alpha particles

negative electrode

positive electrode

negative ion

positive ion

smoke

Learning Outcomes

3.2 Describe the properties of alpha, gamma and neutron radiation

3.7 Explain the effects on the atomic (proton) number and mass (nucleon) number of radioactive decays (α and γ decay)

H 3.8 Use given data to balance nuclear equations

3.19 Recall that nuclei that have undergone radioactive decay often undergo nuclear rearrangement with a loss of energy as gamma radiation

HSW **3** Describe how phenomena are explained using scientific models

How can we predict if an element is likely to be unstable?

How is the N–Z curve used

In nature the balancing of forces results in stability, whether in a set of odd-shaped rocks or in sub-atomic particles.

A The forces on these rocks balance exactly, resulting in a stable structure.

All the **isotopes** of an element have the same number of protons but different numbers of neutrons. Some isotopes are **stable** and will stay in that arrangement indefinitely; others are **unstable** and will **decay**. When all the isotopes of different elements are compared a pattern emerges, as shown in Figure B.

1 Why is carbon towards the bottom left corner of the graph in Figure B?

Skills spotlight

The interpretation of data provides evidence to develop theories by making predictions to test. How does the N-Z curve enable scientists to predict the stability and decay of isotopes?

ResultsPlus
Watch Out!

When plotting or reading an N-Z curve, students often wrongly use the mass number instead of the number of neutrons for N. The variables that are plotted on the N-Z curve are the number of neutrons (N) against the number of protons (Z).

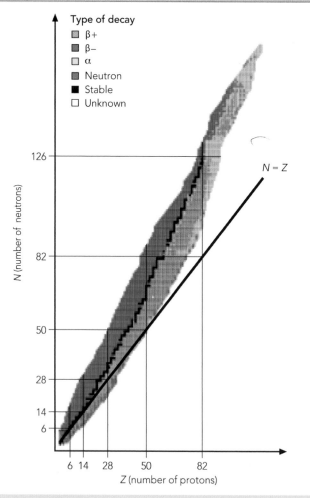

Type of decay
- □ β+
- ■ β−
- □ α
- ■ Neutron
- ■ Stable
- □ Unknown

N = Z

N (number of neutrons)

Z (number of protons)

B Graph of number of neutrons (N) against number of protons (Z) showing the kind of decay each isotope will undergo.

Lighter elements appear in the bottom left corner and heavier elements towards the top right. The straight line labelled N = Z indicates where elements will appear if they have the same number of protons as neutrons.

The dark dots show stable isotopes; they form a line called the **N-Z curve**, sometimes referred to as the 'stability curve'. This line stops at Z = 82 because above this all isotopes are unstable. At the bottom left the curve is close to the N = Z line but it soon deviates.

Isotopes above the N–Z curve have too many neutrons to be stable and undergo β– decay. Isotopes below the N–Z curve but close to it have too many protons to be stable and usually undergo β+ decay.

Unstable isotopes are **radioactive isotopes**.

Isotopes of the heaviest elements (Z above 82), found to the right of the graph in Figure B usually undergo alpha decay.

The element Tungsten shows that tungsten (symbol W; Z = 74) has four stable isotopes (^{182}W, ^{183}W, ^{184}W and ^{186}W) and one unstable isotope (^{180}W), which is below the stability curve. It undergoes alpha decay:

$$^{180}_{74}\text{W} \rightarrow ^{176}_{72}\text{Hf} + ^{4}_{2}\text{He}$$

The products are an alpha particle and hafnium-176.

> **?**
>
> 2 Do the heavier elements have more neutrons than protons or vice versa?
>
> 3 How could you calculate N if you know the atomic number and the mass number?

> **?**
>
> 4 What is true about N compared with Z for:
> a lighter elements, such as carbon
> b heavier elements, such as iron?
>
> 5 What is formed when:
> a plutonium-238 ($^{238}_{94}$Pu) undergoes α decay?
> b sodium-22 ($^{22}_{11}$Na) undergoes β+ decay?
> c caesium-137 ($^{137}_{55}$Cs) undergoes β– decay?
>
> 6 Is tungsten-180 above or below the N-Z curve?
>
> 7 How could you find out if hafnium-176 is radioactive?
>
> 8 Platinum (symbol Pt; Z = 78) has one unstable isotope (^{190}Pt) and five stable ones (^{192}Pt, ^{194}Pt, ^{195}Pt, ^{196}Pt and ^{198}Pt). Explain what kind of decay ^{190}Pt will undergo and what the decay products will be.

Learning Outcomes

H 3.9 Describe the features of the N-Z curve for stable isotopes

H 3.10 Identify isotopes as radioactive from their position relative to the stability curve

H 3.11 Recall that nuclei with high values of Z (above 82) usually undergo alpha decay

H 3.12 Recall that an isotope above the curve has too many neutrons to be stable and will undergo β– decay

H 3.13 Recall that an isotope below the curve has too many protons to be stable and will undergo β+ decay

HSW 2 Describe how data is used to provide evidence that increases our scientific understanding

What is the role of quarks in beta decay?

'Three quarks for Muster Mark!'

This line from James Joyce's *Finnegan's Wake* inspired the physicist Murray Gell-Mann to name some newly discovered particles. We now believe that there are many different 'colours' and 'flavours' of quark but when the name was chosen only three were known.

A *James Joyce, author of the novel* Finnegan's Wake.

1 a What is the combined mass of two up quarks and a down quark?
b What is their combined charge?

2 a What is the combined mass of one up quark and two down quarks?
b What is their combined charge?

It was once thought that protons and neutrons were the smallest particles in the nucleus. It is now believed that they are formed from even smaller objects called **quark** particles. These quarks exist within larger particles, called hadrons (which include protons and neutrons). The two types of quark we need to consider are 'up' and 'down' quarks.

A proton consists of two 'up' quarks and a 'down' quark. A neutron consists of one 'up' quark and two 'down' quarks.

Quarks can change from one into another and this explains how a proton can change into a neutron and vice versa.

Quark	Up	Down
Mass	$\frac{1}{3}$	$\frac{1}{3}$
Charge	$+\frac{2}{3}$	$-\frac{1}{3}$

B

3 Look at the quarks present in protons and neutrons. What is the difference between an up quark and a down quark in terms of:
a mass
b charge?

4 What needs to happen to the quarks in a proton to turn it into a neutron?

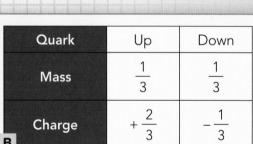

proton p = udu

$u + d + u = p$
$+\frac{2}{3} - \frac{1}{3} + \frac{2}{3} = +1$
so total charge = +1e

neutron n = dud

$d + u + d = n$
$-\frac{1}{3} + \frac{2}{3} - \frac{1}{3} = 0$
so total charge = 0

C *The arrangement of quarks in protons and neutrons*

Some radioactive elements undergo β+ decay when an up quark changes into a down quark.

Other radioactive elements undergo β− decay when a down quark changes into an up quark.

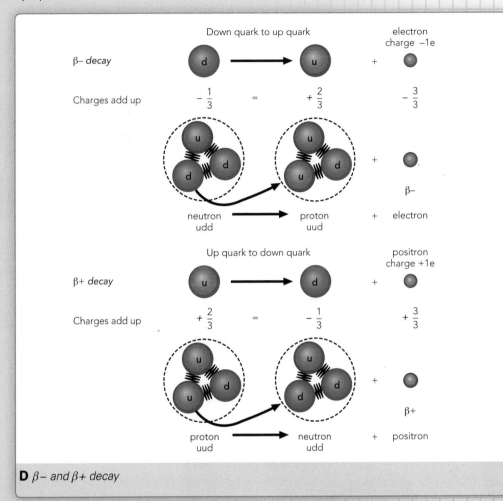

D *β− and β+ decay*

5 What effect will an up quark changing into a down quark have on:
a the atomic number
b the mass number?

6 What effect will a down quark changing into an up quark have on:
a the atomic number
b the mass number?

★ **Skills spotlight**

Explanations can be developed using scientific models. How can you use the quark model to explain beta decay?

ResultsPlus
Watch Out!

Up and down quarks have different charges ($+\frac{2}{3}$ and $-\frac{1}{3}$). You might remember this by thinking of the phrase 'two steps forward and one step backwards'.

7 Write a balanced nuclear equation for the following decay processes, stating what type of decay it is and explaining it in terms of quarks.
a Decay of caesium-137 to barium-137.
b Decay of sodium-22 to neon-22.

Learning ⊙utcomes

Ⓗ **3.14** Recall that the proton and neutron each contain three particles called quarks

Ⓗ **3.15** Describe the arrangement of up and down quarks in protons and neutrons

Ⓗ **3.16** Use given data to explain the arrangement of up and down quarks in protons and neutrons in terms of charge and mass

Ⓗ **3.17** Explain β− decay as a process that involves a down quark changing into an up quark (a neutron becomes a proton and an electron)

Ⓗ **3.18** Explain β+ decay as a process that involves one up quark changing into a down quark (a proton becomes a neutron and a positron)

HSW **3** Describe how phenomena are explained using scientific models

What are the dangers of ionising radiation

Over 1000 nuclear tests have been conducted since 1945 by the USA alone. Radiation and fallout from early tests were later found to have claimed the lives of more than 11 000 Americans.

> **?** 1 Why can we not identify a 'safe level of radiation'?
>
> 2 How may radiation damage cells?

Any increase in radiation levels results in an increased probability of illness and death. The radiation may kill cells or stimulate the growth of cancers. It has been estimated that about 1% of us will develop cancer in our lifetime as a result of radiation exposure.

A *Many nuclear tests conducted above ground were watched by thousands of spectators.*

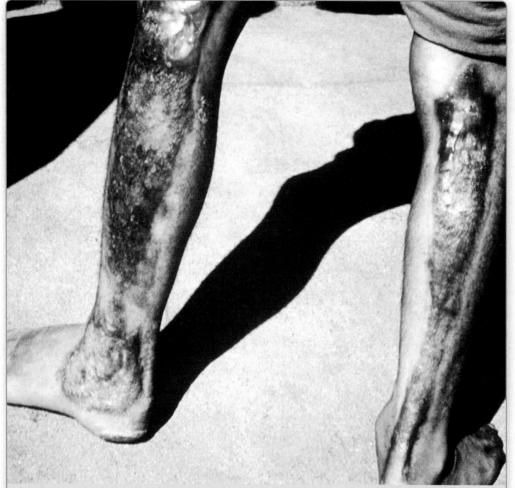

B *Radiation burns caused by the nuclear bomb dropped on the city of Hiroshima on the 6th August 1945. The blast killed at least 80 000 people and left many others with terrible injuries.*

There is a risk to living cells of damage to their DNA. Radiation can cause **mutations** (changes) in the structure of the DNA, which may then be copied over to new cells. Mutations in DNA can cause cancers or harmful changes to the function of genes, which are then passed on to the next generation. However, not all mutations are harmful and cells are often capable of repairing all the damage if the radiation **dosage** is low.

Radiation may cause burns depending on the exposure to the radiation and the type of source. Beta burns are on the surface and may look similar to sunburn, whilst gamma burns extend deeper.

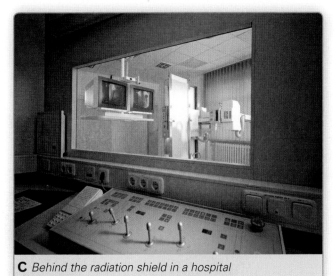

C *Behind the radiation shield in a hospital*

Medical staff working with radioactive sources have their exposure limited in a number of ways, including increasing their distance from the source, shielding, containment of the source and minimising the time they spend in the presence of sources. Their exposure is also closely monitored. Some patients may be exposed to a dose of radiation for the purpose of diagnosis or treatment, but the dosage is carefully controlled.

3 Why is it essential that workers know what type of radioactive source they have been exposed to?

4 What kinds of radiation are workers kept safe from by being some distance from the radioactive source?

5 Why do you think thick concrete is a good material to use to shield workers from radiation?

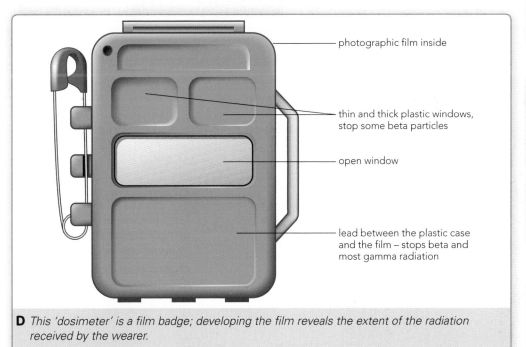

photographic film inside

thin and thick plastic windows, stop some beta particles

open window

lead between the plastic case and the film – stops beta and most gamma radiation

D *This 'dosimeter' is a film badge; developing the film reveals the extent of the radiation received by the wearer.*

6 Explain why ionising radiation needs to be carefully controlled.

7 Describe the methods used to protect people from over-exposure to radiation. Why do the methods need to be varied for different sources of radiation?

Skills spotlight

Scientific and technological developments may involve risks as well as benefits. How are the risks of using radioactive substances in hospital reduced?

ResultsPlus
Watch Out!

Don't assume that all radiation is ionising radiation. The term radiation refers to any energy carried by waves or particles from a source which includes light and infrared.

Learning Outcomes

3.20 Describe the dangers of ionising radiation in terms of tissue damage and possible mutations

3.21 Explain the precautions taken to ensure the safety of people exposed to radiation, including limiting the dose for patients and the risks to medical personnel

HSW **12** Describe the benefits, drawbacks and risks of using new scientific and technological developments

How can lethal types of radiation save lives?

How are radioactive substances used in hospitals?

Alexander Litvinenko had been in the Russian secret service but had been granted asylum in the UK. He wrote a book accusing the Russian government of various crimes and was fatally poisoned with (radioactive) polonium-210 in 2006.

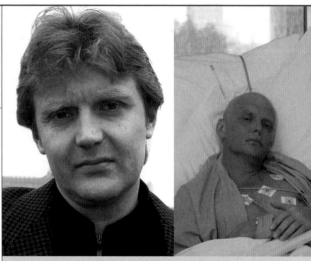

A *Alexander Litvinenko before and after being poisoned*

Radiotherapy is often used to treat cancers, as the radiation can kill cancer cells (or tumours). The radiation can be applied internally (with the source inside the patient, right by the tumour) or externally. A beta emitter, such as iodine-131, is chosen for internal radiotherapy, but external radiotherapy uses a gamma source or high frequency X-rays.

> **1** Why is it important that the radiation is directed only at the tumour and not at healthy tissue?
>
> **2** Why are beta emitters chosen for internal radiotherapy?

Radiotherapy may also be used for **palliative** care, such as shrinking of tumours. In palliative care, a condition won't be cured but the patient will be in less pain and may enjoy a better quality of life.

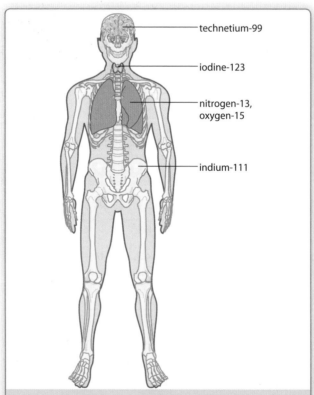

B *Different tracers are absorbed by different parts of the body, for example iodine-123 is absorbed by the thyroid gland.*

technetium-99

iodine-123

nitrogen-13, oxygen-15

indium-111

Diagnosis

Cancers can be diagnosed using a **tracer** that will concentrate in particular organs or in diseased tissues or in cancer tumours. A tracer is usually a substance used by the body (e.g. glucose) which is made using atoms from a certain radioactive isotope. Some elements are directly absorbed by parts of the body (e.g. iodine) and so are used directly as tracers without being incoporated into larger molecules. The radioactive isotope needs to have a short half-life (meaning it loses its radioactivity quickly) so that other parts of the body are affected as little as possible. The patient is injected with or breathes in the tracer and is then given a **PET scan** to locate the tracer.

As the isotopes used in PET scans must have a short half-life, they are made close to where they will be used. They are often used within hours or even minutes of production.

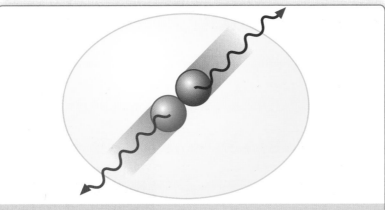

C *The tracer emits a positron, which then interacts with an electron, releasing two gamma rays in opposite directions. The gamma rays are detected by a PET camera.*

3 Why are different tracers used?

4 Radioactive isotopes are produced in cyclotrons. Suggest why cyclotrons are located around the UK, sometimes within hospitals.

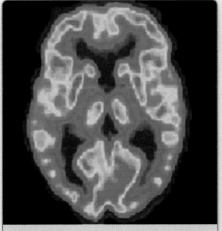

D *In a PET scan the active areas of the brain take up more of the tracer, which a computer shows as brighter colours.*

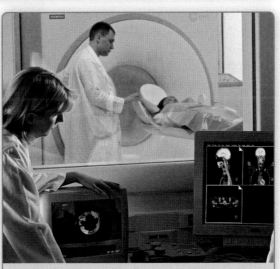

E *A PET scan, using a tracer, taking place*

Skills spotlight

Ethical issues are raised by the use of radiation. Why might a doctor decide not to recommend a diagnosis or treatment that uses radiation?

All medical radioactive techniques carry a risk as they increase the exposure of patients to radioactive sources. Doctors have to decide in each case whether the benefits outweigh the risks.

5 Explain the difference between a cure and palliative care.

6 Explain how PET scanners can reveal useful information about the function of organs.

ResultsPlus
Watch Out!

When asked about the medical uses of ionising radiation, students usually write about using it to produce images to assist in diagnosis but forget about its use in destroying unwanted tissue.

Learning Outcomes

3.1 Evaluate the social and ethical issues relating to the use of radioactive techniques in medical physics

3.22 Compare and contrast the treatment of tumours using radiation applied internally or externally

3.23 Describe palliative care including the use of radiation in some instances

3.24 Explain some of the uses of radioactive substances in diagnosis of medical conditions, including PET scanners and tracers

3.25 Explain why isotopes used in PET scanners have to be produced nearby

HSW 13 Explain how and why decisions that raise ethical issues about uses of science and technology are made

>>>>>>>>>>>>>>>>>>> Where on Earth can you find a fridge that is colder than deep outer space?

What are particle accelerators used for?

The superconducting electromagnets used in the Large Hadron Collider (LHC) at CERN in Geneva, Switzerland are kept at −271 °C, colder than the deepest parts of outer space.

> **1** Explain why it is important that scientists publish scientific papers about the experiments they do. **(?)**

Experiments in **particle physics** help scientists build up a picture of the properties of **sub-atomic particles** and how they are held together. Even particles like protons are made of smaller **fundamental particles**. New theories and models of these particles are tested over time as other scientists repeat experiments and critically evaluate the work published in science journals.

A *ATLAS's powerful magnets bend the paths of charged particles produced in collisions at the LHC. ATLAS could answer questions like why particles have mass.*

Some particle physics experiments are on a small scale, while others study particles at very high kinetic energies and require extremely large and expensive apparatus. Thousands of people from over 100 countries worked together to fund and build the LHC accelerator. The advantage of collaboration is that it brings together expertise from around the world and shares the costs of experiments.

The LHC is a **particle accelerator**. It can accelerate two beams of protons or ions to very high speeds in opposite directions and allow them to collide head-on. Scientists then study the particles created in the collisions and may discover new particles.

B *Hammer thrower in action*

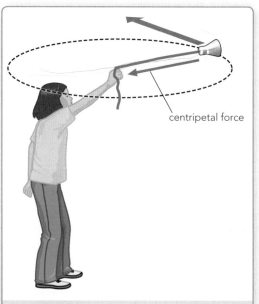

centripetal force

C *Circular motion requires a centripetal force.*

Circular motion

In 'hammer' throwing a heavy mass (the hammer) is swung in a circle and then released.

To keep the hammer moving in a circle a **resultant force** acting inwards along the radius is needed. This is called a **centripetal force**. The centripetal force for the hammer is provided by the tension in the wire. When the hammer is released there is no longer a centripetal force and it travels in a straight line at a tangent to the circular path it had been following.

Cyclotrons are particle accelerators in which moving charged particles are bent into circular or spiral paths, as in the LHC. A constant magnetic field applied at right angles to the particle's motion produces the centripetal force required.

A voltage placed across a gap between two 'D-shaped' magnetic field regions accelerates the charged particles. The path of the particles spirals outwards as their speed increases. On leaving the magnetic field, the particles travel in a straight line towards a specific target. In the LHC, this target is another particle beam.

If a high-energy proton is allowed to collide with a stable element, the nucleus of this element can be changed into an unstable nucleus of a different element. This is a **radioactive isotope**. Small cyclotrons are now used in hospitals to produce the short-lived isotopes needed in **PET scanners**.

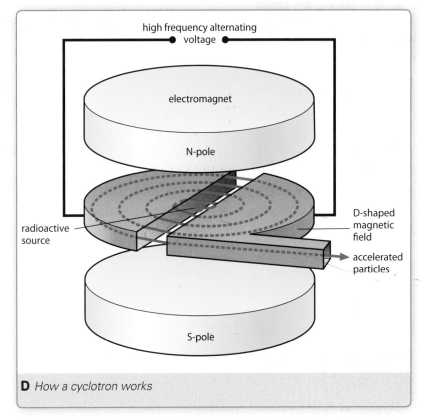

D *How a cyclotron works*

2 What is a centripetal force?

3 A rubber bung is swung on a piece of string in a vertical circle. Where does the resultant centripetal force to keep it moving in a vertical circle come from?

4 Explain why the magnetic field in a cyclotron must be at right angles to the direction of motion of the charged particles to produce circular motion.

5 Explain how a radioactive isotope can be produced from a stable isotope.

6 Suggest some of the advantages of scientists from many countries sharing their expertise on projects such as the LHC.

Learning Outcomes

4.1 Discuss how instruments, including particle accelerators, can help scientists develop better explanations about the physical world

4.2 Discuss reasons for collaborative, international research into big scientific questions, including particle physics

4.3 Explain that for motion in a circle there must be a resultant force known as a centripetal force that acts towards the centre of the circle

4.4 Explain that particle accelerators called cyclotrons cause charged particles to move in a circular or spiral path, due to a magnetic field

4.5 Demonstrate an understanding that certain stable elements can be bombarded with proton radiation to change them into radioactive isotopes

4.6 Describe the use of particle accelerators (cyclotrons) to produce radioactive isotopes for medical purposes

HSW 14 Describe how scientists share data and discuss new ideas, and how over time this process helps reduce uncertainties and revise scientific theories

>>>>>>>>>>>>>>>>> What type of ball can be made to bounce as high as a three storey building?

P3.21 Collisions

 What factors affect the bounce of a ball?

A Super Ball is a toy that was invented in 1965 by Norman Stingley. Its extreme springiness ensured that when dropped it bounced back to more or less the same height it was dropped from and when thrown down against the ground it could leap over a three storey building.

When a ball is dropped onto the ground it undergoes an **inelastic collision**. This means some **kinetic energy** of the ball is transferred to the surroundings. The ball does not rebound to the same height since kinetic energy has been transferred.

A *A ball bounces when it hits the ground*

Your task

You are going to plan an investigation that will allow you to find out the factors affecting the height of rebound of bouncing balls.

Learning Outcomes

4.12 Investigate factors affecting the height of rebound of bouncing balls.

ResultsPlus
Build Better Answers

When planning an investigation like this, one of the skills you will be assessed on is your ability to *evaluate the method used*. There are 6 marks available for this skill. Here are two extracts focusing on this skill. Other skills that you need for the practical assessment are dealt with in other lessons.

Student extract 1 | **A basic response for this skill**

The student has identified a weakness in the method.

> Measuring the height of the rebound was difficult and may have led to some inaccuracies.

This answer is not complete because the student has not suggested how to improve the method nor identified what inaccuracies were caused.

Student extract 2 | **A good response for this skill**

Relating the problems with the method back to the quality of data shows that you have thought about the practical in detail.

> I wanted to test the idea that the same percentage energy was lost on each bounce, irrespective of the height the ball was dropped from. This required accurate and reliable measurement of the bounce height. However, it was difficult to measure the height of the bounce accurately and this may have led to the anomaly in the results. To improve the measurement of the bounce height I could have made a video recording of the bounce. By including a metre rule in the video frame I could then play back the video and stop it when the ball was at the highest point of its bounce and measure the height more accurately. This would improve the accuracy of my results and would mean that I collected better quality results.

This is a good answer because the student has explained what the problem with the method was and related it to the original hypothesis.

The student has indicated how better quality evidence could be collected.

ResultsPlus

To access 2 marks

- Identify a strength or weakness in the method
- Suggest how to improve the method and justify the comments made

To access 6 marks

- Describe strengths and weaknesses in the method and relate them to the hypothesis, and reasons for any anomalies
- Suggests how to improve the method, justifying comments made relating to the hypothesis and how better quality evidence could be produced (including reasons for anomalies)

How is an elastic collision different to an inelastic collision?

Many scientists believe that 90% of the Universe is made out of 'dark matter' but so far, no experiment has detected it. In proton-proton collisions at the Large Hadron Collider, detectors measure the total momentum of the particles before and after collision. If these do not balance, this is evidence that dark matter particles have been produced.

A *Collisions between subatomic particles*

1 a In Figure B how do you know that all the kinetic energy of the grey ball was transferred to the red ball during the collision?
b Is this an elastic collision?
c What evidence is there to suggest that momentum has been conserved during the collision?

Colliding objects have kinetic energy and momentum, which is a measure of the strength of movement (momentum = mass x velocity). Momentum is conserved (remains unchanged) in all collisions. In an **inelastic collision** kinetic energy is not conserved but in an **elastic collision** it is conserved.

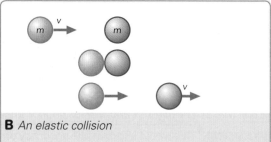

B *An elastic collision*

In Figure B the two balls have equal mass. The grey ball is moving at a constant velocity towards the stationary red ball. On collision the grey ball stops and the red ball carries on with at same velocity that the grey ball had before the collision. This is an elastic collision.

Inelastic collisions

In Figure C two trolleys of equal mass approach each other with equal but opposite velocities, vm/s. When they collide they stick together and instantly stop.

2 a In Figure C what is the value of the total momentum after the collision? Explain.
b How does this show that momentum has been conserved during the collision?

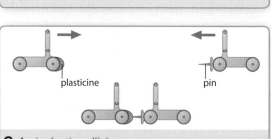

C *An inelastic collision*

Momentum is a **vector** and has both size and direction. In Figure C if the momentum of the trolley moving to the right is positive, then the momentum of the other trolley is negative.

3 Explain what happened to the kinetic energies of the cars in Figure D when they collided.

D *The collision of two vehicles where both vehicles come to a stop is an example of an inelastic collision.*

The moving trolleys each had kinetic energy, but after colliding the total kinetic energy was zero. Kinetic energy has not been conserved. Some has been transformed to heat and sound energy.

Solving problems using momentum conservation

Figure E shows two cars before and after colliding. We can use the conservation of momentum to calculate v, the speed of car B after the collision.

Momentum of an object = mass × velocity

Total momentum before = (500 × 5) + (400 × 2)

$$= 3300 \, \text{kg m/s}$$

Total momentum after = (500 × 3) + (400 × v)

Momentum is always conserved in collisions, so

$$3300 = 1500 + 400 \times v$$

$$v = \frac{1800}{400}$$

$$= 4.5 \, \text{m/s}$$

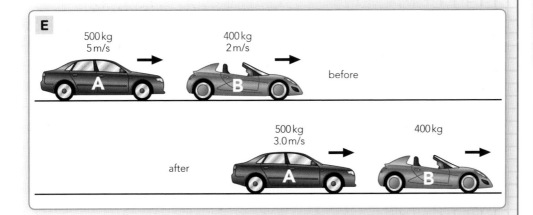

E

500 kg
5 m/s

400 kg
2 m/s

before

A

B

500 kg
3.0 m/s

400 kg

after

A

B

Skills spotlight

Many phenomena can be explained using scientific models and theories. Use the idea of conservation of momentum to explain why a golf ball leaves the surface of a golf club at a much greater velocity than the club was moving before it hit the ball.

H 4 **a** Find out if kinetic energy is conserved in the collision in Figure E. **b** Comment on your answer to part **a**.

Results Plus
Watch Out!

When describing annihilation, students correctly write about the electron and positron being destroyed but forget to mention the production of two gamma rays moving in opposite directions.

H 5 During an experiment, a student pushes a glider of mass 400 g along an air track with a velocity of 2.0 m/s. It collides with a stationary glider of mass 600 g which moves on with a velocity of 1.6 m/s. **a** Find the velocity of the 400 g glider after the collision. **b** Show that the collision is elastic.

6 A car collided head on with another car and both came to a stop. Both cars had the same mass. Describe this collision and explain why the momentum does not change during the accident even though the cars stop moving.

Learning Outcomes

4.7 Demonstrate an understanding that for inelastic collisions momentum is conserved but kinetic energy is not conserved

4.8 Demonstrate an understanding that for elastic collisions both momentum and kinetic energy are conserved

4.9 Analyse collisions in one dimension in terms of momentum and kinetic energy

H 4.10 Carry out calculations using momentum conservation for a two-body collision (in one dimension only)

H 4.11 Carry out calculations using conservation of kinetic energy for a two-body elastic collision (in one dimension only)

HSW 3 Describe how phenomena are explained using scientific theories and ideas

Why do the radioactive isotopes used in PET scans produce pairs of gamma rays?

There's nothing fictional about anti-matter. In 1933 Paul Dirac was awarded the Nobel Prize for Physics for predicting the existence of anti-matter following his analysis of Einstein's work on the equivalence of mass and energy.

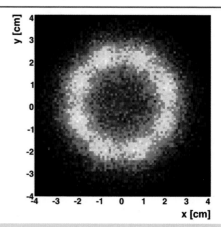

A Anti-hydrogen atoms have been created in collisions at the LHC.

Anti-matter is matter that has particles of the same mass and properties as their counterparts but opposite electrical charges. For example, the anti-matter of an electron is a **positron**. The positron has the same mass as the electron but carries a positive rather than a negative charge.

? 1 What is meant by saying that energy is 'conserved' when something happens?

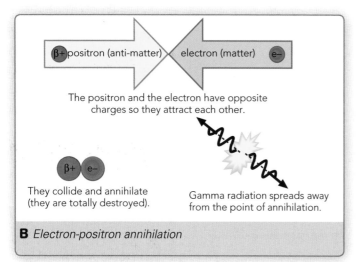

The positron and the electron have opposite charges so they attract each other.

They collide and annihilate (they are totally destroyed).

Gamma radiation spreads away from the point of annihilation.

B Electron-positron annihilation

When an electron and a positron collide, **annihilation** occurs and two gamma rays are produced moving in opposite directions.

The electron and positron have been destroyed so mass seems to have disappeared. This seems to contradict the basic conservation laws of physics, in particular those of mass, momentum and energy.

The answer can be found in Einstein's idea of **mass-energy equivalence**. The masses of the annihilated electron and positron are converted into an equivalent amount of energy. We say mass-energy (the combination of mass and energy) has been conserved.

? 2 In electron-positron annihilation, explain what happens to the electron and positron masses.

In the simplest case, imagine that the electron and positron approach each other with the same speed. This means they have equal but opposite momentum and so the total momentum before collision is zero. Although the gamma rays have no mass they do have energy, which has a mass equivalent. So the gamma rays have momentum. For the total momentum after collision to be zero, two gamma rays of the same energy must be produced, moving in opposite directions. If only one gamma ray were produced, momentum would not be conserved as the single gamma ray would carry momentum in only one direction.

An electron has −1e charge and a positron has +1e charge, so the total charge before collision is zero. After collision, the total charge is still zero since gamma rays carry no charge. Hence charge is also conserved during electron-positron annihilation.

In Einstein's famous equation $E = mc^2$, E is the energy of a system, m is its mass and c is the speed of light, 3×10^8 ms^{-1}.

The mass of an electron is 9×10^{-31} kg, so its energy equivalent is $9 \times 10^{-31} \times (3 \times 10^8)^2$ or 8×10^{-14} J. A positron has the same mass as an electron, so the total energy released by positron-electron annihilation is 1.6×10^{-13} J. Experiments have shown that the total energy of the two gamma rays produced is equivalent to this value.

Positron emission tomography (PET) scanners

During a PET scan the annihilation of an electron and positron is used to produce a gamma ray pair that enables an internal image of the body to be produced. Radio isotopes that emit positrons are injected into the blood in a tracer and the tracer accumulates in various tissues of the body. The positrons emitted by the radioactive isotope travel only a short distance through the tissue before encountering an electron. When this occurs annihilation takes place and a gamma ray pair is produced and detected by sensors positioned round the patient. The detection of the gamma ray pairs in the PET scanner enables a picture of the internal organs to be produced.

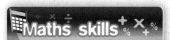

Maths skills

These masses and energies are usually written in **standard form** because they are very small numbers. 1.6×10^{-13} J is actually 0.00000000000016 J, the decimal point has been moved 13 places to the left.

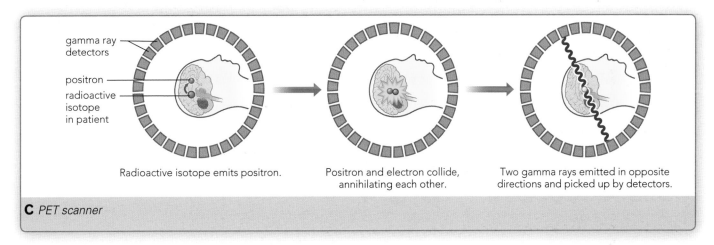

Radioactive isotope emits positron.

Positron and electron collide, annihilating each other.

Two gamma rays emitted in opposite directions and picked up by detectors.

C PET scanner

3 Explain why the observed gamma ray energies from positron-electron annihilation verify Einstein's prediction of the equivalence of mass and energy.

4 Describe how mass energy is conserved in electron-positron annihilation.

5 Suggest why PET scan 'tracers' use radioactive isotopes that produce positrons rather than those that are gamma ray emitters.

6 Why is it not possible in electron-positron annihilation to produce:
a just one gamma ray with a mass energy equivalent to the electron plus the positron
b two gamma rays with a total mass energy equivalent to the electron plus the positron, but moving in the same direction as each other?

Skills spotlight

Conservation of mass-energy is a model that helps explain electron-positron annihilation. Use the model to explain how the energy of the gamma rays produced would change if matter and anti-matter of greater mass annihilated each other.

Learning Outcomes

4.13 Recall that gamma rays can be produced by the annihilation of an electron and a positron

4.14 Apply conservation of momentum and charge to positron electron annihilation

4.15 Apply the idea of conservation of mass energy for positron electron annihilation
   a in a qualitative way (calculations involving $E = mc^2$ will not be required) b in a quantitative way using the equation $E = mc^2$

4.16 Explain the use of radio isotopes in PET scanners to produce gamma rays

HSW 3 Describe how phenomena are explained using scientific models

:::: **What is absolute zero?**

The surface temperature on Triton is the coldest known temperature in the Solar System, at -235 °C. Triton has volcanoes that erupt with ammonia lava and geysers that spit out liquid nitrogen.

The **kinetic theory** states that everything is made of tiny particles (atoms or molecules).

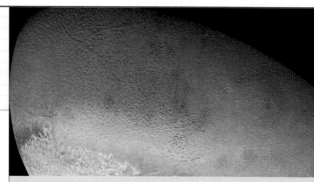

A The surface of Triton, one of the moons of Neptune

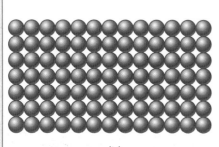
solid

liquid

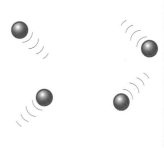
gas

B Particles in the three states of matter

1 Compare how the particles move in solids, liquids and gases.

In solids, particles are held closely together by strong forces. They can vibrate but they cannot move around freely.

In liquids, the bonds between the particles are not quite as strong and the particles can move past each other. The particles are still very close together, so liquids are usually incompressible.

In a gas, the particles are far apart and moving around quickly. Gases are compressible, and expand to fill a container. The temperature of a gas is a measure of the average **kinetic energy** of the particles in the gas. The faster the average speed of the particles, the higher the temperature. Heating a gas increases the kinetic energy of the particles, so they move faster and the temperature rises.

Skills spotlight

Scientists often use models to explain how substances behave. Suggest some advantages and disadvantages of representing particles as spheres.

Particles and pressure

The **pressure** of a gas is caused by the forces exerted as the moving particles hit the walls of a container. The faster the particles are moving, the more collisions there will be, and the more force they will exert when they hit the walls. Increasing the temperature of a gas increases the speed of the particles, so it also increases the pressure of the gas. The units for pressure are **pascals (Pa)**, where $1\,Pa = 1\,N/m^2$.

Absolute zero

Figure C shows how the pressure of a fixed volume of gas changes with temperature. The measurements cannot continue below the boiling point of the substance, as the gas will condense to form a liquid. However, the same graph is obtained for all gases, and if the lines are extended to colder temperatures they meet the horizontal axis at −273 °C. The temperature of −273 °C is called **absolute zero**. This is the temperature at which the pressure of a gas would be zero and the particles would not be moving.

The **Kelvin temperature scale** measures temperatures relative to absolute zero. The units are **kelvin (K)**, and 1 K is the same temperature *interval* as 1 °C. Absolute zero is 0 K on this scale.

Temperatures are easily converted:
- to convert from Kelvin to Celsius, subtract 273 degrees
- to convert from Celsius to Kelvin, add 273 degrees.

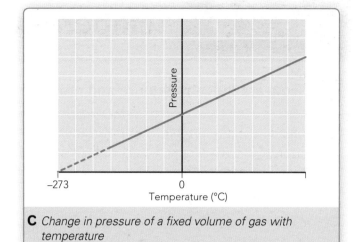

C *Change in pressure of a fixed volume of gas with temperature*

> **e.g.**
>
> What is the boiling point of water in kelvin?
>
> boiling point = 100 °C + 273 = 373 K

The average kinetic energy of the particles in a gas is directly proportional to the Kelvin temperature of the gas.

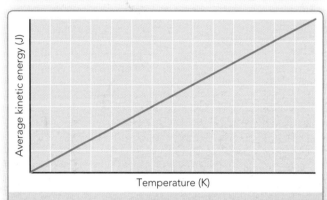

D *The relationship between the average kinetic energy of gas particles and the Kelvin temperature of the gas*

---

2 What causes pressure in a gas?

3 Why does increasing the temperature of a fixed volume of gas increase its pressure?

4 What are the following temperatures on the Celsius scale?
a 500 K   b 100 K

5 If the temperature of a gas is increased from 200 K to 400 K, what happens to the kinetic energy of the particles?

6 Explain why the Kelvin temperature scale is useful.

Watch Out!

Remember that pressure depends on the *average* kinetic energy of the particles. Some particles will be moving faster than the mean speed, and some will be moving more slowly.

Learning Outcomes

5.1 Use a simple kinetic theory model to describe movement of particles in the three states of matter

5.2 Explain the pressure of a gas in terms of the motion of its particles

5.3 Describe the effect of changing the temperature of a gas on the speed of its particles

5.4 Describe the term absolute zero, −273 °C, in terms of the lack of movement of particles

5.5 Convert between the Kelvin and Celsius scales

5.6 Recall that the average kinetic energy of the particles in a gas is directly proportional to the Kelvin temperature of the gas

HSW **3** Describe how phenomena are explained using scientific models

P3.25 Temperature and volume for a gas

How are the temperature and pressure of a gas related?

A bullet has shattered this rose because the rose has been frozen by dipping it into liquid nitrogen. Liquid nitrogen is obtained by liquefying air. This is done by suddenly expanding air to make its temperature drop.

The temperature of a gas can be changed by changing its volume. You can feel this for yourself by letting down a bicycle tyre – the air coming out of the valve expands as it leaves the tyre, and you can feel that it is colder than the air around you.

A Bullet shattering a frozen rose.

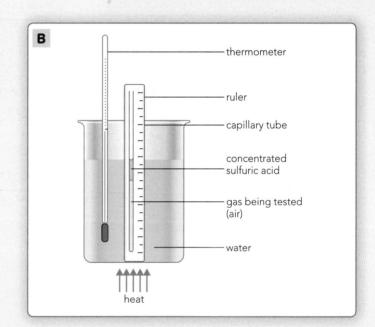

B
- thermometer
- ruler
- capillary tube
- concentrated sulfuric acid
- gas being tested (air)
- water

heat

Your task

You are going to plan an investigation that will allow you to find out how the temperature of a gas depends on its volume. You will be given a narrow glass tube, sealed at one end, with a bead of liquid inside it.

Learning Outcomes

5.7 Investigate the temperature and volume relationship for a gas

Build Better Answers

When planning an investigation like this, one of the skills you will be assessed on is your ability to *choose suitable equipment*. There are 2 marks available for this skill. Here are two extracts focusing on that skill. Other skills that you need for the practical assessment are dealt with in other lessons.

Student extract 1 — A basic response for this skill

You don't get any marks for listing something that you were told in the student brief.

> I will use a thin glass tube with some liquid in it. I will use a water bath

There are several pieces of equipment missing from this answer. It is important to provide a full list.

Student extract 2 — A good response for this skill

This is good because it explains *why* you need the thin glass tube.

> I will use a thin glass tube with some liquid in it. This traps a fixed mass of air and allows the volume to change at a constant pressure (atmospheric pressure). I will use a water bath to change the temperature of the tube and a thermometer to measure the temperature. I will use a ruler to measure the length of the trapped air in the tube, which will give me a measure of its volume.

This student has listed all the apparatus needed *and* explained why each piece of apparatus is needed.

 ResultsPlus

To access 2 marks

- Choose the most relevant resources or equipment
- Explain the reasons for your choices and the choices are fully relevant to method

P3.26 Volume and pressure for a gas

How are the volume and pressure of a gas related?

Joseph Kittinger set the current record for the highest altitude free-fall parachute jump in 1960, jumping from an altitude of 31 300 m. High altitude parachutists wanting to break this record all jump from helium-filled balloons. These balloons are not filled completely on the ground, or they would burst as the balloon ascends and the gas inside them expands.

As the balloon shown in Figure A ascends into the atmosphere, both the pressure and the temperature of the air around it change. The pressure and temperature of the outside air affect the volume of the gas inside the balloon. You can also see the effect of changing the pressure on the volume of a gas when you blow up a balloon or pump up a bicycle tyre.

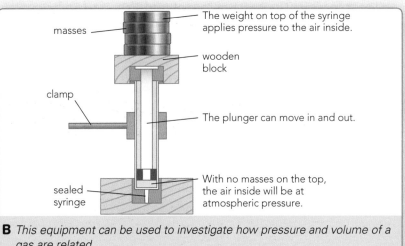

B This equipment can be used to investigate how pressure and volume of a gas are related.

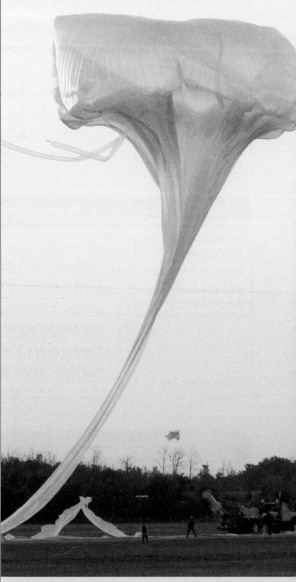

A A high altitude balloon being launched.

Your task

You are going to plan an investigation that will allow you to find out how the pressure and volume of a gas are related.

Learning Outcomes

5.9 Investigate the volume and pressure relationship for a gas

ResultsPlus
Build Better Answers

When planning an investigation like this, one of the skills you will be assessed on is your ability to *plan an investigation*. There are 4 marks available for this skill. Here are two extracts focusing on that skill. Other skills that you need for the practical assessment are dealt with in other lessons.

| Student extract 1 | A basic response for this skill |

The student has explained the range of observations that will be made.

I will change the pressure on the air in the syringe by putting masses on top of it. Each time I add a mass I will measure the volume of the air. I will do this for 5 different masses, starting with nothing and adding 1 kg for each measurement.

This explains how the student is going to change the pressure and what they are going to measure.

| Student extract 2 | A good response for this skill |

This part explains *why* the student is going to change the pressure.

This explains *why* the student has chosen the masses.

I am investigating the relationship between the pressure and volume of a gas, so I need to change the pressure on a fixed quantity of gas and measure the volume. I will do this by trapping air in a syringe and adding masses to the syringe. I can calculate the pressure on the air from the mass and the area of the syringe. I will add 1 kg each time until I have 5 different pressures, as this will give me a large enough range of values to show a pattern on the graph.

This explains *how* they are going to do it.

 ResultsPlus

To access 2 marks

- Arrange the method logically so that it produces results
- Choose a range of data/observations that would test the hypothesis

To access 4 marks

- Arrange the method logically to produce results and include an explanation of why it would test the hypothesis
- Choose a range of data/observations that would test the hypothesis and explain why the range was chosen

How can we calculate the pressure or volume of a gas?

Freedivers swim underwater while holding their breath. The record time for staying underwater without breathing is about 11 minutes. People who work underwater usually need to stay underwater longer than this. They carry the air they need with them, compressed and stored in metal cylinders.

A

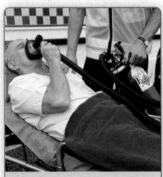

B *Paramedics using gas to relieve pain.*

Bottled gases are important in medicine. Patients with breathing difficulties are often given oxygen and some gases are also used for pain relief. Gases take up large volumes at atmospheric pressure and so they need to be compressed and stored at higher pressures.

Engineers who design the bottles for storing pressurised gases need to understand the relationships between pressure, temperature and volume to work out how much compressed gas can be stored and to make sure the bottles are strong enough.

If the volume of a gas increases at a constant temperature, the pressure decreases. The volume and pressure are related by this equation:

$$V_1 P_1 \ = \ V_2 P_2$$

where V_1 and V_2 are volumes (in m³) and P_1 and P_2 are pressures (in Pa).

? 1 Describe two uses for bottled gases.

2 What volume of gas (at atmospheric pressure) is stored at 230 000 000 Pa in a 0.15 m³ bottle?

> **e.g.**
>
> A cylinder of oxygen contains 0.3 m³ of gas at a pressure of 14 000 000 Pa. If all the oxygen is released from the cylinder without changing temperature, what will its volume be? Atmospheric pressure is approximately 100 000 Pa.
>
> You need to use this version of the equation:
>
> $$V_2 \ = \ \frac{V_1 P_1}{P_2}$$
>
> $$= \ 0.3 \,\text{m}^3 \ \times \ \frac{14\,000\,000 \,\text{Pa}}{100\,000 \,\text{Pa}}$$
>
> $$= \ 42 \,\text{m}^3$$

ResultsPlus
Watch Out!

Students often forget that in volume/temperature calculations the temperature must be on the Kelvin scale. See Page 227 for how to convert between Celsius and Kelvin.

If the temperature of a gas is increased at a constant pressure, the volume increases. The volume and temperature are related by this equation:

$$V_1 \ = \ \frac{V_2 T_1}{T_2}$$ where V_1 and V_2 are volumes (in m³) and T_1 and T_2 are temperatures (in K).

A hot air balloon contains $2000\,m^3$ of air at $100\,°C$ ($373\,K$). What volume of air at $5\,°C$ ($278\,K$) is needed to fill the balloon?

e.g.

$$V_1 = \frac{V_2 T_1}{T_2}$$

$$= 2000\,m^3 \times \frac{278\,K}{373\,K}$$

$$= 1491\,m^3$$

C

Combining the equations

The two equations given above can be combined. $\dfrac{P_1 V_1}{T_1} = \dfrac{P_2 V_2}{T_2}$

H

where P_1, V_1 and T_1 are the initial pressure, volume and temperature, and P_2, V_2 and T_2 are the final pressure, volume and temperature.

A $0.1\,m^3$ gas cylinder can stand a pressure of $20 \times 10^7\,Pa$ before breaking. It is filled with gas at $2 \times 10^7\,Pa$ at $20\,°C$. What temperature can it stand before it explodes?

e.g.

$$T_2 = \frac{P_2 V_2 T_1}{P_1 V_1} \qquad \frac{20 \times 10^7\,Pa \times 0.1\,m^3 \times 293\,K}{2 \times 10^7\,Pa \times 0.1\,m^3} = 2930\,K$$

3 A bicycle pump compresses $0.000\,025\,m^3$ of air at atmospheric pressure to a volume of $0.000\,010\,m^3$. What is the pressure of the compressed gas?

?

H 4 The gas bottle in question 2 is normally stored at $20\,°C$. What is the pressure in the bottle if the temperature rises to $40\,°C$?

5 Hospitals use a lot of oxygen and other gases. Explain why these gases are stored above atmospheric pressure and how engineers can calculate the amount of gas at atmospheric pressure that can be stored in a cylinder.

Skills spotlight

Observations that involve numbers are quantitative. Observations described in words rather than numbers are qualitative.
a Which of these statements is quantitative?
'If you put an empty paint tin on a fire it will explode.'
'This gas cylinder can store gas at $300\,000\,000\,Pa$ without breaking.'
b Explain why one statement *needs* to be quantitative but the other does not.

Learning Outcomes

5.8 Use the relationship: $V_1 = \dfrac{V_2 T_1}{T_2}$ to calculate volume for gases of fixed mass at constant pressure (rearranging not required)

5.10 Use the relationship: $V_1 P_1 = V_2 P_2$ to calculate volume or pressure for gases of fixed mass at constant temperature

H 5.11 Use the equation:

$$\frac{\text{initial pressure}}{\text{(pascal, Pa)}} \times \frac{\text{initial volume (metre}^3, \text{m}^3)}{\text{initial temperature (kelvin, K)}} = \frac{\text{final pressure}}{\text{(pascal, Pa)}} \times \frac{\text{final volume (metre}^3, \text{m}^3)}{\text{final temperature (kelvin, K)}} \qquad \frac{P_1 V_1}{T_1} = \frac{P_2 V_2}{T_2}$$

5.12 Apply an understanding of the equation in 5.11 to the use of bottled gases in medicine, including the need for a pressure above atmospheric and the calculation of the volume of gas released at atmospheric pressure

HSW **10** Use qualitative and quantitative approaches when presenting scientific ideas and arguments, and recording observations

*These questions are indicative of the type of questions use
in the exam. Refer to page 6 for information on the grades*

The human eye

1. (a) Draw one straight line from each part of the eye to the job it does. One has been done for you.

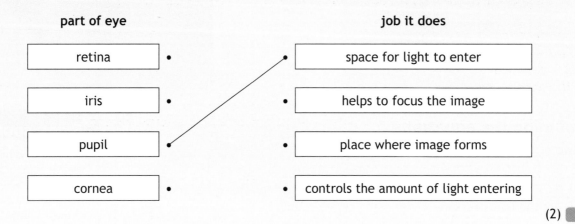

part of eye	job it does
retina	space for light to enter
iris	helps to focus the image
pupil	place where image forms
cornea	controls the amount of light entering

(2)

(b) The near point of the average adult eye is

   A   25 cm
   B   infinity
   C   the same as the focal length
   D   the distance between the cornea and the retina   (1)

(c) Describe how you can find an approximate value for the focal length of a
   converging (convex) lens.   (2)

(d)

$$\text{power of lens (D)} \quad = \quad \frac{1}{\text{focal length (m)}}$$

   Find the power of a lens which has a focal length of 50 cm.   (2)

(e) The diagram shows an eye which is not working correctly.

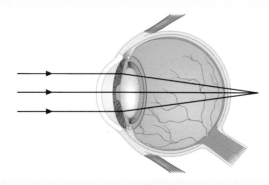

   Explain the symptoms and causes of the problem and how it can be corrected.
   You may draw a diagram to help your explanation.   (6)

Pulse oximetry

2. (a) A pulse oximeter is connected to a finger. The light emitting diode is connected on one side and the detector is on the other side. The detector works because the light is

    A emitted
    B reflected
    C absorbed
    D transmitted   (1)

(b) The graph shows how oxygenated and deoxygenated blood absorb electromagnetic radiation at different wavelengths.

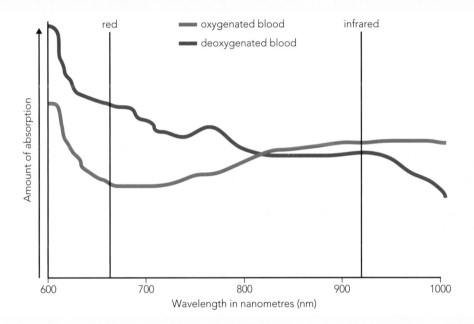

Two wavelengths have been highlighted — one for red visible light and the other for infrared.

(i) Most absorption for oxygenated blood occurs at a wavelength of

    A 600 nm
    B 800 nm
    C 915 nm
    D 1000 nm   (1)

(ii) Describe how the absorption of oxygenated blood changes with wavelength.   (2)

(iii) Compare the absorption of oxygenated and deoxygenated blood at the red and infrared wavelengths marked.   (2)

(c) One method of finding oxygen saturation is to test a sample of blood withdrawn from the patient. Suggest two ways in which a pulse oximeter is superior to a conventional blood test.   (2)

Radioactive and stable nuclei

3. The graph shows a curve for isotopes which are stable.

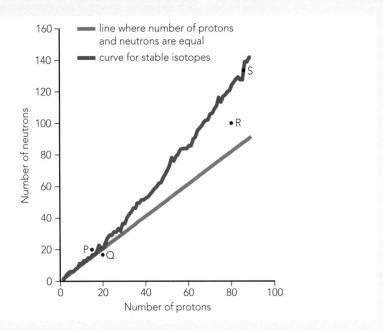

(a) State the letter which corresponds to the isotope which decays by positron emission. (1)

(b) State the difference between a positron and an electron. (1)

(c) Explain what happens when a positron collides with an electron. (2)

(d) A rule for nuclear stability has been suggested. It is called the odd-even rule. The table shows the likely stability of a nucleus depending on the number of protons and neutrons it contains.

number of protons	number of neutrons	numbe of stable isotopes	stability
even	even	168	most stable
even	odd	57	↓
odd	even	50	
odd	odd	4	least stable

Predict which of these isotopes is most likely to be stable.

A $^{17}_{8}O$

B $^{36}_{17}Cl$

C $^{40}_{20}Ca$

D $^{195}_{80}Ha$ (1)

(e) Explain in terms of protons, neutrons, electrons and quarks what happens during β-minus decay. (3)

(f) Complete this equation which shows β-minus decay. (3)

$$+ \quad {}^{195}_{80}\text{Hg} \quad \rightarrow \quad \text{Tl} \quad + \quad \beta$$

Electrons in motion

4. An electron (P) is fired at 100 m/s (towards the right) at another electron (Q), which is initially stationary.

$$\bullet \qquad\qquad\qquad \bullet$$

P   Q
→   stationary
100 m/s

The mass of an electron is 9×10^{-31} kg.

Imagine that there are no other particles which can affect the arrangement.

(a) Draw on the diagram the direction of the initial force acting

   i   on P due to Q
   ii on Q due to P   (2)

(b) Explain what will happen to Q initially.   (1)

(c) What is the initial momentum of P?   (1)

(d) Suggest how P and Q are moving when they are closest together.
    (You do not need to give any numerical values)   (2)

(e) When P becomes stationary, explain the motion of Q.   (3)

Gases

5. The graph below shows how the pressure of a fixed mass of gas varies with volume at different temperatures.

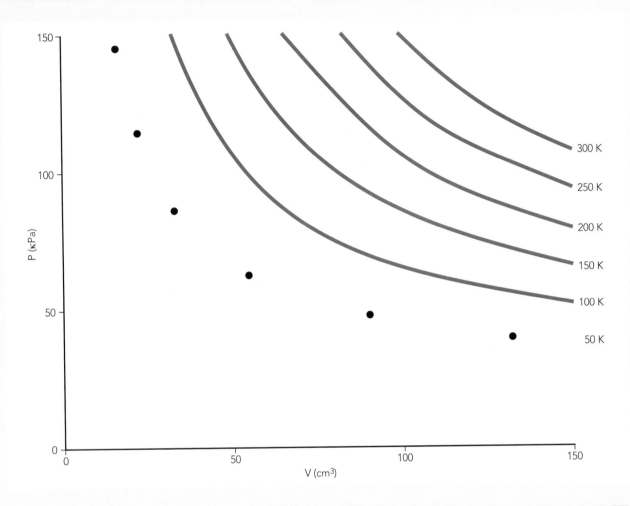

(a) What is the pressure when the gas has a volume of 140 cm³ and the temperature is 200 K? (1)

(b) Complete the line for the temperature of 50 K. (1)

(c) (i) A gas bottle at a hospital contains a fixed mass of the gas. The volume of the bottle is constant. Use the kinetic theory model to explain why the gas exerts a pressure. (2)

(ii) Sketch a graph to show how the average kinetic energy of the gas particles varies with the temperature. (2)

(d) Find values of temperature and pressure from the graph for a gas with a volume of 150 cm³. Use these data to plot a graph to show how pressure varies with temperature. (4)

Heating gases

6. (a) Which of the following is measured in Kelvins?

    A volume
    B mass
    C temperature
    D pressure

    (1) ▢

    (b) The temperature of some gas in a metal container is raised. Explain why the pressure of a gas increases if the temperature is increased.

    (2) ▢

    (c) A temperature of 50 K is the same as a temperature of

    A −323 °C
    B −223 °C
    C 223 °C
    D 323 C

    (1) ▢

    (d) Explain how changes in the speed of gas particles provide evidence for the idea of an absolute zero of temperature.

    (2) ▢

    (e) A bottle of gas has a pressure of 400 000 Pa and a temperature of 100 K. Its volume is doubled. What is its new pressure, if the temperature stays the same?

    (2) ▢

Glasses

7. (a) The unit for power of a lens is the dioptre, D. Which of these brings rays of light from a distant object to a focus nearest to the lens.

    A −1 D
    B −2 D
    C +1 D
    D +2 D

    (1) ▢

    (b) John's glasses say +2.
    Alan's glasses say +3.
    This means

    A John is more short-sighted than Alan
    B John is more long-sighted than Alan
    C John is less short-sighted than Alan
    D John is less long-sighted than Alan

    (1) ▢

(c)

$$\frac{1}{f} = \frac{1}{u} + \frac{1}{v}$$

An object is placed 30 cm in front of a lens of power +4. How far from the lens is the image formed?

(4)

(d) John is slightly long-sighted and Sally is very short-sighted. They both wear glasses to correct their vision. By comparing the materials, shape and power of the lenses, explain how each person's glasses improve their vision.

(6)

X-rays

8. The diagram illustrates a simple tube for producing X-rays.

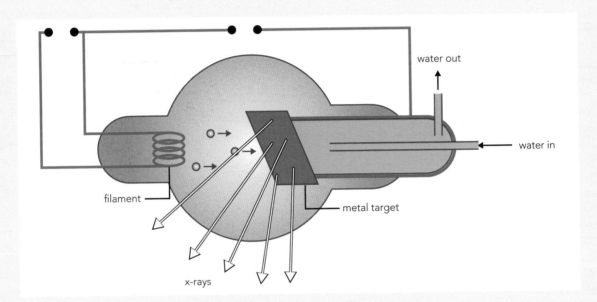

When the filament is heated, electrons escape from the cathode. Eventually, some produce X-rays.

(a) Complete the following sentence. The electrons escape into the space between filament and metal target by a process called _____ .

(1)

(b) The tube is only about 1% efficient at producing X-rays. Suggest why water flows through the target.

(1)

(c) Which row of the table is correct for the electrons once they have escaped from the cathode?

	the electrons move	because the metal target is
A	at constant speed	positive
B	faster and faster	positive
C	faster and faster	negative
D	at constant speed	negative

(1)

(d) State how these electrons form an electric current. (1)

(e) If the current measured is 0.05 mA, how many electrons strike the target per second? (2)

(f) Ali is a doctor and Ben is his patient. They are discussing a problem that Ben has.

I think you need to go for a CAT-scan and then maybe we can use X-rays to treat you.

Dr Ali

Yes, but I have read that X-rays are dangerous because ...?

Ben

Suggest risks that Ben might have read about. What might Dr Ali say to reassure him about the precautions which will be taken? (6)

Cyclotrons

9. A cyclotron is a particle accelerator. The diagram shows how a charged particle moves in a cyclotron.

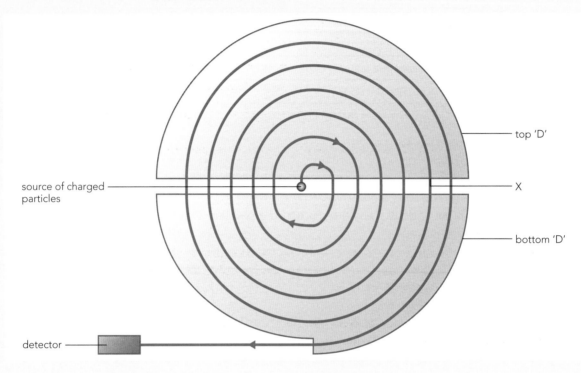

adapted from http://commons.wikimedia.org/wiki/File:Cyclotron.svg

(a) Which one of these cannot be accelerated by a cyclotron?

A a proton
B a neutron
C an electron
D an alpha particle
(1)

(b) (i) The name of the resultant force which must be supplied for an object to move in a circle is called a _____ force.
(1)

(ii) Explain what supplies this resultant force in a cyclotron.
(2)

(c) The first cyclotron to be built was 4 inches in diameter. The Large Hadron Collider at CERN is a successor to cyclotrons. It stretches over a radius of 10 km. Explain why major research institutions such as CERN result from collaboration on an international scale.
(2)

(d) There is a potential difference between the top D and the bottom D. The top D is negative and the bottom positive when a proton is at position X. The proton is moving clockwise round the cyclotron. Explain the effects on this particle if the magnetic field and/or the potential difference (voltage) between the Ds are switched off either separately or both together.
(6) ▨

Quarks

10. The table shows some of the properties of up and down quarks.

type of quark	Up (↑)	Down (↓)
mass	$\frac{1}{3}$	$\frac{1}{3}$
charge	$\frac{2}{3}$	$-\frac{1}{3}$

(a) A sub-atomic particle contains two down quarks and one up quark. What is its charge? (1) ▢

(b) State what happens to the atomic number of the product nucleus when an up quark changes into a down quark. (1) ▢

(c) Explain how the idea of quarks affected scientists' view of protons. (1) ▢

(d) The 'baryons' are a group of particles which contain 3 quarks.
In baryons there are four possible combinations containing only quarks which are up and/or down. Two of these are the proton and the neutron. Give the atomic numbers and mass numbers of the other two. (3) ▢

(e) Explain, using the quark model, what happens to a nucleus of radium ($^{226}_{88}$Ra) when it decays by emitting an alpha particle. (6) ▢

Here are three student answers to the following question. Read the answers together with the examiner comments around and after them.

Question | Dangers of ionising radiation | Grade | D–A*

A cyclotron that is used in a hospital produces dangerous radiation when it is in operation. The hospital also makes regular use of radioactive isotopes. Hospital workers are at risk from the radioactive isotopes and from radiation produced by the cyclotron.

Explain the dangers and how the risks can be reduced for hospital workers.

Student answer 1 | Extract typical of a level ① answer

You should mention how the coveralls prevent penetration to the body by absorbing the X-rays

Hospital workers reduce the risk by wearing lead cuveralls. These stop the dangerous radiations getting at their bodies. They should also leave the room when they can so they aren't exposed to radiations too long. Being exposed a long time will cause damage to their bodies.

Lead coveralls would be effective protection, but would be very heavy and difficult to move around in. Take care to spell all words correctly, even non-scientific terms.

Good – reducing the time workers are exposed to radiation is an effective way to reduce risk.

Examiner summary
This answer outlines two main methods of protection: shielding and reduced exposure time. However the shielding method suggested is not really practical. It would be helpful to include some of the scientific reasons behind the protection methods, and medical reasons why protection is needed.

Student answer 2 | Extract typical of a level ② answer

Good – the main medical danger from radiation is an increased risk of cancer.

This is a much better explanation of how the effects of radiation are reduced with increasing distance.

Any rays reaching you will cause damage to your internal organs like the liver and cause cancer. So they need to be stopped from reaching you. Hospital workers should stay as far away from radiation as possible. The further you are away, the less chance a ray has of finding you. Wearing lead absorbs the radiation and the less time you spend near it the safer you are. But lead is very heavy. So a hospital worker using the cyclotron should work behind lead screens as far away as possible, since the rays spread out and so the dose is less with distance. The lead will absorb all the radiation

Keeping as far away as possible from a radiation source is a way to reduce the danger. However, you should try to use scientific terms to describe this as rays do not 'find' someone.

Examiner summary
This answer explains why radiation is dangerous to humans. It also mentions two ways of reducing exposure (shielding and distance), It would help to include something about how reducing the time exposed to radiation reduces risk, and how exposure is monitored to ensure safety.

When working with or near radioactive sources it is very important that you are well protected otherwise you may get cancer or your cells may mutate. The longer you are exposed the more cells will be damaged. So one way of protecting workers is to keep the exposure time down. They can wear little badges with photographic film in them. The film goes dark if the worker is exposed for too long.

Another way of protection is to use thick lead screens. These absorb the radiation. Keeping far away from the radiation also helps. This can be done by using remote control and watching what they are doing on a screen. The further away you are the smaller the danger because the rays spread out according to an inverse square law – double the distance a quarter the dose.

This explains why shielding works – the material absorbs the radiation.

Good – this is a simple and effective way to check radiation exposure.

A good explanation of how radiation doses reduce with distance.

Examiner summary

This answer shows good understanding of the three main ideas involved. It would have been useful to further expand on working practices which can ensure the minimum time of exposure.

 ResultsPlus

Move from level ① to level ②

To move to level 2, you need to give more details about how and or why something is done. For example, the lead stops the radiation getting to the body by absorbing it.

You should also be careful that you do not overuse words like 'it' and 'they'. Too many of these words make it difficult to keep check on what the word refers to.

Move from level ② to level ③

To move to level 3, you need to organise your answer more clearly. Jot down the main points you want to make and think about the order you want to put them in. Then start writing properly. To move to the top level, you must explain the dangers and what will be damaged by the rays. You should mention all the important factors that affect radiation exposure.

Here are three student answers to the following question. Read the answers together with the examiner comments around and after them.

Question — Radiation in hospitals — Grade D–A*

Fluorine–18 is built into molecules which act like glucose. Tumour cells use more glucose than ordinary cells. Fluorine–18 collects in the tumour cells, where it decays and emits positrons. Explain how positron emission enables the tumour to be located accurately to help the consultant with his assessment. You may use a labelled diagram to help your answer.

Student answer 1 — Extract typical of a level ① answer

Don't get your radiation types mixed up. The radiation produced is actually gamma rays – pure energy, not alpha particles.

> The fluorine produces a positive and a negative electron which produce two alpha rays which are 180° to each other. These are detected by two out of many detectors on a circle on opposite sides of the machine. The tumour is somewhere along that line between the two detectors. Exactly where depends on the time difference between the two detections. Three lines are taken because the tumour is in 3-D. In actual practice, during the scan, thousands of readings are taken to pinpoint the tumour exactly.

It would be better to use the technical term 'positron' to describe the anti-particle to a normal electron.

You need to explain *how* taking several readings helps to pinpoint the tumour.

Examiner summary
This would be a much better answer if it correctly identified the radiation emitted as gamma rather than alpha. Try not to get the different types of radiation mixed up. Also, learn technical terms such as 'positron' so that you can use them in your answers. It would be helpful to give more details about why more than one line is needed to pinpoint the tumour's position.

Student answer 2 — Extract typical of a level ② answer

It is important to say that the two gamma rays are detected at almost the same time otherwise they may have come from different positrons initially.

> The positron and an electron disappear when they collide and are replaced by two gamma rays moving in opposite directions since $E = mc^2$. They will be detected diametrically opposite across the machine and so the tumour is along the diameter. For this the two gamma rays must be detected at almost the same time. Since the positron has only moved a little since it was produced the gamma rays come from very near the tumour if not inside it. So the tumour is along that diameter. If you wait for two pairs to be detected, then where they cross is the centre of the tumour. There will be many pairs produced and this makes it better.

The answer correctly mentions that they disappear but it is better to use the technical term 'annihilate'.

It is good to include this explanation of how the tumour can be pinpointed by detecting gamma rays, given off in several different directions. However you could make it clearer by improving the sentence structure of the answer. A plan would help with this.

Examiner summary

This answer outlines most of the important points but does not show complete understanding of the process. How do you know the two gamma rays detected come from the same electron-positron collision? It would be better to explain why they are detected at almost the same time. It also needs to explain more clearly how detecting several pairs of gamma rays can pinpoint the tumour. Finally, it would be useful to explain why the gamma rays travel at almost 180° to each other.

Student answer 3 | **Extract typical of a level ③ answer**

Momentum is always conserved but the emissions are not always at exactly 180°

A labelled diagram is good if it helps to explain the answer.

The F-18 concentrates in the tumour and so is like a source of positrons. When a positron is emitted it quickly meets an electron. They immediately annihilate each other producing two gamma rays when particle meets antiparticle. The gamma rays move almost at 180° to each other because of momentum conservation.

Good technical vocabulary, but the sentence is a little confused as there is too much information given at once.

gamma ray tracks

ring of detectors

They travel very fast and so reach the detectors on opposite sides at almost the same time. It is important to only count pairs of detections which arrive very close together (picoseconds) because otherwise the gamma rays may have come from two different annihilations. Once a pair of detections has been established, the scientists know that the tumour is along the line joining them. To find the position on that line, they have to take at least two readings. In practice, many readings are taken during the scan.

The explanation of how several readings pinpoint the tumour's position is not stated very clearly.

Examiner summary

This is a reasonably comprehensive account of how positron emission can be used to detect tumours.

 Results**Plus**

Move from level ① to level ②

To improve your mark to a level 2, you must try to include more science, such as why two lines enable you to pinpoint the tumour better than just one line. This topic depends on knowledge of technical terms. Make sure you learn the terms and are able to use them in your answers.

Often a quick sketch diagram can save a lot of words.

Move from level ② to level ③

To move to the next level, include in your explanation the very important reason for counting only those pairs of gamma rays that are detected almost at the same time. If we accept gamma-ray pairs that are not almost simultaneous, the rays may have come from different annihilations and so will not help to pinpoint the tumour. Be precise with your choice of words. For example, 'better' can mean 'cured' or 'more reliable', or many other things.

Build Better Answers

Here are three student answers to the following question. Read the answers together with the examiner comments around and after them.

Question	Volume and pressure for a gas	Grade	D–A*

The oxygen cylinders used in a hospital are different from the cylinders used in an ambulance. Hospital oxygen cylinders are larger, made of aluminium and they need a separate device to adjust the flow rate. These cylinders contain more oxygen, but work at a lower pressure.

Oxygen cylinders used on an ambulance are often made from steel, but the latest ones are carbon-fibre reinforced aluminium. The device to adjust the flow rate is built into the cylinder. Explain how the different cylinders make them suited to their use.

Student answer 1 — Extract typical of a level ① answer

This would be better with some explanation, for example showing how the high pressure can be created, using ideas from the kinetic theory of gases.

> The cylinders used in hospitals are bigger than those in ambulances. They have to be small to fit into an ambulance and light enough for the doctors to carry. If they were too big they would not be able to carry them to where an injured patient was if it was at the top of a mountain. They probably also have to have a high pressure to have enough oxygen to last until they get to hospital. An ambulance cylinder should be strong so that it doesn't explode in an accident due to the high pressure inside them.

This repeats information given in the question, so won't gain any marks. However it does go on to explain the benefits of this, which will gain marks.

Examiner summary
This answer is quite detailed about one area of the subject, You should make sure you cover all areas, not just one. The treatment of this topic does not contain much science – when explaining why ambulance oxygen cylinders are at high pressure, you should give an explanation from the kinetic theory of gases.

Student answer 2 — Extract typical of a level ② answer

This section tries to explain about pressure and volume, but it is quite confused. Be sure to include the mass (amount) of gas in your explanation.

> In an ambulance there could be a crash so the cylinders must be as strong as steel. They must also be strong because of the high pressure in them. This is possible because the pressure is inversely proportional to the volume. Small volume – large pressure. For the small volume, the pressure must be high otherwise there would not be enough to use. It is very cramped in an ambulance. It must be well over atmospheric pressure to get enough into a small volume. The device to adjust the flow rate is built into it to make it stronger and ready for emergency use.

This mentions the need for strength but not the downside of using steel – its weight. Carbon-fibre reinforced aluminium gives nearly the same strength but is much lighter.

In the last four sentences, the word 'it' is used to mean the conditions in an ambulance, the oxygen in the cylinder and the oxygen cylinder itself. This makes the meaning unclear.

Examiner summary

When considering gases, there are four possible variables: pressure, volume, temperature and mass of gas needed. These variables all depend on each other. This answer correctly mentions the first two variables, showing some good scientific understanding which takes it to level 2. It could also discuss the temperature changes in an ambulance which are greater than in a hospital.

Student answer 3 | **Extract typical of a level ③ answer**

> People in hospital who need oxygen receive it from a permanent supply but those on ambulances are moving and only need it for a short time. In an ambulance there will be a maximum of 2 patients needing oxygen. In towns the ambulance would be close to the hospital but in the country you can be over an hour away. So there must be enough oxygen to last 2 people for this long.
>
> The oxygen cylinder in an ambulance must be strong to prevent explosions in an accident. Steel is strong but heavy; carbon-fibre reinforced aluminium is just as strong, but lighter. Ambulances are small, so there is limited space for equipment to be stored. To store enough oxygen in a small space, the pressure must be higher than in a hospital oxygen cylinder. The pressure gauge on an ambulance cylinder is for only one or two people. It can be on the cylinder so it is handy for the operator. It also needs to be attached to the cylinder because you might take the cylinder out of the ambulance, up a mountain etc and you don't want to forget it until you are half-way up! A carbon-fibre reinforced cylinder is lighter to carry.
>
> In hospitals there is more space for cylinders, and they don't have to move. So they can be fixed to the wall permanently and connected up as needed.
>
> Finally, in a hospital, the temperature is well controlled while there will be a lot of different temperatures in an ambulance. If the temperature rises, the pressure in the cylinder will rise in proportion and so again it must be strong.

This would be a good opportunity to discuss the amount of gas and the pressure and the relationship between pressure and volume for a fixed mass and temperature.

An interesting point!

A good introduction referring to the supply of oxygen to different patients

Some good, relevant points about the weight problem of transporting a cylinder to remote places

A good discussion of the differences in demand between hospital and ambulance supplies

Examiner summary

This answer is a level 3, however, it could use kinetic theory to explain more fully the relationships between pressure, volume, temperature and mass.

  ResultsPlus

Move from level ① to level ②

To move to level 2, you should try to show what science you know and what you can do with it. There is quite a lot of information given in the question which is often ignored. These ideas are given to help you cover the range of material relevant to the question.

Move from level ② to level ③

To move to level 3, apply your scientific knowledge and ideas to the situation. The kinetic theory of particles in a gas enables you to discuss how the effect of temperature variation and the need for a large mass in a small volume affect the design of the container. Your answer should include the differences in design between cylinders used in ambulances and those for hospitals.

Here are three student answers to the following question. Read the answers together with the examiner comments around and after them.

Temperature and volume for a gas Grade D–A*

Joshim investigates how changing the temperature of a gas affects its volume. He starts with some gas in a syringe and seals it. Then he varies the temperature and measures how this affects the volume of the gas in the syringe. The table shows Joshim's results.

Temperature (°C)	0	20	45	55	70	90	100
Volume (cm³)	120	130	140	150	160	160	170

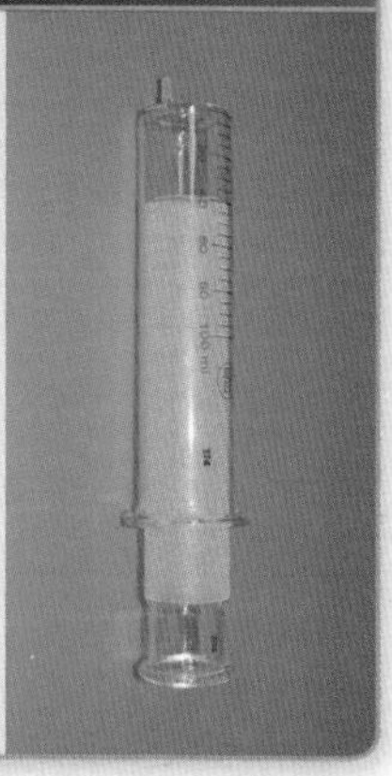

Suggest how Joshim should process the data to find a value for absolute zero and how he could improve the experiment to collect further good quality data.

Student answer 1 — Extract typical of a level ① answer

Be clear about which axis you are referring to. Extending these results back to absolute zero involves drawing a line through one axis to meet the temperature axis.

Joshim should repeat his readings three times. He needs to draw his graph on the right hand side of the paper leaving room on his scale for a temperature of about −300 to the left. Then he should plot his graph line back to the axis. The reading on the axis is the absolute zero of temperature. If he had more time he could have repeated the experiment. He could check the values with his mates and if they were all similar it must be correct. He should use more accurate thermometers.

Taking multiple readings is a good way to help spot any mistakes made when taking readings.

It would help to explain that the absolute zero of temperature is where the volume of the gas becomes 'zero'.

Examiner summary

This answer describes some good procedures but the reasons for using them are not always clear. Unless you are lucky, accepting what your mates say is risky. Some of their results may not be good; if you all do the same wrong thing then this will affect everyone's results.

Student answer 2 — Extract typical of a level ② answer

You suggest making extra readings, but you don't mention why. This is a good way to spot any anomalies in the readings.

The results of an experiment are better if you take more readings. Joshim took 7 but he needs at least 10. He should plot a graph and then continue it back until it meets the x-axis. He will get a more accurate value of the absolute zero where his line meets the temperature axis if he is careful to draw a very straight line. Some points further to the left of those he took would also help. At the absolute zero the gas volume is zero and you cannot get less than this. We could take a class average to get a better value.

Extending a line on a graph is called extrapolation. It is better to use the scientific term. State how far it goes, i.e. until it meets the temperature axis.

You should also explain why the gas volume becomes zero. Is it really zero?

Examiner summary

In this experiment Joshim has to go well beyond his readings to make use of the idea that the volume of a gas is zero at the absolute zero of temperature. This should be explained scientifically in terms of the fact that at absolute zero the particles making up the gas are no longer moving. Extrapolating the results back so far means that it is more important than usual to plot points accurately, using a straight ruler. You might also suggest how you can measure gas volumes at very low temperatures.

Student answer 3 | **Extract typical of a level ③ answer**

> Absolute zero is the temperature when the gas particles stop moving and take up zero volume. Joshim can plot his results on a graph and extrapolate them back until the line reaches the temperature axis. This temperature is the absolute zero. To improve his investigation he could take more readings between 0 and 100 °C, but it would be more useful to take as many measurements as possible below zero. He could use for instance liquid nitrogen or solid CO_2 to get lower temperatures. To process the data he could stick three pieces of graph paper together and plot the results on the right hand one. He can then extrapolate back from this graph on the other pieces. This is better than drawing the whole graph on one piece of paper as the results would be too squashed and the pencil line too thick. The precautions he should take include tapping the syringe to make sure the piston can move freely. Pressure also affects the volume so he must make sure the pressure of the atmosphere stays the same. It would be better also to use a more detailed scale on the syringe since this one has thickish markings every 2mm. He would also need a thermometer that could take readings at very low temperatures.

Good but you need to be careful that the scale is continuous.

Plotting the results on a fairly large scale like this helps to improve the accuracy of the extrapolated line.

This is good – these are practical things to improve the experiment.

Examiner summary

This answer has some valuable suggestions for improving the experiment. To make sure it reaches level 3, it should explain the science behind each suggestion made.

ResultsPlus

Move from level ① to level ②

To move to level 2, you should try to include more science, perhaps by explaining why taking more readings are better, or explaining why the experiment should work.

In practical questions like this it is good to discuss several ways to improve the experiment - using the right instruments is only one way.

Move from level ② to level ③

To move to level 3, you should be able to use the scientific method carefully, including taking precautions *and* explaining how they will help. The science behind the investigation should be included whenever possible. Other factors that might affect the gas volume, such as pressure, should also be mentioned.

Be the examiner

ResultsPlus

The diagram on the right shows a satellite S moving at a constant speed in orbit around a planet.

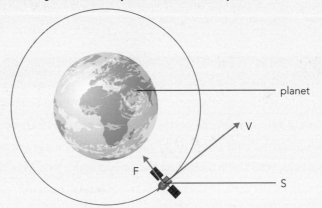

planet

V

F

S

not to scale

a) (i) Add an arrow to the satellite to show the direction of its velocity. Label this arrow V. (1)

(ii) Add another arrow to show the direction of the force acting on the satellite. Label this arrow F. (1)

▲ The red arrows on the diagram show the correct answers.

● Most students got the force arrow correct, but many did not draw the velocity arrow in the correct direction. Only about a quarter of students got both marks.

b) Explain why the satellite is accelerating even though it is moving at constant speed. (2)

▲ Any two points from the following would have gained both marks:
- There is a resultant force towards the centre (or gravity force) acting.
- The velocity is constantly changing.
- Velocity is a vector (or the direction of the satellite is changing).
- Acceleration is a change in velocity.

● Only about a fifth of students gained both marks, and almost half got no marks at all on this part.

ResultsPlus
Exam question report

The diagram below show an overhead view of a fairground ride. The ride turns at a steady speed. Which of these describes the motion of one of the cars?

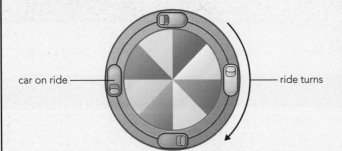

car on ride

ride turns

	Velocity of car	Acceleration of car
A	changing	constant size
B	steady	zero
C	steady	constant size
D	changing	zero

Answer: The correct answer is A.

How students answered

0 marks

Most students got this wrong.

1 mark

Don't forget that if the direction changes, the velocity changes too and so the car is accelerating.

ResultsPlus

Francine is a flight attendant. She has heard that cosmic radiation is a problem for people who fly a lot. Francine normally works on routes that go over the North Pole. Francine discovers that she is pregnant.

(a) State a possible ill-effect to her unborn baby caused by exposure to cosmic radiation. (1)

▲ **Correct answer:** It could lead to mutations in the baby's DNA that would affect its growth.

■ Not many students gained the mark for this, because their answers were too vague, just saying things such as 'damage cells' or 'cancer'.

(b) She wants to continue working for another six months. Suggest what she could do to protect her unborn baby. (1)

▲ **Correct answer:** Change to lower altitude flights, or switch to routes flying over the equator.

The first part of this question (not given above) was about the different doses of cosmic radiation people would receive for flights at different altitudes, and there was also a comparison between flights over the poles and over the equation. There were huge hints for answering this part of the question.

■ Most students ignored these hints and made silly suggestions such as wear lead-lined underwear, fly in lead aeroplanes, or even advice not to fly over the equator.

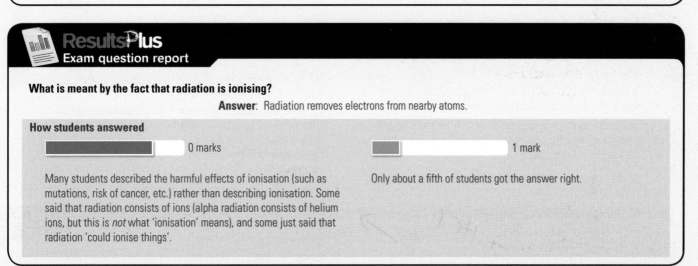

ResultsPlus
Exam question report

What is meant by the fact that radiation is ionising?

Answer: Radiation removes electrons from nearby atoms.

How students answered

0 marks

Many students described the harmful effects of ionisation (such as mutations, risk of cancer, etc.) rather than describing ionisation. Some said that radiation consists of ions (alpha radiation consists of helium ions, but this is *not* what 'ionisation' means), and some just said that radiation 'could ionise things'.

1 mark

Only about a fifth of students got the answer right.

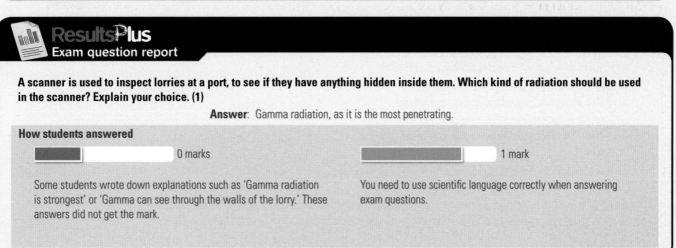

ResultsPlus
Exam question report

A scanner is used to inspect lorries at a port, to see if they have anything hidden inside them. Which kind of radiation should be used in the scanner? Explain your choice. (1)

Answer: Gamma radiation, as it is the most penetrating.

How students answered

0 marks

Some students wrote down explanations such as 'Gamma radiation is strongest' or 'Gamma can see through the walls of the lorry.' These answers did not get the mark.

1 mark

You need to use scientific language correctly when answering exam questions.

Glossary

absolute zero   The temperature at which the pressure of a gas drops to zero. It is −273°C or 0K.

acrosome   Cap-like structure on the head of a sperm cell that produces enzymes used to penetrate an egg.

action potential   Change in voltage across a neurone or the membrane of a cardiac muscle cell when an electrical impulse travels along it.

Ⓗ ADH (antidiuretic hormone)   A hormone made by the pituitary gland that causes the kidneys to retain water in the body.

aerobic   A process that takes place with oxygen.

Ⓗ African Eve   A woman who lived in Africa between 130000 and 200000 years ago, and passed on mtDNA to all humans living today.

agitation   Mixing the contents of a liquid, such as by stirring.

Agrobacterium tumefaciens   A bacterium used as a vector in genetic modification.

Ⓗ alcohol   Carbon compound which contains one or more hydroxyl (−OH) groups.

alkali   A solution which contains excess OH⁻ ions, and has a pH greater than 7.

alkane   A hydrocarbon in which all the bonds between the carbon atoms are single bonds.

alkene   A hydrocarbon in which there are one or more double bonds between carbon atoms.

Ⓗ allele   Different forms of a gene.

alpha decay   Emission of alpha particles from a radioactive isotope.

alpha (α) particle   Particle made of two protons and two neutrons, emitted as ionising radiation from some radioactive isotopes.

ampere (A)   The unit for measuring current. 1 ampere is a flow of 1 coulomb of charge per second.

anaerobic   A process that does not use oxygen.

analysis   Investigation into the kinds and/or amounts of substances present in a sample.

angle of incidence   The angle between the normal and the wave or ray when it hits a surface.

angle of reflection   The angle between the normal and the reflected wave or ray when it leaves the surface.

anion   Negatively charged ion, formed by gaining electrons (usually a non-metal ion).

annihilation   The total destruction of matter. In the context of matter and anti-matter particles this means the destruction of the masses of the particles involved, turning their masses into energy.

anode   Positive electrode.

antibody   A protein produced by lymphocytes. It attaches to a specific antigen on a microorganism and helps to destroy or neutralise it.

antidiuretic hormone   See ADH.

antigen   A protein that white blood cells recognise as foreign, for example, on the surface of a bacterium.

anti-matter   Matter composed of anti-particles that has the opposite charge but the same mass as the corresponding particle, which it annihilates on contact.

Ardi   The name given to the individual of a human-like species that lived 4.4 million years ago, whose fossil bones were discovered in Ethiopia.

aseptic   Free from microorganisms

aseptic precaution   See aseptic technique.

aseptic technique   Any method to ensure that living microorganisms do not come into contact with something.

atmosphere (atm)   A unit of pressure.

atomic (proton) number   The number of protons in the nucleus of an atom.

Avogadro's number   The number of particles or 'formula units' in a mole of any substance. One mole contains 6×10^{23} particles.

Ⓗ B lymphocyte   A type of lymphocyte that produces antibodies.

Ⓗ *Bacillus thuringiensis*   A bacterium that produces a substance that is toxic to insects that destroy crop plants. Some crop plants have been genetically modified with a gene from this bacterium.

base   A substance that will react with an acid to form only salt and water.

behaviour   The responses of an animal to what is going on around them.

beta (β) decay   Emission of an electron or a positron.

beta (β) particle   High kinetic energy electrons (β−) or positrons (β+) emitted as ionising radiation from some radioactive isotopes.

Ⓗ β+ decay   Radioactive decay in which a neutron becomes a proton, which remains in the nucleus, and a positron, which is emitted from the nucleus. One up quark changes into a down quark.

β− decay   Radioactive decay in which a neutron becomes a proton, which remains in the nucleus, and an electron, which is emitted from the nucleus. Ⓗ One down quark changes into an up quark.

biofuel   A fuel made from plants or microorganisms.

biological clock   A timing mechanism in the body that helps to control various rhythms, such as sleeping and waking.

biomolecule   A substance made by living organisms.

biotechnology   The alteration of natural biomolecules using science and engineering to provide goods and services.

bladder   The organ where urine is stored.

body language   Body positions and gestures that give observers information about the way an animal is feeling.

Bowman's capsule   The part of a kidney tubule where blood is filtered.

Ⓗ Bt toxin   A poison produced by a bacterium (*Bacillus thuringiensis*) when eaten by insects. The gene for the toxin has been transferred to some crop plants to reduce damage by insect pests.

burette   Apparatus used to accurately measure the volume of solution that has been added during a titration.

carbohydrate   A compound made up from carbon, hydrogen and oxygen.

carboxyl group   A group of two oxygen atoms, one carbon and one hydrogen, usually written as $-COOH$ or CO_2H.

carboxylic acid   An acid that contains a carboxyl group.

Ⓗ carrier   An individual with one copy of a recessive allele; they are not affected by the allele but can pass it on to their offspring.

CAT (computerised tomography) scan   An X-ray picture that shows a slice through the body.

Ⓗ catalyst   A substance that speeds up the rate of a reaction without being used up in the reaction.

Ⓗ catalytic hydrogenation   A reaction in which hydrogen is added to a compound using a catalyst to speed up the reaction, such as the addition of hydrogen to unsaturated oils with alkene C=C double bonds to produce a compound with only single bonds.

cathode   Negative electrode.

cation   Positively charged ion, formed by losing electrons (usually a metal ion).

centripetal force   Resultant force needed for circular motion in an inwards direction, towards the centre of the circle. Because the direction of motion is constantly changing the object is accelerating even though the speed does not change.

choice chamber   A device that offers small invertebrates such as woodlice two or more contrasting environments. The different conditions provide a stimulus to which the invertebrates respond.

chymosin   A protein-digesting enzyme used to make cheese that can be produced by genetically modified bacteria or yeast.

ciliary muscles   Muscles that relax or contract to change the shape of the lens of the eye.

circadian rhythm   A daily rhythm.

classical conditioning   A process in which learning causes a reflex action to happen in response to a different stimulus.

Ⓗ clone   A cell or organism that is genetically identical to the parent cell or organism.

Ⓗ co-evolution   The way in which two different species affect each other's evolution.

collecting duct   The final part of a kidney tubule, where water is reabsorbed.

communication   The exchange of information between organisms.

concentration   A measure of how much solute is dissolved in a solvent. The units are $g\,dm^{-3}$ or $mol\,dm^{-3}$.

conventional breeding   Producing offspring using the natural technique of cross-breeding.

converge   Bring closer together.

converging lens   A lens that brings light rays together (converges).

convoluted tubule   A part of the kidney tubule where glucose and other useful substances are reabsorbed into the blood.

cornea   Outer transparent layer of the eye that refracts light entering the eye.

Ⓗ corpus luteum   A structure that develops in an ovary after an egg has been released, which secretes progesterone.

corrosion   Chemical changes to metals converting them to compounds, as in rusting of iron.

corrosive   Material that corrodes, wears away and destroys.

coulomb (C)   The unit for measuring charge.

courtship behaviour   Actions that help male and female organisms to attract one another, and to maintain the bond between them.

Ⓗ cracking   A type of chemical reaction in which large alkane molecules are decomposed into two or more smaller molecules to form smaller alkanes and alkenes.

critical angle   The smallest angle of incidence at which the angle of refraction is 90° or total internal reflection occurs.

crop rotation   Where a different crop is planted in the same field each year in a 3- or 4-year cycle, such as potatoes, oats, beans and cabbages. This helps to control the build-up of soil pests for each crop.

crystallise   To make something from crystals.

cyclotron   Type of particle accelerator which uses a magnetic field to cause charged particles to travel in a circular path and also increases their speed.

cytoplasm   The liquid gel which makes up a lot of the body of a cell and is where many chemical reactions take place.

decay   The process of transforming to another element or isotope when a radioactive isotope emits ionising radiation.

decompose   The breakdown of the bodies of dead plants and animals by microorganisms called decomposers.

Ⓗ dehydration   Removing water.

diagnosis   Identifying a medical condition by its signs and symptoms or from a medical imaging scan.

dialysis   Process used to clean the blood of people with kidney failure, using membranes to filter out waste products.

dioptre (D)   Unit for power of a lens.

diploid   A cell that has two sets of chromosomes. In humans, almost all cells except the sperm and egg cells are diploid.

discharged   Conversion of ions to elements by electron transfers at the electrodes during electrolysis.

diverging lens   A lens that spreads out (diverges) light rays.

Ⓗ DNA ligase   An enzyme that joins two DNA molecules together.

dosage   In radiation treatment, the total amount of radiation absorbed by the patient.

Ⓗ dynamic equilibrium   When the forwards and backwards reactions are occurring at the same rate.

egg donation   Using an egg from one woman to produce an embryo that can be implanted into another woman.

elastic collision   A collision where there is conservation of kinetic energy.

electrocardiogram(ECG)   A graph showing the change in potential difference produced by the heart, used to monitor heart action.

electrode   A rod made of metal or carbon which carries the current in the electrolyte.

electrolysis   The process in which electrical energy from a d.c. supply decomposes some compounds. A chemical change.

electrolyte   Ionic liquid where moving ions carry the current during electrolysis.

electron   A negative particle of negligible mass and charge −1 (relative to a proton).

electron gun   A heated cathode that emits electrons, and the apparatus that focuses the beam of electrons.

electroplating   Covering one metal with a thin layer of another, using electrolysis.

endoscope   A tube that can be inserted into the body. It uses total internal reflection in optical fibres to send light into the body and reflect a picture back of what's inside.

Ⓗ endothermic   A type of reaction that takes in heat energy, e.g. photosynthesis.

enzyme   A protein produced by living organisms that acts as a catalyst to speed up the rate of a reaction.

ester   Carbon compound made from the reaction of an acid (often a carboxylic acid) with an alcohol.

ethanoic acid   The carboxylic acid which contains two carbon atoms, and which is the active ingredient in vinegar.

ethanol   The chemical name of the alcohol in alcoholic drinks.

ethology   The study of animal behaviour.

eutrophication   The build up of nitrates and phosphates in water which encourages excessive plant growth, leading to the depletion of light and oxygen supplies. This in turn leads to other organisms in the water dying off.

evacuated tube   A tube from which the air has been removed so that there is a vacuum.

evolution   The development of new species over time through a process of natural selection.

evolutionary strategy   A process that affects how a species changes over time and spreads, such as parental care that helps more offspring to survive for longer.

excess   Reactants that are not used up when the reaction is finished.

Ⓗ exothermic   A type of reaction that releases heat energy, e.g. combustion.

exponential growth   When the growth rate of a population is proportional to the population's current value.

far point   The farthest point at which the eye can focus.

fermentation   When microorganisms break down large molecules, using enzymes to produce different substances, including foodstuffs and drugs. For example, the conversion of glucose into ethanol (alcohol), using enzymes found in yeast.

fermenter   A container in which microorganisms are cultured to produce a useful substance on a large scale – the product is collected from the solution in which the microorganisms have grown.

fertilisation   The joining together of the nuclei of two gametes, e.g. a sperm and an egg.

fertiliser   Substance containing minerals that is added to the ground to increase plant growth.

filament A thin wire. In thermionic emission a heated filament emits electrons and forms the cathode when current is passed through an evacuated tube.

filtrate The product of filtration; a fluid that has passed through a filter.

filtration Separating large molecules from smaller ones using a partially permeable membrane, as in the Bowman's capsule of a nephron.

filtration The separation of undissolved solids from a liquid by filtering.

flame test An analytical test to find out which metal ion is present in a substance. Different metals produce different colours in a Bunsen burner flame.

flavonoid A coloured substance found in plant flowers and leaves.

fluoroscope A device that uses X-rays and a fluorescent screen to obtain moving pictures of the inside of the body.

focal length The distance from a lens to the focal point.

focal point The point at which nearly parallel light rays converge after passing through a lens (also the point where the image of a very distant object is produced).

Ⓗ follicle Fluid-filled sac in the ovary that contains the egg.

Follicle Stimulating Hormone See FSH.

fractional distillation A method of separating a mixture of liquids with different boiling points into individual components (fractions).

fractions The different mixtures produced by fractional distillation.

frequency The number of cycles of a wave per second, measured in hertz (Hz). 1 hertz is 1 wave per second.

Ⓗ FSH (follicle stimulating hormone) A hormone produced by the pituitary gland, which causes eggs to mature in the ovaries.

fundamental particle A particle that cannot be broken down into smaller units. At present quarks, electrons and their anti-particles (anti-quarks and positrons) are thought to be fundamental.

Fusarium A type of fungus that is grown in fermenters to produce mycoprotein as a food source.

gamete A sex cell (egg or a sperm cell).

gamma (γ) radiation Ionising radiation in the form of pulses of electromagnetic radiation with very short wavelengths.

general formula Formula showing the proportions of different atoms in a molecule for a series of compounds (a homologous series) that have similar properties. For example, alkenes have the general formula C_nH_{2n} (where '*n*' is a constant).

genetic modification Adding a gene for a particular characteristic from one organism into another so that the second organism shows the characteristic.

genotype The alleles of a particular gene (or genes) possessed by an organism.

germinate A process in which a seed begins to grow into a young plant.

global food security The ability to produce enough food in the future to feed everyone in the world.

glomerulus A network of blood capillaries in a kidney.

Haber process The industrial process in which ammonia is made from the reaction between hydrogen and nitrogen.

habituation A process in which an animal learns not to respond to a repeated stimulus.

Ⓗ haemophilia A disorder of blood clotting, caused by a recessive allele on the X chromosome.

Ⓗ half-equation Ionic equation showing electron transfers in reduction or oxidation.

haploid Containing a single set of chromosomes, as in gametes.

hard water Water which contains dissolved calcium or magnesium ions and does not easily form a lather with soap.

homologous series A family of compounds which have the same general formula and similar properties, but have different numbers of carbon atoms.

hormone Chemical messengers that are made in one part of the body and are carried in the blood to other parts which they affect, such as melatonin which changes the actions of parts of the body so we feel sleepy.

Ⓗ hybridoma A cell made by fusing a lymphocyte with a cancer cell.

Ⓗ hydration Adding water.

hydrocarbon A compound of hydrogen and carbon only.

hydrogen ions, $H^+(aq)$ Positively charged hydrogen ion. The more hydrogen ions in solution the greater the acidity.

Ⓗ hydrogenated A substance such as a vegetable oil which has had hydrogen added to it; converting an unsaturated C=C double bond to a single bond.

hydrophilic 'Water-loving' substances which are attracted to water and mix with it.

hydrophobic 'Water-hating' substances which are repelled by water and do not mix (e.g. oil).

hydroxide ions, OH⁻(aq) One hydrogen and one oxygen atom carrying a negative charge, acts as a base.

hydroxyl An oxygen atom joined by covalent bonds to a hydrogen atom (an −OH group).

immune response The response of the body to attack by invading pathogens.

immunisation Making someone immune, for example by vaccinating them.

imprinting The process in which young animals bond with or become attached to animals (including humans) or moving objects they see immediately after hatching or birth.

impure Not pure, a mixture.

incident Falling or striking of radiation on something.

indicator Substance which can change colour depending on the pH of a solution.

inelastic collision A collision where kinetic energy is not conserved. Some of the kinetic energy of the system is transferred to the surroundings, for example, as heat or sound energy, or as work done. Most collisions that take place in nature are inelastic.

inert Unreactive material, unlikely to take part in chemical reactions.

infection The entry of a pathogen into the body; an illness caused by a pathogen.

infertile Unable to reproduce.

innate Inborn; innate behaviour is behaviour that does not have to be learnt and is automatic, not thought about.

insoluble Substance which does not dissolve in a given solvent.

insulin The hormone which decreases blood glucose concentration. Used in treatment of Type I diabetes.

integrated pest management Reducing the populations of insects and other pests by a coordinated treatment of different pest control strategies.

intensity The strength of a wave defined as power of incident radiation/area.

inverse square law Any law of physics in which the value of a physical quantity is inversely proportional to the square of the distance from the source of that physical quantity. Applies to the strength of electromagnetic radiation.

invertase An enzyme (also known as sucrase) that catalyses conversion of sucrose into glucose and fructose.

ion exchange column Device used to soften hard water. Contains a resin with an excess of Na^+ ions. When hard water passes through the column, the Ca^{2+} ions in the water are exchanged for Na^+ ions.

ionic compound Substance containing ions from two or more elements.

ionic equation Equation which only shows the ions changed by a reaction, with the other ions omitted.

ionising radiation Radiation that can cause charged particles to be formed by knocking outer electrons out of the atom, or giving them enough energy to break free from the atom. Causes tissue damage and may cause mutations.

iris Coloured ring that controls the size of the pupil and hence controls how much light enters the eye.

IVF (in vitro fertilisation) Fertilising an egg by placing it in a sterile container and then adding sperm.

kelvin (K) The unit in the Kelvin temperature scale. One kelvin is the same temperature interval as 1 °C.

Kelvin temperature scale A temperature scale that measures temperatures relative to absolute zero.

kidney One of the organs in the abdomen that removes urea and extra water from the blood, by producing urine.

kidney transplant Taking a healthy kidney from one person and putting it into the body of another person.

kinetic energy The energy that a particle has due to its movement. Calculated using the equation K.E. = $\frac{1}{2} mv^2$. The units are joules (J).

kinetic theory The theory that explains the different states of matter in terms of the movement of particles.

lactase An enzyme that catalyses the breakdown of lactose (milk sugar). The enzyme is produced by the digestive system and by bacteria used in yogurt manufacture. Lactose-intolerant individuals do not produce this enzyme and cannot digest lactose.

lactic acid The substance that gives the sour taste to yogurt, produced when certain bacteria ferment the sugar lactose in the absence of oxygen.

lactose A sugar found in milk that is converted to lactic acid in the manufacture of yogurt.

laser correction Using a laser to permanently reshape the curvature of the cornea so that the focal length of the eye is changed.

law of reflection The angle of reflection equals the angle of incidence for a wave or ray at a surface.

learning Behaviour which changes as a result of previous experience.

lens Further converges light rays (which have been refracted by the cornea) to focus them on the retina.

(H) lens equation Equation linking the object distance, image distance and focal length for a lens forming either a real or a virtual image.

(H) LH (luteinising hormone) A hormone produced by the pituitary gland, which causes ovulation.

lipase An enzyme that catalyses the breakdown of lipids (fats and oils).

litmus A natural acid/alkali indicator, obtained from lichen. Turns red in acidic solutions and blue in alkaline solutions.

liver cirrhosis A disease of the liver which is linked to excess consumption of alcohol.

long sight Eyesight problem when someone can see distant objects clearly but cannot focus properly on near objects. Caused by light rays being focused to a point behind the retina. Can be corrected by different lenses **(H)** or by cornea surgery.

loop of Henlé Part of a kidney nephron that loops down and then sharply upwards; helps with osmoregulation.

Lucy The name given to the individual of a human-like species that lived 3.2 million years ago, whose fossil bones were discovered in Ethiopia.

lymphocyte A type of white blood cell that produces antibodies.

mass (nucleon) number The total number of protons and neutrons in the nucleus of an atom.

mass-energy equivalence The idea that the *mass* of a body can be interchanged with energy. This means that energy can appear through the disappearance of mass, such as when a positron and electron annihilate and two gamma rays are produced. **(H)** The equivalence is described by the famous equation $E = mc^2$, where E is energy, m is mass, and c is the speed of light in a vacuum.

medium (plural media) Material through which electromagnetic waves travel.

memory lymphocyte A lymphocyte that remains in the blood for a long time after an infection or vaccination.

menstrual cycle A monthly cycle involving the reproductive organs in women.

menstruation The breakdown and loss of the lining of the uterus, at the start of a woman's menstrual cycle.

metabolic reaction A chemical reaction that takes place in a living organism.

middle section Part of a sperm cell immediately behind the head, which contains mitochondria.

(H) mitochondrial DNA The DNA found inside mitochondria, which is passed by the mother to all offspring without any mixing; sons do not pass down their mother's mtDNA to their children.

mitochondrion (plural mitochondria) The site of cellular respiration where glucose is broken down using oxygen to release energy, which is needed for reactions in the cell.

molar volume The volume of one mole of any gas at room temperature and pressure ($24\,dm^3$).

mole The quantity of a substance which is equivalent to its relative formula mass in grams.

(H) molecular formula The formula that shows the actual number of atoms of each element that combine to make a molecule of a compound.

momentum Measure of motion, mass multiplied by velocity. The units are kgm/s. Since momentum is a vector quantity it will have both size and direction.

(H) monoclonal antibodies Many identical antibodies.

mutation A change in the base sequence of DNA.

mycoprotein A protein-rich food made from fungi, sold as Quorn™.

near point The closest point in front of the eyes that an object may be clearly focussed. Usually about 25 cm.

(H) negative feedback A control mechanism in which a change in a factor causes an action that reverses the change.

nephron A kidney tubule.

neutralisation reaction Reaction in which a base or alkali reacts with an acid.

neutron Particle found in the nucleus, having zero charge and mass of 1 (relative to a proton) and **(H)** made up of one up quark and two down quarks.

neutron radiation Ionising radiation in the form of neutrons emitted during radioactive decay.

nitrogenous fertiliser Fertiliser that contains nitrogen compounds such as nitrates.

non-ionising radiation Radiation that does not cause charged particles to be formed.

(H) non-renewable A resource that we are using up faster than it can possibly be replaced and will eventually run out, e.g. coal or oil.

normal An imaginary line drawn at right angles to the surface of a mirror or lens where a ray of light hits it.

(H) nuclear DNA The DNA found in the nucleus of a cell.

(H) nuclear equation Equation representing a nuclear reaction, i.e. a change in the nucleus due to radioactive decay, balancing the atomic number and mass number.

nucleon number See mass number.

nucleon Particle found in the nucleus (neutron or proton).

nutrient A substance required by an organism for growth or energy.

(H) N-Z curve (stability curve) Line on a graph of number of neutrons (N) against number of protons (Z) for all the isotopes of different elements, showing the stable isotopes. Isotopes above the curve have too many neutrons and undergo β- decay. Isotopes below the curve have too many protons and undergo β+ decay.

oestrogen A hormone produced by the ovaries, important in the menstrual cycle.

operant conditioning A process in which an animal changes its behaviour as a result of experiencing rewards or unpleasant consequences.

optical fibre Tight bundle of glass fibres which transmits light from one end to the other by total internal reflection.

optimum pH The pH at which an enzyme's rate of reaction is greatest, or at which a population of microorganisms grows most rapidly.

optimum temperature The temperature at which an enzyme's rate of reaction is greatest, or at which a population of microorganisms grows most rapidly.

osmoregulation The maintenance of an organism's water content and dissolved salt concentration; a function performed by the kidneys.

ovulation The release of an egg from an ovary.

oxidation A reaction in which oxygen is added to a chemical; loss of an electron by a negative ion.

pacemaker A device which helps the heart to beat properly by detecting the action potentials and applying electrical signals to regulate the heart action.

palliative care A medical intervention that does not cure a condition but may reduce pain or other symptoms.

particle accelerator Device used to accelerate charged particles to very high speeds. Using particle accelerators it is possible for particle physicists to collide particles at high energies and through this to break down matter into smaller particles.

particle physics The study of subatomic and fundamental constituents of matter.

pascals (Pa) A unit of pressure. $1\,Pa = 1\,N/m^2$.

pasteurisation When foods, such as milk, are heated briefly to kill the bacteria in them.

pathogen An organism (usually a microorganism such as a bacterium or virus) that causes disease.

permanent hardness Property of hard water that cannot be removed by boiling the water.

pest Animals such as insects or larger herbivores that eat and damage crop plants.

PET scanner A medical scanning technique. The image of metabolically active sites inside the body is computed by detecting gamma rays coming from positron–electron annihilation.

phenolphthalein An indicator. Turns colourless in acidic solutions and pink in basic solutions.

phenotype The characteristics of an organism.

pheromone A substance produced by one organism that diffuses into the environment and causes responses in another organism (a chemical signal).

photoperiodism The way in which living organisms respond to changes in daylength.

pipette Apparatus used to accurately measure a set volume of a solution, which can be used in a titration.

(H) pituitary gland Gland at the base of the brain that secretes many different hormones, including FSH and LH.

(H) plant chemical defence Some plants have evolved to defend themselves against attack from herbivores by producing toxic compounds; some insects have co-evolved an adaptation to allow them to eat the plant.

(H) pollination Transfer of pollen (the male gamete in plants) from one flower to another, enabling fertilisation.

polyester A type of plastic made from long chains of esters, which can be used to make drinks bottles and fibres for clothing.

positron The anti-particle of an electron, having the same mass but opposite charge. Positron emission is a type of beta decay.

potential difference Another word for voltage. It is the difference in the energy carried by electrons before and after they have flowed through a component.

power of a lens A measure of how much a lens refracts light rays, related to the shape of the lens, measured in dioptres (D). Calculated from the equation power = 1 divided by focal length in metres. Diverging lenses have negative power.

precipitate Insoluble solid formed when two solutions are mixed together and a precipitation reaction occurs.

precipitation reaction A reaction in which an insoluble product is formed from soluble reactants.

preservative A substance that is added to food to keep it edible for longer.

pressure The force on a certain area, measured in pascals or N/m^2.

primary response The way in which the immune system responds on the first occasion that a particular pathogen enters the body.

progesterone A hormone produced by the ovaries and placenta, which helps to maintain the thick lining of the uterus.

protease An enzyme that catalyses the breakdown of proteins.

proton Positive particle found in the nucleus, having charge of +1 and mass of 1, and **H** made up of two up quarks and one down quark.

proton number See atomic number.

pulse oximeter Device placed on the surface of the body that uses LEDs and light detectors to measure the amount of oxygen in the blood from how much infrared radiation the blood absorbs, and measures pulse rate from the time interval between peaks in infrared absorbance.

pulse oximetry Using a pulse oximeter to measure the pulse rate and the amount of oxygen in the blood.

Punnett square A chart used in genetic diagrams to show the possible genotypes (and sometimes phenotypes) that can result from the fusion of the gametes involved.

pupil The round hole in the centre of the iris of the eye. It can change size in response to changes in light levels.

purity Measure of the amount of the main substance present in a sample related to the amount of impurity present.

qualitative analysis Investigation into the kind of substances present in an unknown sample.

quantitative analysis Investigation into the amount of each substance present in an unknown sample.

H **quark** Particle from which protons and neutrons are made. Protons and neutrons each contain three quarks.

radiation The emission of energy from a source, as sound, electromagnetic waves or moving particles.

radioactive isotope Unstable isotope that emits radiation, as alpha particles, beta particles (electrons and positrons), gamma rays or neutrons.

radiotherapy Treating cancer by killing cancer cells or reducing the size of a tumour with ionising radiation.

real image An image that can be projected onto a screen.

H **real is positive sign convention** Convention for the lens equation that real images have positive image distances and distances measured from the other side of the lens are negative.

recessive Version of a gene (allele) that will only have an effect if the other allele is also recessive.

H **recombinant DNA technology** Genetic modification; the addition of new DNA to an organism's cells.

H **red-green colour blindness** A sex-linked genetic disorder in humans where the affected individual cannot distinguish the colours red and green, much more common in men than women.

reduction Gain of an electron by a positive ion.

refine Increase the purity of a material, such as a metal.

reflection When a wave or particle bounces off a surface.

reflex An automatic reaction to a stimulus.

refract The change in direction of a wave due to a change in wave speed at an interface between two media.

H **refractive index** The ratio of the speed of light in a vacuum to the speed of light in a particular material.

reject To refuse or get rid of, such as when the body reacts to the foreign tissue of a transplant and kills it.

relative atomic mass The mean mass of an atom relative to the mass of an atom of carbon-12, which is assigned a mass of 12.

relative formula mass The sum of the relative atomic masses of all the atoms in a formula.

renal artery An artery that delivers blood to the kidneys.

renal vein A vein that carries blood away from the kidneys.

renewable Something that can be made without diminishing the resources used to make it, such as biofuels made from plants that can be grown again.

reproductive quality The ability of an individual to produce healthy offspring.

resazurin dye Dye used as a qualitative test for the presence of significant numbers of bacteria in milk, thereby checking whether it is fit for sale.

H **restriction enzyme** An enzyme that cuts DNA molecules into pieces.

resultant force The total force that results from two or more forces acting on a single object. It is found by adding the forces together, taking into account their direction.

retina Tissue at the back of the eye that contains light receptors.

reversible reaction A chemical reaction that can work in both directions.

Saccharomyces cerevisiae   A species of yeast, a single-celled fungus, used in biotechnology, for example, to cultivate the enzyme invertase.

salt   A compound formed by neutralisation of an acid by a base. The first part of the name comes from the metal in the metal oxide, hydroxide or carbonate. The second part of the name comes from the acid.

Ⓗ **saturated**   A molecule which contains only single bonds between the carbon atoms and has the maximum possible number of atoms attached to the carbon chain.

scum   Insoluble precipitate formed when the dissolved calcium and magnesium ions in hard water bind with soap.

Ⓗ **secondary response**   The way in which the immune system responds on the second occasion that a particular pathogen enters the body.

selective reabsorption   Taking back useful substances into the blood, from the fluid inside a nephron.

sex cell   A gamete; a cell such as egg or a sperm.

sex chromosome   One of the chromosomes that helps to determine an organism's sex; in humans, these are the X and Y chromosomes.

Ⓗ **sex-linked genetic disorder**   A condition caused by an allele of a gene carried on either the X or Y chromosome.

short sight   Eyesight problem when someone can see nearby objects clearly but cannot focus properly on distant objects. Caused by light rays being focused to a point in front of the retina. Can be corrected by different lenses Ⓗ or by cornea surgery.

Ⓗ **Snell's law**   A law for the refraction of light rays or any type of wave, which states that when a wave passes from one medium to another the ratio of the sine of the angle of incidence to the sine of the angle of refraction is a constant.

social behaviour   The way in which organisms that live in groups interact with one another.

soft water   Water which forms a good lather with soap.

soluble   Substance which dissolves in a given solvent.

solute   The solid or liquid that dissolves in a given solvent to form a solution.

solution   The clear mixture that forms when a solute dissolves in a given solvent.

solvent   The liquid that dissolves the solute. (solute + solvent → solution)

Ⓗ **stability curve**   See N-Z curve.

stable isotope   Isotope that is unlikely to decay.

sterilise   To destroy bacteria, viruses, mould and pests such as insects on an object. It can be carried out using radioactive sources.

Ⓗ **sticky end**   A length of DNA with only one strand, that will easily join with other pieces.

Ⓗ **structural formula**   A formula that shows the way that all the atoms are arranged and joined together in a molecule.

subatomic particle   Particles smaller than atoms, including protons, neutrons, electrons and quarks.

sucrase   An enzyme (also known as invertase) that converts sucrose to glucose and fructose.

surrogate mother   A female organism that has had the embryo of a different female placed in her uterus.

symptom   The visible effects of a disease, such as a fever or rash.

temporary hardness   Property of hard water that can be removed by boiling the water.

thermionic emission   The process of emitting an electron from the surface of a heated metal, usually a hot filament.

time period   The time taken for one cycle of a regularly repeating event. Related to frequency by the equation frequency = 1/time period in seconds.

titration   Technique in volumetric analysis, used to find the exact volumes of solutions which react with each other.

titre   The volume of solution delivered by the burette at the 'end point' when the indicator changes colour.

total internal reflection   When all of a wave is reflected from a boundary instead of being refracted. Occurs when the angle of incidence is greater than the critical angle.

tracer   A radioactive substance that is injected into the body and emits gamma rays that can be detected outside the body to monitor how a part of the body is working.

training   Changing an animal's behaviour by giving it rewards or punishments.

transgenic plant   A plant containing genes that have been taken from another species.

tumour   An abnormal growth of rapidly dividing cells that may or may not be cancerous (malignant).

ultrasound   Sound waves with a frequency above 20 000 Hz, which is too high for the human ear to detect.

Ⓗ **unsaturated**   A molecule which contains one or more double bonds between the carbon atoms, allowing extra atoms to be added on to the carbon chain.

unstable isotope   Isotope that is likely to decay.

urea   A waste product produced in the liver from excess amino acids.

ureter   One of the tubes that carry urine from the kidneys to the bladder.

urethra   The tube that carries urine from the bladder to the outside of the body.

urinary system   The body system that produces and removes urine, including the kidneys, ureters, bladder and urethra.

urine   A fluid produced by the kidneys, containing urea and other waste substances dissolved in water.

uterus   The organ in which a foetus develops (womb).

vaccine   A substance containing dead or weakened pathogens (or parts of them), introduced into the body to make a person immune to that pathogen.

vector   A 'go-between' that is used in genetic modification, to transfer genes from the cells of one organism to another.

vector   A physical quantity that has a magnitude (size) and direction. Force and velocity are examples of a vector. Speed, mass and volume are not vectors.

virtual image   An image that cannot be projected onto a screen.

X-ray   Electromagnetic (EM) wave with a high frequency and high energy. X-rays are ionising radiation.

yield   The amount of product formed in a reaction.

The Periodic Table of the Elements

1	2												3	4	5	6	7	0
																		4 **He** helium 2
7 **Li** lithium 3	9 **Be** beryllium 4												11 **B** boron 5	12 **C** carbon 6	14 **N** nitrogen 7	16 **O** oxygen 8	19 **F** fluorine 9	20 **Ne** neon 10
23 **Na** sodium 11	24 **Mg** magnesium 12												27 **Al** aluminium 13	28 **Si** silicon 14	31 **P** phosphorus 15	32 **S** sulfur 16	35.5 **Cl** chlorine 17	40 **Ar** argon 18
39 **K** potassium 19	40 **Ca** calcium 20	45 **Sc** scandium 21	48 **Ti** titanium 22	51 **V** vanadium 23	52 **Cr** chromium 24	55 **Mn** manganese 25	56 **Fe** iron 26	59 **Co** cobalt 27	59 **Ni** nickel 28	63.5 **Cu** copper 29	65 **Zn** zinc 30		70 **Ga** gallium 31	73 **Ge** germanium 32	75 **As** arsenic 33	79 **Se** selenium 34	80 **Br** bromine 35	84 **Kr** krypton 36
85 **Rb** rubidium 37	88 **Sr** strontium 38	89 **Y** yttrium 39	91 **Zr** zirconium 40	93 **Nb** niobium 41	96 **Mo** molybdenum 42	[98] **Tc** technetium 43	101 **Ru** ruthenium 44	103 **Rh** rhodium 45	106 **Pd** palladium 46	108 **Ag** silver 47	112 **Cd** cadmium 48		115 **In** indium 49	119 **Sn** tin 50	122 **Sb** antimony 51	128 **Te** tellurium 52	127 **I** iodine 53	131 **Xe** xenon 54
133 **Cs** caesium 55	137 **Ba** barium 56	139 **La*** lanthanum 57	178 **Hf** hafnium 72	181 **Ta** tantalum 73	184 **W** tungsten 74	186 **Re** rhenium 75	190 **Os** osmium 76	192 **Ir** iridium 77	195 **Pt** platinum 78	197 **Au** gold 79	201 **Hg** mercury 80		204 **Tl** thallium 81	207 **Pb** lead 82	209 **Bi** bismuth 83	[209] **Po** polonium 84	[210] **At** astatine 85	[222] **Rn** radon 86
[223] **Fr** francium 87	[226] **Ra** radium 88	[227] **Ac*** actinium 89	[261] **Rf** rutherfordium 104	[262] **Db** dubnium 105	[266] **Sg** seaborgium 106	[264] **Bh** bohrium 107	[277] **Hs** hassium 108	[268] **Mt** meitnerium 109	[271] **Ds** darmstadtium 110	[272] **Rg** roentgenium 111								

1
H
hydrogen
1

Elements with atomic numbers 112–116 have been reported
but not fully authenticated

Key

relative atomic mass
Atomic symbol
name
atomic (proton) number

* The lanthanoids (atomic numbers 58–71) and the actinoids (atomic numbers 90–103) have been omitted.
The relative atomic masses of copper and chlorine have not been rounded to the nearest whole number.

There are a number of formulae that you will be expected to be able to use in your physics examination for Unit P3. However, you do not need to learn them by heart. You will be a given a formulae sheet in the examinations which will contain all the formulae from the unit. They are also shown below.

Specification statement	Equation
1.4	$$\text{intensity} = \frac{\text{power of incident radiation}}{\text{area}}$$ $$I = \frac{P}{A}$$
1.7	$$\text{power of lens (dioptre, D)} = \frac{1}{\text{focal length (metre, m)}}$$
Ⓗ 1.9	$$\frac{1}{f} = \frac{1}{u} + \frac{1}{v}$$ (f = focal length (m), u = object distance (m), v = image distance (m)) the use of the real is positive sign convention is preferred and will be used in the exam
Ⓗ 2.4	current (ampere, A) = number of particles per second (1/second, 1/s) × charge on each particle (coulomb, C) $$I = N \times q$$
Ⓗ 2.5	kinetic energy (joule, J) = charge on the electron (coulomb, C) × accelerating potential difference (volt, V) $$\text{KE} = \frac{1}{2} mv^2 = e \times V$$
2.12	$$\text{frequency (hertz, Hz)} = \frac{1}{\text{time period (second, s)}}$$ $$f = \frac{1}{T}$$
5.8	$$V_1 = \frac{V_2 T_1}{T_2}$$ to calculate volume for gases of fixed mass at constant pressure (rearranging not required)
5.10	$$V_1 P_1 = V_2 P_2$$ to calculate volume or pressure for gases of fixed mass at constant temperature
Ⓗ 5.11	$$\text{initial pressure (pascal, Pa)} \times \frac{\text{initial volume (metre}^3\text{, m}^3)}{\text{initial temperature (kelvin, K)}} =$$ $$\text{final pressure (pascal, Pa)} \times \frac{\text{final volume (metre}^3\text{, m}^3)}{\text{final temperature (kelvin, K)}}$$ $$\frac{P_1 V_1}{T_1} = \frac{P_2 V_2}{T_2}$$

Index

Published by Pearson Education Limited, a company incorporated in England and Wales, having its registered office at Edinburgh Gate, Harlow, Essex, CM20 2JE. Registered company number: 872828
Edexcel is a registered trademark of Edexcel Limited

Text © Pearson Education Limited 2011

The rights of Mark Levesley, William Beales, Iain Brand, Peter Ellis, Steve Gray, Penny Johnson, Mary Jones, Jim Newall, Ray Oliver, Damian Riddle, Ed Walsh, Gemma Young, Mark Grinsell, Sue Jenkin, Ian Roberts, Julia Salter, David Swann to be identified as authors of this work have been asserted by them in accordance with the Copyright, Designs and Patents Act 1988.

First published 2011

10 9 8 7 6 5 4 3

British Library Cataloguing in Publication Data

A catalogue record for this book is available from the British Library

ISBN 978 184690 886 6

Typeset by EMC Design Ltd
Illustrated by Oxford Designers and Illustrators
Picture research by Louise Edgeworth and Alison Prior
Printed in the UK by Scotprint

Acknowledgements

The publisher would like to thank all the teachers and students who helped in the development and trialling of this course, including:

Steven Rowe, Graham Hartland, David French and students at Tomlinscote School; Alex Dawes and students at the Jewish Free School; Suzanne Mycock, Sandra Fox and students at Chelmer Valley High School; David Liebeschuetz, Richard Brock, Elizabeth Andrews and the science team at Davenant Foundation School; Peter Bowen-Walker; Carol Chapman; Fay Dodds; Ben Lovick; Esther Ruston and Rupert Turpin.

We are grateful to the following for permission to reproduce copyright material:

Graph on page 30 from Agency BATS, www.bats.ch<http://www.bats.ch> Copyright of BATS Centre for Biosafety and Sustainability, reproduced with permission; Graph on page 51 adapted from Animal Behaviour, *Tinbergen revisited: a replication and extension of experiments on the beak colour preferences of herring gull chicks*. Copyright of Elsevier, reproduced with permission; Graph on page 210 adapted from *N-Z Chart* from Bechtel Marine Propulsion Corporation (BMPC), reproduced with permission.

In some instances we have been unable to trace the owners of copyright material, and we would appreciate any information that would enable us to do so.

The publisher would like to thank the following for their kind permission to reproduce their photographs:

(Key: b-bottom; c-centre; l-left; r-right; t-top)

Alamy Images: A T Willett 138, Alaska Stock 82, Arco Images GmbH 50b, Art Gallery Collection 40, Ben Nottridge 80tr, Bon Appetit 70, Catchlight Visual Services 50t, Classic Stock 148t, Danita Delimont 32, David Grossman 150, David Noton Photography 112cl, Dennis MacDonald 148b, doc-stock 215, Fancy 58tr, Guy Croft Scitech 110tr, imagebroker 92, Jan Baks 188, Jochen Tack 155l, Joerg Boethling 74, Kumar Sriskanda 155r, Lebrecht Music & Arts Photo Library 212, Mark Burnett 128, MBI 180bl, Media blitz images (UK) ltd 153, Mike Goldwater 55l, Noble Images 210, Paul Glendell 110l, Philip Bramhill 112t, Photos 12 320, Pixonnet.com 31, Qaphotos.com 104l, Razor Pix 152t, Ros Drinkwater 30tr, Science Photos 104 (ii), Scott Camazine 37, Shout 222bl, Stuart Abraham 106tr, ukscapes 192, Warren Mcconnaughie 144l; Ardea: Kenneth W Fink 48b, Stefa Meyers 50c; The Art Archive: 166; Better Equipped Educational Supplies Ltd: 250; Bridgeman Art Library Ltd:Private Collection 186; CERN Geneva: 218t, 224; Copyright Nielsen Norman Group, reprinted from htttp://www.useit.com/alertbox/banner-blindness. html by permission: 54tr; Corbis: Adrianna Williams 68, Bettmann 146t, DLILLC 76, Jim Sugar 42, Larry Downing 36, Miek Chick 48t; David Olsen: 180tr; DK Images: 56tl, 56tc, 56bl, 56br; Dr Carlos Jared: 49t; E M Clements Photography: 190; FLPA Images of Nature: James Christensen / Minden Pictures 78, Jim Brandenberg 140;Fotolia. com: Irmina Mamof 232tr, Jean-Marc Gandy 233; Geoff Jones: 29, 58b, 63; Getty Images: 137, 181, 216tr, AFP / David Boily 230, Bloomberg 136r, Colin Anderson 60t, Colorful HIgh Speed Photographs / Flickr 228, DAGO C 46, Eightfish 79c, Ferdaus Shamin 154, Mark Dadswell 218b; image courtesy of NASA Earth Observatory: 226; Image courtesy of The Advertising Archives: 200tr, 220; iStockphoto: 61r; Jennifer Burton/IWCP: 184; John Chapman/Photographers Direct:146b; John Innes Institute: 80l; Kathleen Cohen: 62t; Martyn F. Chillmaid: 112b; NHPA Ltd / Photoshot Holdings: Stephen Dalton 56tr; Pearson Education Ltd: Corel Professional Photos 116r, Dynamic Graphics, Inc. 116l, Imagestate. John Foxx Collection 66, Jupiter Images / Brand X / Alamy 202b, Oxford Designers & Illustrators Ltd 52bl, Photodisc. Getty Images 52, Trevor Clifford 130b; Pearson Education Ltd: David R Frazier / Alamy 122t, Steve Hamblin 118t, Trevor Clifford 113, 120b, 122bl; Reprinted with permission, courtesy of Pfizer Limited.: 124t; Photolibrary.com: Custom Medical Stock Photo 111b, Dennis Kunkel 69r, Paul Kay 54b, Rawdon Wyatt 72tr, Roland Symons 49b; Press Association Images: Alistair Fuller 216tl, AP Photo / Toby Talbot 134; Press Office: John James 133; Reuters: Christian Charisius130t, Tobias Schwarz 182, You Sung-Ho 198; Rex Features: Sipa Press 57; Andy Rouse Wildlife Photography: 26; Sally Farndon: 72l; Science Photo Library Ltd: 51, 110b, 202t, 204, Adam Hart-Davies 232cl, Andrew Lambert Photography 104 (i), 104 (iii), 104 (iv), 105 (i), 105 (ii), 105 (iii), 105 (iv), 105 (v), 106bl, 118b, Antoine Rosset 178, Arno Massee 200tl, Brad Nelson / Custom Medical Stock 39, BSIP / Raguet 217r, CDC 34, Chris R Sharp 136l, David Nicholls 47, David R Frazier 73, Dr Rob Stepney 79tr, Dr Yorgos Nikas 44b, James Holmes / Celltech 65, JAVIER TRUEBA / MSF 103, Life in View 38b, Living Art Enterprises, LLC 203r, Mark Clarke 104tr, MARTYN F. CHILLMAID 124b, Maximilian Stock Ltd 126, Michael Donne 120t, NASA 208, National Museum of Health and Medicine 214bl, Omikron 222tr, Pasieka 194, Patrice Latron / Look At Sciences 111t, Power and Syred 30bl, Prof David Hall 69l, Robert Brook 132, Scientifica, Visuals Unlimited 217, Sheila Terry 114, 158, Sovereign / ISM 203, Stuart Wilson 56b, Trevor Clifford 152b, US National Archives & Records 214tr, US Navy 55r, Zephyr 38; Seapics.com: Larry Madrigal 28tr;Shutterstock.com: 0, Fritz 59b, Jian Hongyan 64; Stefan Sveinsson/Photographers Direct: 115; SuperStock: age fotostock 128b; Sutton Swimwear: 185t; © The Trustees of The British Museum. All rights reserved.: 144tr; Thinkstock: Hemera 45, 154l, 183, iStockphoto 199; Tim Gainey / Photographers Direct: 59t; Visuals Unlimited: Scientifica 28bl

All other images © Pearson Education

Every effort has been made to trace the copyright holders and we apologise in advance for any unintentional omissions. We would be pleased to insert the appropriate acknowledgement in any subsequent edition of this publication.